TAKING SIDES

Clashing Views on
Controversial Bioethical Issues

Second Edition

Where there is much desire to learn, there of necessity will be much arguing . . .

John Milton

STAFF

Jeremy Brenner — Program Manager
Brenda Filley — Production Manager
Jean Bailey — Designer
Libra Ann Cusack — Typesetting Coordinator
Diane Barker — Editorial Assistant
Lynn Shannon — Graphics Coordinator

TAKING SIDES

**Clashing Views on
Controversial Bioethical Issues**

Second Edition

Edited, Selected and with Introductions by

CAROL LEVINE, The Hastings Center
Hastings-on-Hudson, NY

The Dushkin Publishing Group, Inc.
Guilford, Connecticut 06437

Library of Congress Catalog Card Number: 86-71775

Manufactured in the United States of America

Second Edition, First Printing

CONTENTS

Professor of Law John T. Noonan, Jr., believes that a fetus is conceived
by human parents and it is just as wrong to destroy its life as it would
be to destroy the life of any human. Professor of Christian ethics Beverly
Wildung Harrison argues that women ought to decide whether or not to
bear children on the basis of their own moral preparedness to become
mothers.

Professor of religion Hans O. Tiefel opposes the new technology of *in
vitro* fertilization on the grounds that it may cause harm to both mothers
and embryos. Biologist Clifford Grobstein argues that this technology is
a useful therapy for infertile couples and that we can avoid potential
moral problems by developing sound principles.

Professor of law John A. Robertson believes that infertile couples have a
right to arrange for a surrogate mother to bear the husband's child and
that the ethical and legal problems that might result are not very different from those that already exist in adoption and artificial insemination
by donor. Professor of law Herbert F. Krimmel takes the position that it is
immoral to bear a child for the purpose of giving it up and that surrogate
mother arrangements will put additional strain on our society's shared
moral values.

PART II. DECISIONS ABOUT DEATH

Physician Bernard C. Meyer argues that physicians must use discretion in communicating bad news to patients. Adherence to a rigid formula of truthtelling fails to appreciate the differences in patients' readiness to hear and understand the information. Philosopher Sissela Bok challenges the traditional physicians' view by arguing that the harm resulting from disclosure is less than they think and is outweighed by the benefits, including the important one of giving the patient the right to choose among treatments.

Philosopher James Rachels argues that the conventional distinction between active euthanasia (killing) and passive euthanasia (letting die) has no moral importance. Philosophers Tom L. Beauchamp and James F. Childress hold that the distinction is not only valid morally (it upholds certain principles such as "do no harm") but also practically (it avoids certain harmful consequences, such as loss of patients' trust in physicians).

Professor of religion Gilbert Meilaender maintains that food and water are ordinary care, not medical treatment. Removing them constitutes "aiming to kill" rather than "allowing to die." Physician Joanne Lynn and professor of religious studies James F. Childress claim that nutrition and hydration are not morally different from other life-sustaining medical treatments that may on occasion be withheld or withdrawn, according to the patients' best interests.

Theologian Earl E. Shelp believes that parents should be the ultimate decision-makers about medical treatment for severely diseased or defective newborns. C. Everett Koop, a pediatric surgeon who is now Sugeon General of the United States, calls withholding treatment from newborns "infanticide" and faults the medical profession for acceding to the wishes of the families instead of protecting their patients.

Mary Rose Barrington, a British solicitor (attorney), argues that humane and advanced societies must embrace the notion of "rational suicide" in a world that is increasingly populated by the aged, who would prefer a "planned death" to a long wait to be "arbitrarily extinguished." Psychiatrist Herbert Hendin emphasizes that suicide is a pathological response to life's problems and that, instead of intellectual attempts to rationalize or glorify suicide, we need efforts to improve our lives together.

PART III. TREATING THE MENTALLY ILL

California Supreme Court Justice Mathew Tobriner asserts that when a psychotherapist learns that a patient plans to commit a violent act against a third person, the public interest requires that the therapist warn that person, even if it violates the patient's right to privacy. Former Justice William Clark argues that if patients cannot be assured of confidentiality, those who need treatment will not seek it.

Professor of law Stephen Cohen argues that the insanity defense as it now exists should be abolished because it is so difficult to tell whether mental illness has impaired the defendant's capacity for free will. Professor of law Richard J. Bonnie counters with the view that the insanity defense should not be abandoned because it is fundamentally wrong to condemn and punish a person whose rational control over his or her behavior was impaired by mental illness.

Psychiatrist Thomas S. Szasz maintains that the detention of persons in mental institutions against their will is a crime against humanity. People are not committed because they are "mentally ill" or "dangerous," but because society wants to control their behavior. Psychiatrist Paul Chodoff believes that the rights of the mentally ill to be treated are being set aside in the rush to give them their freedom. He favors a return to the use of medical criteria by psychiatrists, albeit with legal safeguards.

PART IV. HUMAN AND ANIMAL EXPERIMENTATION

The late psychologist Stanley Milgram believed that the central moral justification for allowing deceptive experiments is that the vast majority of subjects who take part in them find them acceptable after the rationale is explained. Social psychologist Thomas H. Murray argues that deception research is not only bad for subjects but also harmful to researchers and to the goals of science itself.

Minister and physician Jack W. Provonsha claims that because of medical advances, implanting a baboon heart in Baby Fae offered a real measure of hope to save her life. Attorney George J. Annas maintains that the experiment on Baby Fae did not receive adequate ethical review or appropriate consent and that it was unjustified and premature.

Applying the principle of a "bias for life," theologian Seymour Siegel
concludes that no experimental procedures likely to harm a fetus, even
when it is to be aborted, are justifiable. Ethicist John C. Fletcher and
physician Joseph D. Shulman argue that current guidlelines on fetal
research need to be reexamined in the light of new knowledge. More
risks might be allowed in carefully designed studies.

Philosopher Peter Singer claims that much experimentation involving
animals is brutal and serves no direct benefit of humans and that alternative scientific methods achieve the same knowledge. The Office of
Technology Assessment acknowledges the conflict of interests between
the use of animals for human ends, and the need of animals to be free
from suffering, but concludes that when suffering inflicted on animals is
unavoidable to satisfy human objectives, the human interest will be
controlling.

PART V. PUBLIC POLICY AND BIOETHICS

Physician Alfred M. Sadler, Jr., and attorney Blair Sadler maintain that
the system of encouraged voluntarism increases the supply of organs
without infringing on the rights of individuals and families. Philosopher
Arthur L. Caplan argues that current laws should be overridden in favor
of a system of required request, in which physicians would have to ask
the families of newly-dead persons if they will permit the retrieval of
organs.

The Working Group on Mechanical Circulatory Support of the NHBLI
concludes that effective, fully implantable, long-term, mechanical circula-

tory support systems—that is, artificial hearts—could provide a significant increase in life span, with acceptable quality of life, for 17,000 to 35,000 patients a year. Cardiologist Thomas A. Preston opposes further development of the artificial heart without stringent regulations because claims for its theraputic benefits are unwarranted and the costs to society for the limited gains it might provide are too high.

Physician Percy Brazil asserts that cost containment in medical care is a fact of life, and that the responsibility of the medical profession should be to ensure that the new system provides quality care. Psychiatrist Allen R. Dyer argues that the physician's primary responsibility is to the patient. To ask conscientious physicians to bear the responsibility for lowering costs creates a conflict of interest that threatens to alter the nature of the doctor-patient relationship.

The health and life insurance industries believe that their obligation to use sound underwriting practices requires the use of screening tests for antibodies to HTLV-III, the virus that causes AIDS. Attorney Mark Scherzer argues that maintaining insurance coverage for AIDS serves important social goals and that the insurance industry has exaggerated its potential losses.

Philosopher Hans Jonas believes that expanding the uses of genetic engineering from bacteria to humans would open a Pandora's box of evils. We should not tamper with the inviolability of the human image. The President's Commission concludes that genetic engineering is not intrinsically wrong for humans and sees no fundamental danger to world safety or human values in any current or planned forms of the technology.

FOREWORD

These days even our successes cause anxiety. Nowhere is this more true than in the realm of medicine. The last forty years have seen the conversion of medicine from a care-and-comfort profession into a life-saving enterprise. However, the pride in accomplishment seems almost completely submerged in the tragic dilemmas that accompany such awesome power.

If a life can be saved now by an artificial organ, whose life should it be, and on what basis should we decide? If a dying individual can be sustained on a respirator to a point where the distinction between life and death is blurred, how shall we examine when the border of no return has been passed, and by whose criteria and under whose authority will treatment be terminated? When antisepsis permits us to do unheard-of surgery of sweeping and dramatic power to save the life of a cancer patient, how shall we decide if the radical deformity which extends life is worth the extra days of living for the mutilated patient? How are we to equate the *number* of days a patient survives with the *quality* of those days?

These are only some of the tragic dilemmas considered in this book. We are all now—by demand, not choice—philosophers in pursuit of an evasive truth. Medicine has forced a renewed interest in ethics, and all of us—physicians, philosophers, and citizens who inevitably will be caught up in these decisions—are groping for answers.

The answers do not come easily, and each resolution involves a compromise in which something treasured—privacy, autonomy, days of life—may have to be abandoned to preserve something else equally treasured—a sense of justice, human dignity, the common good. I tend to distrust anyone who is comfortable with any decision in these areas. They are hard choices, and most of us come to our conclusions reluctantly, with a sense of anguish and humiliation. And so it should be when one deals with life and death.

The cases offered here are presented in an adversarial way to sharpen your awareness of the dilemmas involved. Every attempt has been made to play with a fair deck, by having the strongest and best case made on each side of the issue. It is hoped that by the time you have finished this book you will be fully aware of the extraordinary extent of the problems that have been created by the Biological Revolution—that you will be informed of the major decisions that you, not some experts, will be called upon to make in the not too distant future, either directly in your personal life or through your legislative representatives. Finally, it is hoped that, as a testament to any good educative effort, on completion of this book you will be left with fewer, rather than more, answers.

Willard Gaylin, MD
President
The Hastings Center

PREFACE

This is a book about choices—hard and tragic choices, as Willard Gaylin points out in the Foreword. The choices are hard not only because they often involve life and death but also because there are convincing arguments on both sides of the issues. An ethical dilemma, by definition, is one that poses a conflict not between good and evil but between one good principle and another which is equally as good. The choices are hard because the decisions that are made—by individuals, groups, and public policy makers—will influence the kind of society we have today and the one we will have in the future.

Although the views expressed in the selections in this volume are strong—even passionate—ones, they are also subtle ones, concerned with the nuances of the particular debate. *How* one argues matters in bioethics; you will see and have to weigh the significance of varying rhetorical styles and appeals throughout this volume.

Although there are no easy answers to any of the issues in the book, the questions will be answered in some fashion—partly by individual choices and partly by decisions that are made by professionals and government. We must make them the best answers possible, and that can only be done by informed and thoughtful consideration. This book, then, can serve as a beginning for what ideally will become an ongoing process of examination and reflection.

ACKNOWLEDGMENTS

I would like to thank Jeremy Brenner of the Dushkin Publishing Group for his editorial guidance; not only did he provide excellent advice on particular matters, but he also knew when to reassure and when to urge onward. All the staff and contributors to The Hastings Center's work have contributed indirectly to this volume, but several people were helpful in specific ways. Eric Feldman provided valuable research assistance for the first edition, and Marna Howarth and Arthur Caplan read and commented on portions of the manuscript. Paul Homer made a significant contribution to this reorganized, expanded, and updated second edition. I would particularly like to thank Daniel Callahan, director of the Center, and Willard Gaylin, its president, not only because they encouraged me to undertake this project but also because they have made The Hastings Center a place where intellectual rigor and a tolerance for clashing points of view—the foundations of this book—are not just an academic ideal but a way of life. Finally, for reasons they alone will understand, I thank my parents, Betty and King Solomon; my husband, Howard Levine; and my children, Jenny, Judy, and Charlie Levine.

Carol Levine
Hastings-on-Hudson, NY
September 1986

INTRODUCTION: MEDICINE AND MORAL ARGUMENTS IN AMERICAN LIFE

Carol Levine

In the fall of 1975, a twenty-one-year-old woman lay in a New Jersey hospital—as she had for months—in a coma, the victim of a toxic combination of barbiturates and alcohol. Doctors agreed that her brain was irreversibly damaged and that she would never recover. Her parents, after anguished consultation with their priest, asked the doctors and hospital to disconnect the respirator that was artificially maintaining their daughter's life. When the doctors and hospital refused, the parents petitioned the court to be made her legal guardian so that they could authorize the withdrawal of treatment. After hearing all the arguments, the court sided with the parents, and the respirator was removed. Contrary to everyone's expectations, however, the young woman did not die but began to breathe on her own (perhaps because, in anticipation of the court order, the nursing staff had gradually weaned her from total dependence on the respirator). She lived for ten years until her death in June 1985—comatose, lying in a fetal position and fed with tubes—in a New Jersey nursing home.

The young woman's name was Karen Ann Quinlan, and her case brought national attention to the thorny ethical questions raised by modern medical technology: When, if ever, should life-sustaining technology be withdrawn? Is the sanctity of life an absolute value? What kinds of treatment are really beneficial to a patient in a "chronic vegetative state" like Karen's? And (perhaps the most troubling question), who shall decide?

These and similar questions are at the heart of the growing field of "biomedical ethics" or (as it is usually called) "bioethics." Other questions have been raised by the development of techniques to screen fetuses for birth defects and, in a few cases, to treat them in the womb; the ability to control behavior thorugh psychotropic, or mind-altering, drugs, or through psychosurgery; the development of the artificial kidney and heart machines and organ transplants; the possibility of fertilizing human eggs outside a woman's body and implanting them in her (or another woman's) uterus; and the capacity to create new life forms through direct manipulation of DNA, the basic genetic material. All these technological advances have brought enormous promise for improving the health and quality of life for many people, but they have also created problems in deciding when to use these techniques, for whom, and at what cost (both in terms of money and effort and in terms of the other human values that may be compromised in the process).

Ethical dilemmas in medicine are, of course, nothing new. They have been recognized and discussed in Western medicine since a small

1

group of physicians—led by Hippocrates—on the Isle of Cos in Greece around the fourth century B.C., subscribed to a code of practice that newly graduated physicians still swear to uphold today. But unlike earlier times, when physicians and scientists had only limited abilities to change the course of disease, today they can intervene in profound ways in the most fundamental processes of life and death. Moreover, ethical dilemmas in medicine are no longer considered the sole province of professionals. Professional codes of ethics, to be sure, offer some guidance, but they are usually unclear and ambiguous about what to do in specific situations. More important, these codes assume that whatever decision is to be made is up to the professional, not the patient. Today, to an ever-greater degree, lay people—patients, families, lawyers, clergy, and others—want to and have become involved in ethical decision making not only in individual cases, such as the Quinlan case, but also in large societal decisions, such as how to allocate scarce medical resources, including high technology machinery, newborn intensive care units, and the expertise of physicians. While questions of the physician-patient relationship and individual cases are still prominent in bioethics (see, for example, Issue 4 on truth-telling and Issue 7 on withholding treatment from newborns with birth defects), today the field covers a broad range of other decisions as well: such as the abolition of the insanity defense (Issue 10), harvesting of organs (Issue 16), containing the costs of health care (Issue 18), and the future of genetic engineering (Issue 20).

This involvement is part of broader social trends: a general disenchantment with the authority of all professionals and, hence, a greater readiness to challenge the traditional belief that "doctor knows best;" the growth of various civil rights movements among women, the aged, and minorities—of which the patients' rights movement is a spinoff; the enormous size and complexity of the health care delivery system, in which patients and families often feel alienated from the professional; the increasing cost of medical care, much of it at public expense; the growth of the "medical model" in which conditions that used to be considered outside the scope of physicians' control, such as alcoholism and behavioral problems, have come to be considered diseases.

Bioethics began in the 1950s as an intellectual movement among a small group of physicians and theologians who started to examine the questions raised by the new medical technologies that were starting to emerge as the result of the heavy expenditure of public funds in medical research after World War II. They were soon joined by a number of philosophers who had become disillusioned with what they saw as the arid abstractions of much analytic philosophy at the time, and by lawyers who sought to find principles in the law that would guide ethical decision making or, if such principles were not there, to develop them by case law and legislation or regulation. Although these four disciplines—medicine, theology, philosophy, and law—still dominate the field, today bioethics is an interdisciplinary effort, with political scientists, economists, sociologists, anthropologists, nurses, allied health professionals, policymakers, psychologists, and others contributing their special perspectives to the ongoing debates.

From its modest beginnings bioethics has become a major enterprise. Academic departments have been established in many universities and colleges; it is taught as part of science, philosophy, and other courses and has become part of the curriculum of medical schools, nursing schools, and other professional training; scholars devote their careers to it. Regional and national centers have been established—the best known of which are The Hastings Center in Hastings-on-Hudson, New York, and the Kennedy Institute of Ethics, Center for Bioethics, which is part of Georgetown University in Washington, D.C. The bioethics literature has burgeoned, with encyclopedias, books, periodicals, articles, and newsletters all devoted to the subject matter. Philosophers and other specialists in the humanities have been invited to join the staffs of medical centers and to participate in discussions about decision making, both at the level of individual cases and institutional policies. Two federal commissions—The National Commission for the Protection of Human Subjects of Biomedical and Behavioral Research (1974-1978) and the President's Commission for the Study of Ethical Problems of Medicine and Biomedical and Behavioral Research (1978-1983)—have contributed major reports and recommendations to federal policymakers. And the media have discovered in bioethics an unending source of stories. Scarcely a day goes by without some bioethical dilemma making news: the plight of a family seeking a liver transplant for their baby; a controversial government regulation establishing a "hotline" that people can call when they suspect treatment is being unjustifiably withheld from a baby with a birth defect; a man with leukemia trying to compel a medical center to contact a woman and convince her to donate the bone marrow he hopes will save his life.

The issues discussed in this volume attest to the wide range of bioethical dilemmas, their complexity, and the passion they arouse. But if bioethics today is at the frontiers of scientific knowledge, it is also a field with ancient roots. It goes back to the most basic questions of human life: What is right? What is wrong? How should people act toward others? And why?

While the "bio" part of "bioethics" gives the field its urgency and immediacy, we should not forget that the root word is "ethics."

APPLYING ETHICS TO MEDICAL DILEMMAS

To see where bioethics fits into the larger framework of academic inquiry, some definitions are in order. First, *morality* is the general term for an individual's or a society's standards of conduct, both actual and ideal, and of the character traits that determine whether people are considered "good" or "bad." The scientific study of morality is called *descriptive ethics;* a scientist—generally an anthropologist, sociologist, historian, or other social scientist—can describe in empirical terms what the moral beliefs, judgments, or actions of individuals or societies are and what reasons are given for the way they act or believe. The philosophical study of morality, on the other hand, approaches the subject of morality in one of two different ways: either as an analysis of the concepts, terms, and method of reasoning (*metaethics*) or as an analysis of what those standards or moral judgments ought to be (*normative ethics*). Metaethics deals with meanings of moral terms and logic; normative ethics, with which the issues in this volume are concerned, reflects on the kinds of actions and principles that will promote moral behavior.

Because normative ethics accepts the idea that some kinds of acts and character traits are more moral than others (and that some are immoral), it rejects the rather popular idea that ethics is relative. Because different societies have different moral codes and values, ethical relativists, such as the anthropologist Ruth Benedict, have argued that there can be no universal moral judgments: What is right or wrong depends on who does it and where, and whether society approves. Although it is certainly true that moral values are embedded in a social, cultural, and political context, it is also true that certain moral judgments are universal. We think it is wrong, for example, to sell people into slavery—whether or not a certain society approved or even whether or not the person wanted to be a slave. People may not agree about what these universal moral values are or ought to be (those who are opposed to abortion, for instance, see the protection of fetal life as one of them while pro-choice advocates don't) but it is hard to deny that some such values exist.

The other relativistic view rejected by normative ethics is the notion that whatever feels good *is* good. In this view, ethics is a matter of personal preference, weightier than one's choice of which automobile to buy, but not much different in kind. Different people, having different feelings, can arrive at equally valid moral judgments, according to the relativistic view. Just as we should not disregard cultural factors, we should not overlook the role of emotion and personal experience in arriving at moral judgments. But to give emotion ultimate authority would be to consign reason and rationality—the bases of moral argument—to the ethical trash heap. At the very least, it would be impossible to develop a just policy concerning the care of vulnerable persons, like the mentally retarded or newborns, who depend solely on the vagaries of individual caretakers.

Thus, if normative ethics is one branch of philosophy, bioethics is one branch of normative ethics; it is normative ethics applied to the practice of medicine and science. There are other branches—business ethics, legal ethics, journalism ethics, or military ethics. One common term for the entire grouping is *applied and professional ethics,* because these ethics deal with the ethical standards of the members of a particular profession and how they are applied in the professionals' dealings with each other and the rest of society. Bioethics is based on the belief that some solutions to the dilemmas that arise in medicine and science are more moral than others and that these solutions can be determined by moral reasoning and reflection.

ETHICAL THEORIES

If the practitioners of bioethics do not rely solely on cultural norms and emotions, what are their sources of determining what is right or wrong? The most comprehensive source is a theory of ethics—a broad set of moral principles (or perhaps just one overriding principle) that is used in measuring human conduct. Divine law is one such source, of course, but even in the Western religious traditions of bioethics (both the Jewish and Catholic religions have rich and comprehensive commentaries on ethical issues, and the Protestant religion a less cohesive but still important tradition) the law of God is interpreted in terms of human moral principles. A theory of ethics must be acceptable to many groups, not just the followers of one religious tradition. Most writers outside the religious traditions (and some within them) have looked to one of three major traditions in ethics: teleological theories, deontological theories, and natural law theories.

Teleological theories are based on the idea that the end or purpose (from the Greek *telos* or end) of the action determines its rightness or wrongness. The most prominent teleological theory is *utilitarianism*. In its simplest formulation, an act is moral if it brings more good consequences than bad ones. Utilitarian theories are derived from the works of two English philosophers: Jeremy Bentham (1748-1832) and John Stuart Mill (1806-1873). Rejecting the absolutist religious morality of his time, Bentham proposed that "utility'—the greatest good for the greatest number—should guide the actions of human beings. Invoking the hedonistic philosophy of Epicurean Greeks, Bentham said that pleasure (*hedon* in Greek) is good and pain is bad. Therefore, actions are right if they promote more pleasure than pain and wrong if they promote more pain than pleasure. Mill found the highest utility in "happiness," rather than pleasure. (Mill's philosophy is echoed, you will recall, in the Declaration of Independence's espousal of "life, liberty, and the pursuit of happiness.") Other utilitarians have looked to a range of utilities, or goods (including friendship, love, devotion, and the like) that they believe ought to be weighed in the balance—the utilitarian calculus.

Utilitarianism has a pragmatic appeal. It is flexible, and it seems impartial. However, its critics point out that utilitarianism can be used to justify suppression of individual rights for the good of society ("the ends justify the means") and that it is difficult to quantify and compare "utilities," however they are defined.

Utilitarianism, in its many forms, has had a powerful influence on bioethical discussion, partly because it is the closest to the case-by-case risk/benefit ratio that physicians use in clinical decision making. Joseph Fletcher, a Protestant theologian who was one of the pioneers in bioethics in the 1950s, developed a utilitarian theory that he called "situation ethics." He argued that a true Christian morality does not blindly follow moral rules but acts from love and sensitivity to the particular situation and the needs of those involved. He has enthusiastically supported most modern technologies on the grounds that they lead to good ends.

Another forceful supporter of utilitarianism is Peter Singer, an Australian philosopher who is represented in this volume in Issue 15. Singer's utilitarian calculus includes not only an assessment of the pain and pleasure a particular act causes humans but also how it affects animals. Other writers in this volume who use a utilitarian theory to arrive at their moral judgments are Bernard C. Meyer (Issue 4), who defends the withholding of the truth from dying patients on the grounds that it leads to better consequences than truth-telling, and Clifford Grobstein (Issue 2), who supports in vitro fertilization.

The second major type of ethical theory is *deontological* (from the Greek *deon* or duty). The rightness or wrongness of an act, these theories hold, should be judged on whether it conforms to a moral principle or rule, not on whether it leads to good or bad consequences. The primary exponent of a deontological theory was Immanuel Kant (1724-1804), a German philosopher. Kant declared that there is an ultimate norm, or supreme duty, which he called the "Moral Law." He held that an act is moral only if it springs from what he called a "good will," the only thing that is good without qualification.

We must do good things, said Kant, because we have a duty to do them, not because they result in good consequences or because they give us pleasure (although that can happen as well). Kant constructed a formal "Categorical Imperative," the ultimate test of morality: "I ought never to act except in such a way that I can also will that my maxim should become a universal law." Recognizing that this formulation was far from clear, Kant said the same thing in three other ways. He explained that a moral rule must be one that can serve as a guide for everyone's conduct; it must be one that permits people to treat each other as ends in themselves, not solely as means to another's ends; and it must be one that each person can impose on himself by his own will, not one that is solely imposed by the state, one's parents, or God. Kant's Categorical Imperative, in the simplest terms, says that all persons have equal moral worth and no rule can be moral unless all people can apply it autonomously to all other human beings. Although on its own, Kant's Categorical Imperative is merely a formal statement with no moral content at all, he gave some examples of what he meant: "Do not commit suicide," and "Help others in distress."

Kantian ethics is criticized by many who note that Kant gives little guidance on what to do when ethical principles conflict, as they often do. Moreover, they say, his emphasis on autonomous decision making and individual will neglects the social and communal context in which people live and make decisions. It leads to isolation and unreality. These criticisms notwithstanding, Kantian ethics has stimulated much current thinking in bioethics. The idea that certain actions are in and of themselves wrong underlies, for example, Sissela Bok's appeal to truth-telling (Issue 4) and Thomas Murray's attack on deception in research (Issue 12).

Two modern deontological theorists are the philosophers John Rawls and Robert M. Veatch. In his book *A Theory of Justice* (1971), Rawls places the highest value on equitable distribution of society's resources. He believes that society has a fundamental obligation to correct the inequalities of historical circumstance and natural endowment of its least well-off members. According to this theory, some action is good only if it benefits the least well-off. (It can also benefit others but that is secondary.) His social justice theory has been influential in bioethical writings concerning the allocation of scarce resources.

Robert M. Veatch has applied Rawlsian principles to medical ethics. In his book *A Theory of Medical Ethics* (1981), he offers a model of a social contract among professionals, patients, and society that emphasizes mutual respect and responsibilities. This contract model will, he hopes, avoid the narrowness of professional codes of ethics and the generalities and ambiguities of more broadly-based ethical theories.

The third strain of ethical theory that is prominent in bioethics is *natural law theory*, first developed by St. Thomas Aquinas (1223-1274). According to this theory, actions are morally right if they accord with our nature as human beings. The attribute that is distinctively human is the ability to reason and to exercise intelligence. Thus, argues this theory, we can know the good, which is objective and can be learned through reason. References to natural law theory are prominent in the works of Catholic theologians and writers; they see natural law as ultimately derived from God, but knowable through the efforts of human beings. The influence of natural law theory can be seen in this volume in John T. Noonan, Jr.'s, attack on abortion (Issue 1) and Hans O. Tiefel's condemnation of in vitro fertilization (Issue 2).

The *theory of virtue*, another ethical theory with deep roots in the Aristotelian tradition, has recently been revived in bioethics. This theory stresses not the morality of any particular actions or rules but the disposition of individuals to act morally, to be virtuous. In its modern version its primary exponent is Alasdair MacIntyre, whose book *After Virtue* (1980)urges a return to the Aristotelian model. Gregory Pence has applied the theory of virtues directly to medicine in *Ethical Options in Medicine* (1980); he lists temperance in personal life, compassion for the suffering patient, professional competence, justice, honesty, courage, and practical judgment as the virtues most desirable in physicians. Although this theory has not yet been as fully developed in bioethics as the utilitarian or deontological theories, it is likely to have particular appeal for physicians—many of which have resisted formal ethics education on the grounds that moral charcter is the critical factor and that one can best learn to be a moral physician by emulating the actions of one's mentors.

Although various authors, in this volume and elsewhere, appeal in rather direct ways to either utilitarian or deontological theories, often the various types are combined. One may argue both that a particular action is immoral in and of itself and that it will have bad consequences (some commentators say even Kant used this argument). In fact, probably no single ehtical theory is adequate to deal with all the ramifications of the issues. In that case we can turn to a middle level of ethical discussion. Between the abstractions of ethical theories (Kant's Categorical Imperative) and the specifics of moral judgments (always obtain informed consent from a patient) is a range of concepts—ethical principles—that can be applied to particular cases.

ETHICAL PRINCIPLES

In its four years of deliberation, the National Commission for the Protection of Human Subjects of Biomedical and Behavioral Research grappled with some of the most difficult issues facing researchers and society: When, if ever is it ethical to do research on the fetus (see Issue 14), on children, or on people in mental institutions. This commission—which was composed of people from various religious backgrounds, professions, and social strata—was finally able to agree on specific recommendations on these questions, but only after they had finished their work did the commissioners try to determine what ethical principles they had used in reaching a consensus. (They did not even try to determine what ethical theory they had used or, indeed, if they had used one.) In their Belmont Report (1978), named after the conference center where they met to discuss this question, the commissioners outlined what they considered to be the three most important ethical principles (respect for persons, beneficence, and justice) that should govern the conduct of research with human beings. These three principles, they believed, are generally accepted in our cultural tradition and can serve as basic justifications for the many particular ethical prescriptions and evaluations of human action. Because of the principles' general acceptance and widespread applicability, they are at the basis of most bioethical discussion. Although philosophers argue about whether other principles—preventing harm to others or loyalty, for example—ought to be accorded equal weight with these three or should be included under another umbrella, they agree that these principles are fundamental.

Respect for Persons

Respect for persons incorporates at least two basic ethical convictions, according to the Belmont Report. Individuals should be treated as autonomous agents, and persons with diminished autonomy are entitled to protection. The derivation from Kant is clear. Because human beings have the capacity for rational action and moral choice, they have a value independent of anything that they can do or provide to others. Therefore, they should be treated in a way that respects their independent choices and judgments. Respecting autonomy means giving weight to autonomous persons' considered opinions and choices, and refraining from interfering with their choices unless those choices are clearly detrimental to others. However, since the capacity for autonomy varies by age, mental disability, or other circumstances, those people whose autonomy is diminished must be protected—but only in ways that serve their interests and do not interfere with the level of autonomy that they do possess.

Two important moral rules are derived from the ethical principle of respect for persons: informed consent and truth-telling. Persons can exercise autonomy only when they have been fully informed about the range of options open to them, and the process of informed consent is generally considered to include the elements of information, comprehension, and voluntariness. Thus, a person can give informed consent to some medical procedure only if he or she has full information about the risks and benefits, understands them, and agrees voluntarily—that is, without being coerced or pressured into agreement. Although the principle of informed consent has become an accepted moral rule (and a legal one as well), it is difficult—some say impossible—to achieve in a real-world setting. It can easily be turned into a legalistic parody or avoided altogether. But as a moral ideal it serves to balance the unequal power of the physician and patient.

Another important moral ideal derived from the principle of respect for persons is truth-telling. It held a high place in Kant's theory. In his essay "The Supposed Right to Tell Lies from Benevolent Motives," he wrote: "If, then, we define a lie merely as an intentionally false declaration towards another man, we need not add that it must injure another . . . ; for it always injures another; if not another individual, yet mankind generally. . . . To be truthful in all declarations is therefore a sacred and conditional command of reasons, and not to be limited by any other expediency." (See Issue 4 for a discussion of truth-telling.)

Other important moral rules that are derived from the principle of respect for persons are confidentiality and privacy. (See Issue 9 for a discussion of whether it is justifiable to override the confidentiality that underlies the therapeutic relationship in order to protect a third party from potential violence.)

Beneficence

Most physicians would probably consider beneficence (from the Greek *bene* or good) the most basic ethical principle. In the Hippocratic Oath it is used this way: "I will apply dietetic measures for the benefit of the sick according to my ability and judgment; I will keep them from harm and injustice." And further on, "Whatever houses I may visit, I will comfort and benefit the sick, remaining free of all intentional injustice." The phrase, *Primum non nocere* (First, do no harm), is another well-known version of this idea, but it appears to be a much-later, Latinized version—not from the Hippocratic period.

The philosopher William Frankena has outlined four elements included in the principle of beneficence: (1) one ought not to inflict evil or harm; (2) one ought to prevent evil or harm; (3) one ought to remove evil or harm; and (4) one ought to do or promote good. Frankena arranged these elements in hierarchical order, so that the first takes precedence over the second, and so on. In this scheme, it is more important to avoid doing evil or harm than to do good. But in the Belmont Report, beneficence is understood as an obligation—first to do no harm, and second, to maximize possible benefits and minimize possible harms.

The principle of beneficence is at the basis of the distinction between killing and letting die (see Issue 5); Herbert Hendin's attack on "rational suicide" (see Issue 8) and Joann Lynn and James Childress's defense of withholding fluids and nutrition from some dying patients (see Issue 6).

Justice

The third ethical principle that is generally accepted is justice, which means "what is fair" or "what is deserved." An injustice occurs when some benefit to which a person is entitled is denied without good reason or when some burden is imposed unduly, according to the Belmont Report. Another way of interpreting the principle is to say that equals should be treated equally. However, some distinctions—such as age, experience, competence, physical condition, and the like—can justify unequal treatment. Those who appeal to the principle of justice are most concerned about which distinctions can be made legitimately and which ones cannot.

One important derivative of the principle of justice is the recent emphasis on "rights" in bioethics. Given the successes in the 1960s and 1970s of civil rights movements in the courts and political arena, it is easy to understand the appeal of "rights talk." An emphasis on individual rights is part of the American tradition, in a way that emphasis on the "common good" is not. The language of rights has been prominent in the abortion debate, for instance, where the "right to life" has been pitted against the "right to privacy" or the "right to control one's body." The "right to health care" is a potent rallying cry, though it is one that is difficult to enforce legally. Although claims to rights may be effective in marshalling political support and in emphasizing moral ideals, those rights may not be the most effective way to solve ethical dilemmas. Our society, as philosopher Ruth Macklin has pointed out, has not yet agreed on a theory of justice in health care that will determine who has what kinds of rights and—the other side of the coin—who has the obligation to fulfill them.

WHEN PRINCIPLES CONFLICT

These three fundamental ethical principles—beneficence, respect for persons, and justice—all carry weight in ethical decision making. But what happens when they conflict? That is what this book is all about.

On each side of the issues included in this volume are writers who appeal, explicitly or implicitly, to one or more of these principles. For example, in Issue 11, Thomas S. Szasz sees respect for persons as paramount: Let people decide autonomously, he argues, whether or not they would wish to be treated in a psychiatric hospital against their will. But Paul Chodoff looks to beneficence as the overriding principle, arguing that it is sometimes necessary to ignore autonomy in order to benefit people—and living a life without psychosis is clearly a benefit. In Issue 1, John T. Noonan, Jr., appeals to justice in establishing his case against abortion: Fetuses are human, he declares, and have been considered so for centuries; therefore it is unfair to treat them differently from the way we treat other humans and to allow their destruction. But Beverly Wildung Harrison sees autonomy as more important: Let the woman decide, she says, whether she is morally capable of assuming the responsibilities of motherhood.

Some of the issues are concerned with how to interpret a particular principle: Whether, for example, it is more beneficent to allow old and sick people to commit suicide or to prevent it (Issue 8), or whether a totally voluntary system of obtaining organs for transplant is more just than one that involves some required interventions (see Issue 17).

Will it ever be possible to resolve such fundamental divisions—those that are not merely matters of procedure or interpretation but of fundamental differences in principle? Lest the situation seem hopeless, consider that some consensus does seem to have been reached on questions that seemed equally tangled a few decades ago. The idea that government should play a role in regulating human subjects research was hotly debated, but it is now generally accepted (at least if the research is medical, not social or behavioral in nature and is federally funded). And the appropriateness of using criteria of brain death for determining the death of a person (and the possibility of subsequent removal of their organs for transplantation) has largely been accepted and written into state laws. The idea that a hopelessly ill patient has the legal and moral right to refuse treatment that will only prolong dying is also well established (though it is often hard to exercise because hospitals and physicians continue to resist it). Finally, nearly everyone now agrees that health care is distributed unjustly in this country—a radical idea only a few years ago. There is of course sharp disagreement about whose responsibility it is to rectify the situation—the government's or the private sector's.

But if there is consensus in some areas, in others there is none. As Daniel Callahan, director of The Hastings Center, has noted in an article in the *New England Journal of Medicine,* it may be harder to deal with the next round of problems precisely because they will confront fundamental issues of principle. Such issues are now being questioned in the arguments over abortion and the future of genetic engineering (see Issue 20). Callahan suggests that no single moral principle may be adequate to resolve the issues and that bioethics will have to move into the mainstream of political and social theory—beyond the model of the individual decision maker and into the "thicket of important vested and legitimate private and group interests."

The challenge for bioethics in the future is to avoid the extremes of idiosyncratic ethical decision making and what philosopher Stephen Toulmin has called the "tyranny of principle." Robert S. Morison, a physician who has observed the development of bioethics for more than two decades, wrote in an article in the *Hastings Center Report:* "Perhaps all general truths or principles are useful over only a limited range. Professional wise men like Emerson and Henry Adams have equated maturity with the ability to tolerate ambiguity; even the physicists have found that there comes a point at which they can no longer explain everything in terms either of particles or of waves." This book will introduce you to the particles and the waves of bioethics. Whether we will be able to move beyond them to a realm of moral consensus will depend on society's willingness to struggle with these issues and to make the hard choices that are required.

Photo courtesy of Arkansas Department of Parks and Tourism.

PART I
CHOICES IN
REPRODUCTION

Few bioethical issues could be of greater significance than questions concerning reproduction. This is an area frought with conflicting and competing interests and precedents that are established could have important implications for the future. Advances in medical technology, such as in vitro fertilization, and changes in social mores that have made surrogate mothering more acceptable have opened new possibilities to couples who might otherwise not have been able to have children. With these new capabilities come new ethical questions. The issues in this section come to grips with some of the most perplexing and fundamental questions that confront medical practitioners and society.

Is Abortion Immoral?
_____

Is it Wrong to Create Test-Tube Babies?
_____

Should Women Be Allowed to Bear Babies for a Fee?
_____

ISSUE I

IS ABORTION IMMORAL?

YES: John T. Noonan, Jr., from "An Almost Absolute Value in History," from *The Morality of Abortion: Legal and Historical Perspectives* (Cambridge: Harvard University Press, 1970)

NO: Beverly Wildung Harrison, from *Our Right to Choose: Toward a New Ethics of Abortion* (Boston: Beacon Press, 1983)

ISSUE SUMMARY

YES: Professor of law John T. Noonan, Jr., believes that a fetus is human because it is conceived by human parents and that it is just as wrong to destroy its life as it would be to destroy the life of any human.
NO: Professor of Christian ethics Beverly Wildung Harrison argues that women ought to decide whether or not to bear children on the basis of their own moral preparedness to become responsible mothers.

Abortion is the most divisive bioethical issue of our time. The issue has been a persistent one in history, but in the past twenty years or so the debate has polarized. One view—known as "pro-life"—sees abortion as the wanton slaughter of innocent life. The other view—"pro-choice"—considers abortion as an option that must be available to women if they are to control their own reproductive lives. In the pro-life view, women who have access to "abortion on demand" put their own selfish whims ahead of an unborn child's right to life. In the pro-choice view, women have the right to choose to have an abortion—especially if there is some overriding reason, such as preventing the birth of a child with a severe genetic defect or one conceived as a result of rape or incest.

Behind these strongly-held convictions, as political scientist Mary Segers has pointed out, are widely differing views of what determines value (that is, whether value is inherent in a thing or ascribed to it by human beings), the relation between law and morality, and the use of limits of political solutions to social problems, as well as the value of scientific progress. Those who condemn abortion as immoral generally follow a classical tradition in which abortion is a public matter because it involves our conception of how we

14

ought to live together in an ideal society. Those who accept the idea of abortion, on the other hand, generally share the liberal, individualistic ethos of contemporary society. To them, abortion is a private choice, and public policy ought to reflect how citizens actually behave, not some unattainable ideal.

This is what we know about abortion practices in America today: It has been legal since the 1973 Supreme Court decision of *Roe* v. *Wade* declared that a woman has a constitutional right to privacy, which includes an abortion. It is seven times safer than childbirth, although there are some known risks—primarily psychological—and some unknown ones—primarily the effect of repeated abortions on subsequent pregnancies. Abortion is common; in 1983, the last year for which complete figures are available, 1.15 million abortions were performed. That is, one out of four pregnancies (and half of all unintended pregnancies) ended in abortion. About ninety percent of all abortions are performed within the first twelve weeks of pregnancy by a method called suction aspiration. Eighty percent of the women who have abortions are unmarried, and nearly sixty-three percent are between the ages of fifteen and twenty-four. (In comparison, however, in 1965 there were between 200 thousand and 1.2 million illegal abortions, and twenty percent of all deaths from childbirth or pregnancy were caused by botched abortions.)

If abortion today is legal, safe, and common, it undeniably involves the killing of fetal life, and so the question remains: Is it ethical? At the heart of the issue are two complex questions. Does the fetus have a moral status that entitles it to life, liberty, and the pursuit of happiness as guaranteed by the Constitution? And even if it does, does a woman's rights to the same freedoms outweigh those of the fetus?

In the selections that follow, John T. Noonon, Jr., draws on the long history of religious and humanistic thought to support his claim that, from the moment of conception, a fetus is human and entitled to every protection. Beverly Wildung Harrison draws on another strand in ethical thought—concern for the quality of human life—and combines it with a feminist perspective to assert that some abortions, particularly early ones, are moral because they are the result of a woman's careful assessment of her capacities for motherhood.

YES
John T. Noonan, Jr.

AN ALMOST ABSOLUTE VALUE
IN HISTORY

. . . The most fundamental question involved in the long history of thought on abortion is: How do you determine the humanity of a being? To phrase the question that way is to put in comprehensive humanistic terms what the theologians either dealt with as an explicitly theological question under the heading of "ensoulment" or dealt with implicitly in their treatment of abortion. The Christian position as it originated did not depend on a narrow theological or philosophical concept. It had no relation to theories of infant baptism.[1] It appealed to no special theory of instantaneous ensoulment. It took the world's view on ensoulment as that view changed from Aristotle to Zacchia. There was, indeed, theological influence affecting the theory of ensoulment finally adopted, and, of course, ensoulment itself was a theological concept, so that the position was always explained in theological terms. But the theological notion of ensoulment could easily be translated into humanistic language by substituting "human" for "rational soul"; the problem of knowing when a man is a man is common to theology and humanism.

If one steps outside the specific categories used by the theologians, the answer they gave can be analyzed as a refusal to discriminate among human beings on the basis of their varying potentialities. Once conceived, the being was recognized as man because he had man's potential. The criterion for humanity, thus, was simple and all-embracing: if you are conceived by human parents, you are human.

The strength of this position may be tested by a review of some of the other distinctions offered in the contemporary controversy over legalizing abortion. Perhaps the most popular distinction is in terms of viability. Before an age of so many months, the fetus is not viable, that is, it cannot be removed from the mother's womb and live apart from her. To that extent, the life of the fetus is absolutely dependent on the life of the mother. This dependence is made the basis of denying recognition to its humanity.

There are difficulties with this distinction. One is that the perfection of artificial incubation may make the fetus viable at any time: it may be removed and artificially sustained. Experiments with animals already show that such a procedure is possible.[2] This hypothetical extreme case relates to an actual difficulty: there is considerable elasticity to the idea of viability. Mere length of life is not an exact measure. The viability of the fetus depends on the extent of its anatomical and functional development.[3] The weight and length of the fetus are better guides to the state of its development than age, but weight and length vary.[4] Moreover, different racial groups have different ages at which their fetuses are viable. Some evidence, for example, suggests that Negro fetuses mature more quickly than white fetuses.[5] If viability is the norm, the standard would vary with race and with many individual circumstances.

The most important objection to this approach is that dependence is not ended by viability. The fetus is still absolutely dependent on someone's care in order to continue existence; indeed a child of one or three or even five years of age is absolutely dependent on another's care for existence; uncared for, the older fetus or the younger child will die as surely as the early fetus detached from the mother. The unsubstantial lessening in dependence at viability does not seem to signify any special acquisition of humanity.

A second distinction has been attempted in terms of experience. A being who has had experience, has lived and suffered, who possesses memories, is more human than one who has not. Humanity depends on formation by experience. The fetus is thus "unformed" in the most basic human sense.[6]

This distinction is not serviceable for the embryo which is already experiencing and reacting. The embryo is responsive to touch after eight weeks[7] and at least at that point is experiencing. At an earlier stage the zygote is certainly alive and responding to its environment.[8] The distinction may also be challenged by the rare case where aphasia has erased adult memory: has it erased humanity? More fundamentally, this distinction leaves even the older fetus or the younger child to be treated as an unformed inhuman thing. Finally, it is not clear why experience as such confers humanity. It could be argued that certain central experiences such as loving or learning are necessary to make a man human. But then human beings who have failed to love or to learn might be excluded from the class called man.

A third distinction is made by appeal to the sentiments of adults. If a fetus dies, the grief of the parents is not the grief they would have for a living child. The fetus is an unnamed "it" till birth, and is not perceived as personality until at least the fourth month of existence when movements in the womb manifest a vigorous presence demanding joyful recognition by the parents.

Yet feeling is notoriously an unsure guide to the humanity of others. Many groups of humans have had difficulty in feeling that persons of another tongue, color, religion, sex, are as human as they. Apart from reactions to alien groups, we mourn the loss of a ten-year-old boy more than the loss of his one-day-old brother or his 90-year-old grandfather. The difference felt and the grief expressed vary with the potentialities extinguished, or the experience wiped out; they do not seem to point to any substantial difference in the humanity of baby, boy, or grandfather.

Distinctions are also made in terms of sensation by the parents. The embryo is felt within the womb only after about the fourth month.[9] The embryo is seen only at birth. What can be neither seen nor felt is different from what is tangible. If the fetus cannot be seen or touched at all, it cannot be perceived as man.

Yet experience shows that sight is even more untrustworthy than feeling in determining humanity. By sight, color became an appropriate index for saying who was a man, and the evil of racial discrimination was given foundation. Nor can touch provide the test; a being confined by sickness, "out of touch" with others, does not thereby seem to lose his humanity. To the extent that touch still has appeal as a criterion, it appears to be a survival of the old English idea of "quickening"—a possible mistranslation of the Latin *animatus* used in the canon law.[10] To that extent touch as a criterion seems to be dependent on the Aristotelian notion of ensoulment, and to fall when this notion is discarded.

Finally, a distinction is sought in social visibility. The fetus is not socially perceived as human. It cannot communicate with others. Thus, both subjectively and objectively, it is not a member of society. As moral rules are rules for the behavior of members of society to each other, they cannot be made for behavior toward what is not yet a member. Excluded from the society of men, the fetus is excluded from the humanity of men.[11]

By force of the argument from the consequences, this distinction is to be rejected. It is more subtle than that founded on an appeal to physical sensation, but it is equally dangerous in its implications. If humanity depends on social recognition, individuals or whole groups may be dehumanized by being denied any status in their society. Such a fate is fictionally portrayed in *1984* and has actually been the lot of many men in many societies. In the Roman empire, for example, condemnation to slavery meant the practical denial of most human rights; in the Chinese Communist world, landlords have been classified as enemies of the people and so treated as nonpersons by the state. Humanity does not depend on social recognition, though often the failure of society to recognize the prisoner, the alien, the heterodox as human has led to the destruction of human beings. Anyone conceived by a man and a woman is human. Recognition of this condition by society follows a real event in the objective order, however imperfect and halting the recognition. Any attempt to limit humanity to exclude some group runs the risk of furnishing authority and precedent for excluding other groups in the name of the consciousness or perception of the controlling group in the society.

A philosopher may reject the appeal to the humanity of the fetus because he views "humanity" as a secular view of the soul and because he doubts the existence of anything real and objective which can be identified as humanity.[12] One answer to such a philosopher is to ask how he reasons about moral questions without supposing that there is a sense in which he and the others of whom he speaks are human. Whatever group is taken as the society which determines who may be killed is thereby taken as human. A second answer is to ask if he does not believe that there is a right and wrong way of deciding moral questions. If there is such a difference, experience may be appealed to: to decide who is human on the basis of the sentiment of a given society has led to consequences which rational men would characterize as monstrous.

The rejection of the attempted distinctions based on viability and visibility, experience and feeling, may be buttressed by the following considerations: Moral judgments often rest on distinctions, but if the distinctions are not to appear arbitrary fiat, they should relate to some real difference in probabilities. There is a kind of continuity in all life, but the earlier stages of the elements of human life possess tiny probabilities of development. Consider for example, the spermatozoa in any normal ejaculate: There are about 200,000,000 in any single ejaculate, of which one has a chance of developing into a zygote.[13] Consider the oocytes which may become ova: there are 100,000 to 1,000,000 oocytes in a female infant, of which a maximum of 390 are ovulated.[14] But once spermatozoon and ovum meet and the conceptus is formed, such studies as have been made show that roughly in only 20 percent of the cases will spontaneous abortion occur.[15] In other words, the chances are about 4 out of 5 that this new being will develop. At this stage in the life of the being there is a sharp shift in probabilities, an immense jump in potentialities. To make a distinction between the rights of spermatozoa and the rights of the fertilized ovum is to respond to an enormous shift in possibilities. For about twenty days after conception the egg may split to form twins or combine with another egg to form a chimera, but the probability of either event happening is very small.

It may be asked. What does a change in biological probabilities have to do with establishing humanity? The argument from probabilities is not aimed at establishing humanity but at establishing an objective discontinuity which may be taken into account in moral discourse. As life itself is a matter of probabilities, as most moral reasoning is an estimate of probabilities, so it seems in accord with the structure of reality and the nature of moral thought to found a moral judgment on the change in probabilities at conception. The appeal to probabilities is the most commonsensical of arguments, to a greater or smaller degree all of us base our actions on probabilities, and in morals, as in law, prudence and negligence are often measured by the account one has taken of the probabilities. If the chance is 200,000,000 to 1 that the movement in the bushes into which you shoot is a man's, I doubt if many persons would hold you careless in shooting; but if the chances are 4 out of 5 that the movement is a human being's, few would acquit you of blame. Would the argument be different if only one out of ten children conceived came to term? Of course this argument would be different. This argument is an appeal to probabilities that actually exist, not to any and all states of affairs which may be imagined.

The probabilities as they do exist do not show the humanity of the embryo in the sense of a demonstration in logic any more than the probabilities of the movement in the bush being a man demonstrate beyond all doubt that the being is a man. The appeal is a "buttressing" consideration, showing the plausibility of the standard adopted. The argument focuses on the decisional factor in any moral judgment and assumes that part of the business of a moralist is drawing lines. One evidence of the nonarbitrary character of the line drawn is the difference of probabilities on either side of it. If a spermatozoon is destroyed, one destroys a being which had a chance of far less than 1 in 200 million of developing into a reasoning being, possessed of the genetic code, a heart and other organs, and capable of pain. If a fetus is destroyed, one destroys a being already possessed of the genetic code, organs, and sensitivity to pain, and one which had an 80 percent chance of developing further

19

into a baby outside the womb who, in time, would reason.

The positive argument for conception as the decisive moment of humanization is that at conception the new being receives the genetic code.[16] It is this genetic information which determines his characteristics, which is the biological carrier of the possibility of human wisdom, which makes him a self-evolving being. A being with a human genetic code is man.

This review of current controversy over the humanity of the fetus emphasizes what a fundamental question the theologians resolved in asserting the inviolability of the fetus. To regard the fetus as possessed of equal rights with other humans was not, however, to decide every case where abortion might be employed. It did decide the case where the argument was that the fetus should be aborted for its own good. To say a being was human was to say it had a destiny to decide for itself which could not be taken from it by another man's decision. But human beings with equal rights often come in conflict with each other, and some decision must be made as whose claims are to prevail. Cases of conflict involving the fetus are different only in two respects: the total inability of the fetus to speak for itself and the fact that the right of the fetus regularly at stake is the right to life itself.

The approach taken by the theologians to these conflicts was articulated in terms of "direct" and "indirect." Again, to look at what they were doing from outside their categories, they may be said to have been drawing lines or "balancing values." "Direct" and "indirect" are spatial metaphors; "line-drawing" is another. "To weigh" or "to balance" values is a metaphor of a more complicated mathematical sort hinting at the process which goes on in moral judgments. All the metaphors suggest that, in the moral judgments made, compari-

sons were necessary, that no value completely controlled. The principle of double effect was no doctrine fallen from heaven, but a method of analysis appropriate where two relative values were being compared. In Catholic moral theology, as it developed, life even of the innocent was not taken as an absolute. Judgments on acts affecting life issued from a process of weighing. In the weighing, the fetus was always given a value greater than zero, always a value separate and independent from its parents. This valuation was crucial and fundamental in all Christian thought on the subject and marked it off from any approach which considered that only the parents' interests needed to be considered.

Even with the fetus weighed as human, one interest could be weighed as equal or superior: that of the mother in her own life. The casuists between 1450 and 1895 were willing to weigh this interest as superior. Since 1895, that interest was given decisive weight only in the two special cases of the cancerous uterus and the ectopic pregnancy. In both of these cases the fetus itself had little chance of survival even if the abortion were not performed. As the balance was once struck in favor of the mother whenever her life was endangered, it could be so struck again. The balance reached between 1895 and 1930 attempted prudentially and pastorally to forestall a multitude of exceptions for interests less than life.

The perception of the humanity of the fetus and the weighing of fetal rights against other human rights constituted the work of the moral analysts. But what spirit animated their abstract judgments? For the Christian community it was the injunction of Scripture to love your neighbor as yourself. The fetus as human was a neighbor; his life had parity with one's own. The commandment gave life to what otherwise would have been only rational calculation.

The commandment could be put in humanistic as well as theological terms: Do not injure your fellow man without reason. In these terms, once the humanity of the fetus is perceived, abortion is never right except in self-defense. When life must be taken to save life, reason alone cannot say that a mother must prefer a child's life to her own. With this exception, now of great rarity, abortion violates the rational humanist tenet of the equality of human lives. . . .

NOTES

1   According to Glanville Williams (*The Sanctity of Human Life supra* n. 169, at 193), "The historical reason for the Catholic objection to abortion is the same as for the Christian Church's historical opposition to infanticide: the horror of bringing about the death of an unbaptized child." This statement is made without any citation of evidence. As has been seen, desire to administer baptism could, in the Middle Ages, even be urged as a reason for procuring an abortion. It is highly regrettable that the American Law Institute was apparently misled by Williams' account and repeated after him the same baseless statement. See American Law Institute, *Model Penal Code: Tentative Draft No. 9* (1959), p. 148, n. 12.

2   E.g., R.L. Brinster and J.L. Thomson, "Development of Eight-Cell Mouse Embryos in Vitro," 42 *Experimental Cell Research* 308 (1966).
3   J. Edgar Morison, *Fetal and Neonatal Pathology* 99-100 (1963).
4   Peter Gruenwald, "Growth of the Human Fetus," 94 *American Journal of Obstetrics and Gynecology* 1112 (1966).
5   Morison, *Fetal and Neonatal Pathology supra* n. 175, at 101.
6   This line of thought was advanced by some participants at the International Conference on Abortion sponsored by the Harvard Divinity School in cooperation with the Joseph P. Kennedy, Jr., Foundation in Washington, D.C., Sept. 8-10, 1967.
7   Frank D. Allan, *Essentials of Human Embryology* 165 (1960).
8   Frederick J. Gottleib, *Developmental Genetics* 28 (1966).
9   Allan, *Essentials for Human Embryology supra* n. 179, at 165.
10   See David W. Louisell and John T. Noonan, Jr., "Constitutional Balance," *infra.*
11   Another line of thought advanced at the Conference mentioned in n. 178. Thomas Aquinas gave an analogous reason against baptizing a fetus in the womb: "As long as it exists in the womb of the mother, it cannot be subject to the operation of the ministers of the Church as it is not known to men" (*In sententias Petri Lombardi* 4.6 1.1.2).
12   Compare John O'Connor, "Humanity and Abortion," 12 *Natural Law Forum* 128-130 (1968), with John T. Noonan, Jr. "Deciding Who Is Human," 12 *Natural Law Forum* 134-138.
13   J.S. Baxter, *Frazer's Manual of Embryology* 5 (1963).
14   Gregory Pincus, *The Control of Fertility* 197 (1965).
15   *Idem.* Apparently there is some small variation by region.
16   Gottleib, *Developmental Genetics supra* n. 180, at 17.

NO

Beverly Wildung Harrison

OUR RIGHT TO CHOOSE

THE WIDER MORAL FRAMEWORK FOR THE ACT OF ABORTION

... I argue that a society which would deny the conditions of procreative choice to women, or which treats women merely or chiefly as reproductive means to some purported end of that society's own self-perpetuation, is one that mandates women's inferior status as less than full, rational beings, denying women full claim to intrinsic value in the process. Likewise, a society that incorporates a perdurable structure of coercion, even violence, against women as morally appropriate to its functioning, but claims that it upholds the sanctity of or respect for human life is deluded. ...

It is little wonder, then, that feminist efforts to articulate a moral argument about bodily integrity and its relevance to procreation are met with almost incredulous disbelief, derision, or trivialization in the ethical literature on abortion. To be sure, when fetal life is adjudged full, existent human life, appeals to body-right will not have automatic, overriding force because where two existent human beings are involved there will be a conflict of rights. (Such conflicts occur all the time in our social world.) But this recognition of *possible* conflict of rights is not usually what is assumed in discussions of the morality of abortion. Rather, appeals women make to their right to bodily self-control and self-direction are treated, at best, as nonmoral, morally irrelevant, or ethically confused and, at worst, as selfish, whimsical, or positive evidence of the immorality of women who choose to have or to defend legal abortions.

I claim that the fact of women's biological fertility and capacity for childbearing in no way overrides our moral claim to the "right" of bodily integrity, because this moral claim is inherent to human well-being. Further-more, if the full implications of women's history were comprehended, including the morally onerous attitudes and violent practices toward women, then reproductive self-determination would be understood to reinforce the substantive social justice claim about bodily integrity. Reproductive choice for women is requisite to any adequate notion of what constitutes a good society. Transformed social conditions of reproduction are absolutely critical to all women's well-being. No society that coerces women at the level of reproduction may lay claim to moral adequacy.

I agree strongly with those who have argued that the notion of "rights" is intrinsically social; it pertains to conditions of relationship between existent beings. I would insist one ought not to impute the existence of "rights" in a social relation unless all parties fall within some justifiable definition of "existents" vis-à-vis our human relations. In discussing the moral meaning of fetal life, we cannot afford to overlook the social character of "rights." When anyone invokes the claim that a fetus has "a right to life," we are justified in being wary, unless or until a plausible account is given of the criteria grounding the contention that a fetus is properly a full member of the class of human beings.

I have also stressed a more utilitarian or "concrete consequentialist" argument for procreative choice that correlates with but is logically discrete from the foregoing one: namely that given women's overall, continuing, disadvantaged socioeconomic situation, together with the de facto reality of childbearing, women should have procreative choice. Women most frequently must provide the life energy, physical and emotional support, and, increasingly, the economic wherewithal for infant survival, growth, and development. Under such circumstances, optimal conditions of procreative choice for women are mandatory.

I have constructed my case to put both good society or rights arguments and utilitarian teleological arguments in the forefront, not only because of my own methodological convictions but, even more important, because so much con-

temporary philosophical and religioethical analysis approaches the morality of abortion with such a weak sense of the relevance of these considerations. No moralist would be considered reputable if he or she argued the morality of economic life either by abdicating reflection on the meaning of a good society or by ignoring the concrete effects of economic policy and practice on people's lives. But, indeed, it *is* acceptable to discuss the morality of abortion without examining the implications of our moral judgments on what a "good society" should be and without taking into account the actual condition of women in society. Hence my ongoing contention is that, given the present climate of opinion among ethicists, it is necessary to insist that the positive principle of justice and the issue of social welfare, or social utility, are both at stake in procreative choice, or noncoercion in childbearing.

If one approaches the question of the morality of abortion without an acute sense of the viability of all these moral claims, then the question of the moral valuation of fetal life inevitably appears to be the only relevant question and the moral problematic of abortion seems to pose a fairly simple moral quandary. If, however, one recognizes the moral dubiousness of a society that treats women as less than full persons with an appropriate and serious moral claim to well-being, self-respect, self-direction and noncoercion in childbearing, and if one also recognizes the disadvantaged state of most women's lives, one's approach to the morality of abortion must shift. Even if one holds, as I do *not,* that fetal life is, from conception or at the point when the genetic code is implanted, essentially a *full, existent* human life, it is necessary to comprehend that we are dealing with a genuine moral dilemma, a conflict of "rights," not a moral chimera in which the "innocent party"—the fetal "person"—is, *by defini-tion, the* "wronged" party in the moral equation.

To address the question "When does human life begin?" or to ask more precisely "What is the moral status of fetal life?" is something we are bound to do, given our modern scientific understanding of embryological development. Yet the questions are a far more intricate matter than they may appear at face value. Biological science itself is a complex, cultural construct, and biological scientists themselves differ over the moral implications of their paradigm. None of us nontechnical interpreters of these scientific data proceed untouched by our own operating cultural and social understandings. In fact, beneath the diverse judgments moralists make about the meaning of fetal life lie differing philosophies of nature and of science, including quite disparate views of biological theory, as well as conflicting methodological assumptions about how scientific "fact" and moral valuation interrelate. . . .

Even though there are reasonable grounds for positing the existence of a genetically developed individuated human body form from sometime after the midpoint of pregnancy onward, it does not follow that we should consider a fetus to be "a person" from this earliest possible point of species differentiation. Many have argued that the term *person* should be reserved to designate those who *actually belong* to the moral community by virtue of criteria derived from our understanding of living human beings. In a notable defense of this position, philosopher Mary Anne Warren has proposed the following criteria for "personhood":

> I suggest that the traits which are most central to the concept of personhood, or humanity in the moral sense, are, very roughly, the following:

1. consciousness (of objects and events external and/or internal to the being), and in particular the capacity to feel pain;
2. reasoning (the developed capacity to solve new and relatively complex problems);
3. self-motivated activity (activity which is relatively independent of either genetic or direct external control);
4. the capacity to communicate, by whatever means, messages of an indefinite variety of types, that is, not just with an indefinite number of possible contents, but on indefinitely many possible topics;
5. the presence of self-concepts, and self-awareness, either individual or social, or both.

Warren does not suppose that any of these criteria are indisputable, but what she does maintain, correctly I believe, is that a fetus possesses *none* of the criteria that come to mind when we think normatively of a "person." . . .

In the debate over the morality of abortion, those who correlate "personhood" with any level of gestational maturation seem to me to obscure, or to fail to appreciate, the integrity of arguments formulated by pro-choice supporters about the importance of "quality of life" questions regarding procreation or birth. Whether or not we wish to acknowledge it, the constitutive foundations of personality are bound up not with biological maturation of the human species life form but with the quality of our social relations. For centuries, even millennia, we human beings have permitted ourselves the luxury of imagining that our personal life follows inexorably from our existence as a natural or species life form, ignoring the now growing evidence that it is our human social relations, the quality of our interaction with each other, that conditions all that we become after birth. Ours is a world in which there is "a crisis of the personal"—that is, a loss of the very conditions that make it possible for individuals who share human species being to live, grow, and thrive as genuinely personal beings having deeply centered personal relations to others. A biologically reductionist understanding of our species, which fully conflates the biologically human and the "person," threatens to intensify this crisis in our human moral relations. Ironically, the "fetishizing of fetuses" in the abortion debate may well exacerbate our already overdeveloped tendency to consider ourselves "normatively human" quite apart from the world of social relations our moral action creates. The birth of an infant, understood from the standpoint of organic embryological development, is an event. Birth is an inexorable watershed in organic process, however, because the care and nurturance of a newborn inaugurates an infinitely complex series of actions. . . .

With respect to the abortion controversy, it is worth remembering that any definition of "a human life" or "person" that neglects the moral reality required to nurture and sustain life after birth is very dangerous to our self-understanding. A "pro-life" movement that invites us to "respect" fetal rights from conception or genetic implantation onward actually undermines us by tempting us to imagine that personal rights inhere in natural processes, apart from any genuine covenant of caring, including the human resolve to create viable conditions of life for all who are born among us. Human rights are qualities that ought to inhere in our social relations. Any use of the concept that neglects this fact invites us to take with less than full seriousness the sort of claim we ought to be making when we say that human beings have "a right to life." Early fetal life does not yet possess

even the minimal organic requirements for participation in the sphere of human rights. And like Mary Anne Warren, I do not believe that even the highly developed fetus can yet be said to have "an intrinsic right to life." Even so, I recognize that it is morally wise to extend such respect, de facto, to fetuses in late stages of gestation. But to do so is also and simultaneously to insist that rights are moral relations, born of our freedom as mature, other-regarding persons. In extending "a right to life" to fetuses in late stages of development, we are attesting that it is a good use of our freedom as agents, from a moral point of view, to do so.

To argue that we may appropriately predicate to fetuses, in the late stages of gestation, "a right to life" does not mean, however, that the life of the pregnant woman should be overridden in decisions about late-stage pregnancies. Rather, it means that abortions, at least in the second half of gestation, are not to be undertaken without serious justifications. My own belief is that the physical and emotional well-being of the pregnant woman, as a valuable existent person, still outweighs the incremental value of the fetus her life sustains. Of course, it is true that in the later stages of pregnancy, abortions are matters of high risk for pregnant women. But doctors, who under most existing laws have discretion as to whether an abortion is advisable at this stage, are themselves not likely to be "frivolous" about the decisions that confront them given the danger of late abortions. . . .

[A]bortions will continue to be available whether or not they are legal. Ironically, then, those persons insisting that a human life begins at conception or at an early stage of genetic human development may help to create a situation in which abortions, though they will not cease, will occur at a later stage of gestation. . . .

Persons of authentic theological sensibility must continue to insist that every child who is born among us deserves to be embraced in a covenant of love and affirmation that includes not merely the love of a mother, or a father, but the active concern and respect of the wider community. We must never imagine that the conditions for such deeply humane covenant exist. I noted at the outset that if women did not have to deliberate the questions relating to our procreative power in an atmosphere of taboo, we would be able to turn our attention to the positive moral task I have commended: what it means for us to use our procreative power responsibly. In the present condemnatory atmosphere, such moral reasoning will go largely undeveloped.

Even so, the deepest reappropriation of the theological theme of the covenant that women can make requires our perception of procreation as a moral act, one we must enter into with maximum awareness of what it means to bear a child. We are still a long way from a historical situation in which women really will have the conditions that make such a genuine covenant and choice an easy matter. Safe surgical abortion has created only the negative conditions for procreative choice. We often now live in situations where it is easier to say no than to say yes to this prospective covenant. The current circumstances in which women choose abortions are often dominated by desperation. And yet it is now possible to begin to anticipate what it would mean to incorporate this covenantal image into the total process of species reproduction. When such a covenant of life is embodied in the birth of every child, an incredible reduction in human suffering will have been accomplished.

Any of us who have experienced human joy in the knowledge of our birth at some level have heard God's call to life through the "yes" of our parents. Without that yes, life is immeasurably impoverished. In fact, it is necessary to put the point more strongly. Those who are born in the absence of such an act of human covenant by already living persons (of course, not merely by our biological parents) frequently do not really live at all. Our acknowledgment of each other in relation is not an optional addition to life, an afterthought; it is constitutive of life itself. For a vital human life to be born, a woman must say yes in a strong and active way and enter positively into a life-bearing, demanding, and, at times, extremely painful process. Freedom to say yes, which, of course, also means the freedom to say no, is constitutive of the sacred covenant of life itself. Failure to see this is also failure to see how good, how strong and real, embodied existence is in this world we are making together. . . .

POSTSCRIPT

IS ABORTION IMMORAL?

In June 1983, in a series of cases, the Supreme Court reaffirmed its support of the legality of abortion. In the most important case, it ruled six to three that ordinances passed by the city of Akron, Ohio, requiring an "informed consent" procedure before an abortion could be performed were designed to deter the woman from the procedure and hence were unconstitutional. In June 1986, the Supreme Court reaffirmed by a narrower margin (five to four) the principles enunciated in *Roe* v. *Wade* in the case of *Thornburgh* v. *the American College of Obstetricians and Gynecologists.* That case struck down the state of Pennsylvania's Abortion Control Act of 1982. Despite this decision, it is likely that the abortion issue will come before the Supreme Court again.

The literature on abortion is large and often impassioned. Noonan's view is amplified in his book *A Private Choice: Abortion in America in the Seventies* (The Free Press, 1979). Paul Ramsey's *Ethics at the Edges of Life* (Yale, 1978) is another eloquent statement of the pro-life stance.

Judith Jarvis Thomson's article, "A Defense of Abortion" (*Philosophy and Public Affairs,* Fall 1971), is a classic philosophical defense of the feminist argument that a woman has the right to control her body. In her article, "On the Moral and Legal Status of Abortion" (*The Monist,* January 1973), Mary Anne Warren goes even further, asserting that the fetus is not a person and that abortion is always permissible. In *Abortion and Woman's Choice* (New York: Longman, 1984), Rosalind Pollack Petchesky presents a communitarian view of abortion, stressing the social context in which women must make reproductive choices. *Abortion: Understanding Differences,* edited by Sidney Callahan and Daniel Callahan, is a collection of articles by pro-choice and pro-life women on the relationship of views about abortion to other values (New York: Plenum, 1984). Other volumes that present a range of viewpoints on abortion are Kristin Luker, *Abortion and the Politics of Motherhood* (Berkeley: University of California Press, 1984); and Jay L. Garfield and Patricia Hennessey, eds., *Abortion: Moral and Legal Perspectives* (Amherst: University of Massachusetts Press, 1984).

ISSUE 2

IS IT WRONG TO CREATE TEST-TUBE BABIES?

YES: Hans O. Tiefel, from "Human In Vitro Fertilization: A Conservative View," *Journal of the American Medical Association* 247:23, June 18, 1982

NO: Clifford Grobstein, from "Coming to Terms with Test-Tube Babies," *New Scientist* 96, October 7, 1982

ISSUE SUMMARY

YES: Professor of religion Hans O. Tiefel opposes the new technology of in vitro fertilization on the grounds that it may cause harm to both mother and embryos, which ought to be protected because they are part of humanity.
NO: Biologist Clifford Grobstein argues that this technology is a useful therapy for infertile couples and that we can avoid the "slippery slope" of potential moral problems by developing sound principles.

Few babies have been born to such instant celebrity as Louise Joy Brown. When she was born in Manchester, England, on July 25, 1978, she was the world's first documented "test-tube" baby. Robert G. Edwards, a physiologist, and Patrick C. Steptoe, an obstetrician, had perfected the technique called "in vitro" or, more properly, "external" fertilization. ("In vitro" literally means "in glass"; the fertilization did not take place in a test tube but in a petri dush.)

Simply put, this is the way the procedure works: A ripe egg is removed through surgery from the mother's ovary, then mixed in a special solution with the male sperm. If fertilization occurs, the resulting embryo is implanted after two or three days in the mother's uterine wall, where it develops to term—that is, if all goes well. Like normal fertilization, external fertilization is subject to the vagaries of nature. Like many scientific achievements, Louise Brown's birth was the culmination of many years of experimentation, beginning with tests on animals in the late nineteenth century. Today about 1,500 babies, including a large number of multiple births, have been born as a result of this technique, primarily in England, Australia, and the United States.

External fertilization offers some hope—perhaps the only one—of alleviating infertility in women whose fallopian tubes are blocked. External fertilization might eventually be used to treat more of the nearly 1.5 million American women who are infertile. Thousands of women have applied to the more than 130 American clinics that offer this therapy, even though it is painful, expensive ($3,000 to $6,000 per try, with three to four tries not uncommon), and successful only some of the time. (Success rates vary from institution to institution, depending on experience.)

Since Louise Brown was born, the technology has advanced even further. Scientists have succeeded in freezing externally-fertilized embryos in liquid nitrogen and storing them for future use. These "spare" embryos can also be implanted in another woman—one who cannot produce fertilizable eggs, or who agrees to carry the fetus of another couple to delivery, for instance. In this country, all "spare" embryos are implanted or frozen, and none are destroyed or otherwise manipulated, say the clinic directors.

But if Louis Brown's birth and the subsequent events answered one question—can it be done?—it raised another, more troubling one—ought it be done? In 1979 an Ethics Advisory Board convened by the then-Department of Health, Education, and Welfare (now Health and Human Services) recommended, after a year and a half of hearings and study, that research on in vitro fertilization was "ethically acceptable" under specific conditions. This included a provision that the fertilized embryo not be maintained outside the mother's body beyond fourteen days, the stage normally associated with implantation. However, the board did not recommend what level of federal funding, if any, ought to be given to such research. While the board's work represented the most exhaustive examination of the subject to date in this country, it by no means quieted all fears.

In the following selection, Hans O. Tiefel takes the view that in vitro fertilization is at best a "mixed blessing" and that human embryos ought to be considered as persons and protected from unjustifiable research. Clifford Grobstein, while not denying the existence of ethical problems, believes that external fertilization is beneficial and that calling a halt to the practice is unjustifiable because ethical problems can be overcome by sound guidelines and policies.

YES

Hans O. Tiefel

HUMAN IN VITRO FERTILIZATION: A CONSERVATIVE VIEW

The extracorporeal engendering of human life that led to the birth of Louise Brown in 1978 struck the world as an awesome medical achievement. Even 3½ years later, the 15th—but this nation's first—child so conceived was fittingly welcomed as the "miracle in Norfolk" (*Washington Post,* Dec 31, 1981, p A-14).

This striking accomplishment offers hope to many of the circa half-million American women whose obstructed or missing Fallopian tubes had seemingly ruled out any chance of having children of their own. Relatively few of the more than 6,000 couples who have applied at the Eastern Virginia Medical School, however, can be helped there or at the other three American clinics.

Two authorities on issues of in vitro fertilization and embryo transfer, LeRoy Walters, PhD, director of the Kennedy Institute's Center for Bioethics, and John D. Biggers, DSc, PhD, the Harvard specialist in human reproductive biology, therefore called for federal support for test-tube conceptions a week after the birth of Elizabeth Carr (*Washington Post,* Jan 4, 1982, p A-3). The national government should stop turning its back on childless couples who want babies, according to Dr Walters, particularly since the US Department of Health, Education, and Welfare Ethics Advisory Board had concluded in June 1979 that such funding is "acceptable from an ethical standpoint." The nationwide hearings on whether to lift a 1974 moratorium on such funding, held by the Ethics Advisory Board in 1978 and 1979, elicited similar recommendations. Particularly, medical professionals hope "to break the log jam of prejudice and law, at both state and federal levels, that at present denies infertile couples the blessing of a child by this remarkable method."

This article opposes such recommendations on moral grounds by arguing that this new technology may be a mixed blessing, that federal funding may be blocked not by prejudice but by moral doubts, and that a more cautious or conservative position is justified by valid objections to both means and ends of test-tube babies. . . .

From "Human In Vitro Fertilization: A Conservative View," by Hans O. Tiefel, *Journal of the American Medical Association,* 247:23, June 18, 1982, pp. 3235-3242. Copyright ©1982, American Medical Association.

The [most significant moral] meaning of the charge that this new technology is unnatural refers not to means but to ends, namely, to the fear that this innovation may prove harmful. Such harm would be widely conceived: mental or physical, emotional or social, possible or actual, detracting from health or worth of any or all parties. That, in my judgment, is the crucial issue, especially as it pertains to the offspring. But that problem is more familiar under the rubric of risk or harm.

RISK TO THE WOULD-BE MOTHER

LeRoy Walters succinctly describes the kinds of risks to the woman in in vitro fertilization and embryo transfer:

> (1) pretreatment of the woman with hormones to induce superovulation, a therapy which occasionally produces ovarian cysts; (2) removal of oocytes by means of laparoscopy, a surgical procedure which requires general anesthesia; (3) potential damage to the uterus during embryo transfer . . . (4) the risks which accompany careful monitoring of the pregnancy, for example, the risks of amniocentesis . . . (5) the risk of ectopic pregnancy.

The second of these seems to be the most important. But to assess that risk, one needs statistics of normal impregnation. Biggers concludes that, normally, one can expect between 69% and 78% embryonic loss, which is consistent with data showing that it takes an average of four months of regular inseminations to achieve pregnancy by artificial insemination or four months of sexual activity to achieve normal pregnancy. Thus even under normal conditions, the required number of embryo transfers will, on average, be four times as great as the number of births one can expect.

The success rate for laparoscopies and embryo transfer have been much lower. In their early work, Edwards and Steptoe claimed two births out of 68 laparoscopies. Biggers concluded in February 1981 that when an ovum is discovered, the probability of obtaining a live birth by the Steptoe-Edwards method was about 0.044. That appears to have been the method that yielded 30 failures to impregnate 30 patients in 1980 for Drs Howard and Georgeanna Jones in Norfolk.

With fertility-inducing drugs, however, the odds apparently improve. More than one ovum can be obtained, which allows more than one embryonic implant. In 1981 the Norfolk clinic reported six pregnancies in some 50 tries. Australian results have similarly improved. Steptoe claimed that as of Oct 31, 1981, out of 436 laparoscopies, 337 implantations, and 74 pregnancies, eight babies had been born and 48 women were still pregnant (*Washington Post*, Dec 23, 1981, p A-24).

Despite such improvements and the prospects of better odds in the future, the success rate still resembles lottery statistics more than promising therapy. Infertile couples, perhaps misled by their own desperation and unqualified news stories, present themselves as patients when their role is more that of subjects in clinical trials.

Even if the meager success rate is explained to couples and they consent to the odds, there are moral limits to surgical risk, time, resources, and stress on human relationships. The fact that prospective parents say that they will do anything to have a baby of their own is not necessarily a moral justification. "Doing anything" may not only be inimical to oneself but neglects ties and duties to others. To use an odd example, one research team supports the claim that a pregnancy actually resulted from their transplant by stating that "the subject abstained from intercourse during the entire treatment as a result of her own firm and deliberate decision." There is no word whether the husband shared in that decision, which seemed to benefit only the researchers. Similarly, one wonders if the delivery of these babies by cesarean section is always necessary and should be one of the risks of this procedure.

Low success rates, repeated risks, disruption of lives, unneeded impositions, and financial and emotional costs to would-be parents as well as to those supporting them are serious moral problems. But all such liabilities are voluntarily assumed by those who hope to benefit from this technology. That is not true for the would-be child.

RISK TO THE WOULD-BE CHILD

Is there risk to a child conceived in vitro and transferred in embryo form into the uterus? It seems that nobody knows for sure. A recent review of the probability of producing a congenitally abnormal baby is offered by Biggers. His conclusion, that the danger of increased congenital defects is not high, seems to be based on the spontaneous elimination of most abnormalities before birth rather than on assurance of no increase in abnormal embryos. But there is no guarantee that this would happen, assuming that such loss is reassuring and of little moral relevance.

When the count of children so conceived was 21, only one was reported to have been born with a serious defect, which will be repaired by cardiac surgery, according to the *Washington Post* (Jan 4, 1982, p A-3). But Walters' conclusion that the procedures do not pose "unreasonable risk" is both sanguine and premature.

Not only are there insufficient data about the effects on humans, but the relevance of in vitro studies on animals is in doubt. Thus, some researchers (Mastroianni, Brackett, Gould) call for more animal studies, while others (Soupart, Biggers) dismiss that as irrelevant. The Ethics Advisory Board found a golden mean by giving its imprimatur to both animal and human studies.

In any case, knowledge about risk requires long-range human studies, decades in which to follow up children so conceived into reproductive age and through a normal life span. Not only time but sufficient numbers are required. Schlesselman, in a careful statistical study, concludes that 99.3% to 99.5% of chromosomal abnormalities are eliminated in vivo through spontaneous abortion or fetal death. Such low survival rates of abnormal fetuses imply that even a doubling of abnormalities of in vitro implantations would result in only two or three additional abnormalities per 1,000 live births. Thus, "a large number of births would be required to provide definitive assessment of risk. The morally crucial answer to the question of risk to the would-be child thus requires a great number of births and much time. The answers seem a long way off, and we must make moral judgments without the benefit of knowing all the facts.

Several responses to this factual uncertainty of risk are troubling. Ethicists have stated repeatedly that risk to the child conceived in vitro would be acceptable if it is no greater than risk to children conceived in vivo. But it is not helpful to say that when no one knows the actual risk. Here ethicists avoid the dilemma.

Others recommend that if couples with recessive defects decide to have children, then the assumed lower risk of in vitro fertilization must be acceptable. Or, since "it is not general practice in this country to interfere with reproductive options facing couples who may be at increased risk for having abnormal offspring, it is held to be right to inform and to accede to a couple's decision here as well."

This acceding role of medical conscience is the opposite extreme of paternalism. Implementing the couple's choice unavoidably makes the physician a part of that decision. But surely the physician should be neither father nor slave, but a responsible participant. If medical judgment anticipates harm, he is obligated to keep patients "from harm and injustice" by virtue of the Hippocratic oath.

Medical proponents of extracorporeal fertilization also offer ethical relativism as a way of overcoming the problem of risk. Individual wishes become king. The fact that a couple wants this procedure is held to make it morally right. For example, one researcher claims that "childless couples' rights to utilize whatever methods and techniques are available to produce wanted offspring far exceeds and surpasses the rights and privileges of the critics who would condemn and suppress scientific work directed toward helping them to accomplish this aim."

Disregarding the lese majesty against science, this is ethical relativism, where individual choice or preference settles moral issues. Medicine should avoid such quicksand, for shifting individual preferences offer no solid support for the objective values undergirding medicine and research. If one lets go of objective and universal values to defer to dubious patient choice, one also relinquishes the heart of medicine, whose life is the objective value of healing and of doing no harm.

A PROPOSAL FOR THE ETHICS OF RISK

How, then, is one to assess the moral issue of unknown risk to the would-be child? The subject, the would-be child, must first be clearly defined lest we confuse our responsibilities to existing and to future children. For offspring who are actually on the way, we must allow great risk when that is the only option for their continued existence. To the would-be child that is not yet conceived, we have no such obligation. Our responsibilities to living offspring, before and after birth, should not be undercut by the risks they face. But offspring who are concepts rather than conceptions may not claim that immunity. We literally do not owe them a living.

Though no one knows for sure, there is some justification for deeming in vitro fertilization to be harmful to offspring thus conceived. The great embryonic and fetal loss, compared with natural pregnancies, is good reason for saying that this mode of begetting is more dangerous. Moreover, the dimensions of risk may not even be known. To a layman there are repeated surprises in the way in which risk studies appear about therapies that were long thought to be safe. Even medical professionals seem surprised by the latent effort of thalidomide or diethylstilbestrol. To create an artificial environment, to handle, stimulate, and disturb human life at its very beginning when its building blocks are being laid, is to risk damage to the finished construct, even for those few structures that survive spontaneous collapse and demolition.

As best we can, we owe every child a fair

chance at physical and mental health. This principle, which is so often misused to justify the destruction of seriously ill fetuses or newborns, is fittingly applied to the would-be child. We must weigh the chances for the well-being of the child while we yet have a choice about initiating this life. Would-be parents have moral obligations to a would-be child. The resolve to have a child of one's own must be tied to a love that seeks the best for that child. To be sure, no parents can guarantee health to future offspring. Nor can they secure safety from nuclear war, a harmful environment, or other dangers over which they have little or no control. But every parent owes every child-to-be reasonable care not to take chances with its health, as every obstetrician explains to every mother-to-be. And the uncertain risks inherent in in vitro fertilization are definitely avoidable by abstinence from this particular technology.

It makes good moral sense never to beget offspring when would-be-parents cannot reasonably ensure a future child a fair chance at health. When there are untried risks and even indications of greater than normal risk, "one cannot ethically choose for a child the unknown hazards that he must face, and simultaneously choose to give him life in which to face them." For would-be mothers to undertake risks and burdens for themselves and for consenting partners is one thing. For them knowingly to place future children at risk is quite another. No one has the moral right to endanger a child while there is yet the option of whether the child shall come into existence. That is the crucial and decisive ethical argument against the clinical use of in vitro fertilization. That also makes this procedure unnatural in the sense of being possibly harmful to human beings.

It is misleading and flippant to object that we should ask the children so conceived what they thought of the risks as objections to their being conceived. For if they turn out to be healthy, they are lucky winners in this technological gamble. If handicapped, they would only have the choice between their burdened life or no existence at all. Whether they say yes or no, the moral choice for actually existing children should generally be for life. That is why the choice exists only for would-be children. The dilemma of risk before conception cannot be resolved after the fact.

Ramsey made the crucial moral point about risk to the future child a decade ago. That seems to have made little impact. A survey of the literature yields no medical researcher who thinks that this is one procedure that should not be used. None of the medical experts rejects this risky technology that is being tested even as it is used on women and their babies.

One subtle but significant threat to children so conceived has not yet been mentioned because it is one of the certain rather than likely problems. The suspicion—and guilt on the part of parents—will be unavoidable that whatever health problems develop are the result of this unique genesis. And uncertainty about the future is apt to create anxiety. The possibility of unknown problems yet to come will overshadow the lives of these children, of their parents, and surely also of their medical "creators" and monitors. . . .

FREEZING HUMAN EMBRYOS

Superovulation yields more ova, more implants, and reduces the need for repeated laparoscopies. But what should be done with "surplus" embryos? Both Australian and British centers have temporarily resolved the problem by "putting it on ice." Freezing was the alternative to discarding the embryos, which could be sustained in no other way.

Freezing also makes sense in another way. The hormones used to induce superovulation may have a detrimental effect on implantation and on early embryonic development. Freezing oocytes or embryos would allow implantation in the subsequent cycle when the woman no longer suffers aftereffects from hormones or from surgery and anesthesia.

A third proposed benefit, recommended by Steptoe and Edwards, lies in banks of frozen embryos for donation to other women, permitting "prenatal adoption" by infertile couples (*New York Times*, Feb 11, 1982, p A-26).

How is one to evaluate this morally? Freezing embryos is particularly unnerving to persons who think that even the earliest forms of human life are special. Here human life is put on hold, as it were. Even if one wants to avoid the judgment that this is unnatural, prolonged freezing may rob a thawed and growing life of its genetic progenitors, of its roots and support. Such a Buck Rogers of the 21st century would lack memories of lost ties, but genuine bonds might well be lost. It is also not too farfetched to think that once the progenitors are forgotten or gone, these suspended beings may lose their natural protectors to become interesting research material, as may already be happening with embryos incidentally recovered during hysterectomies.

Freezing even for long periods seems to damage only the quantity but not the quality of animal embryos, but whether this is true for humans is again unknown. Therefore, the same worries about risk of in vitro fertilization apply here. It would be preferable to freeze ova rather than embryos, since the former are not yet genetically unique lives. And—assuming that the

earlier moral arguments against extracorporeal conception will not dissuade anyone—it would be the lesser evil to freeze surplus embryos. The only other practical option, once they have been conjured into existence, is to discard them, a practice that has been described as "a matter solely between a doctor and his plumber." Even if freezing were to entail additional risks, including those of experimentation, it would at least give embryos a chance to live.

As to prenatal adoption, the legal unclarities of who belongs to whom and who owes what to whom would be legion. But again, an acknowledgment of the intrinsic value of the human embryo might also see this mode of life as better than none. . . .

THE STATUS OF THE EMBRYO

The ethics of nonclinical in vitro fertilization hangs on the decision about status. The Ethics Advisory Board agreed "that the human embryo is entitled to profound respect: but this respect does not necessarily encompass the full legal and moral rights attributed to persons." That amounts to a polite bow in the direction of the embryo before dispatching it for tissue cultures. The key question is whether one may use the embryo in nontherapeutic experiments, whether one may use it up. The board said that, at least for 14 days, one may do so. How much profound respect the embryo enjoys as it is being fixed in slides remains in doubt. In any case, the respect due falls short of never using such human life as a means only.

This peculiar use of "respect" also explains the board's strange conclusion that research on human in vitro fertilization was "ethically acceptable" in the sense of still being legitimately controverted. That controversy hinges on embryonic status.

2. IS IT WRONG TO CREATE TEST-TUBE BABIES?

Neither the board nor I can prove our beliefs about embryonic status, but I shall nevertheless offer reasons for a more inclusive vision of humanity.

The problem with embryonic status lies partly in our inconsistency. On the one hand, we know that we, at least our bodily selves, began as embryos. If we are special, embryos are special. Even Mr Edwards is reported to have said at the birth of Louise Brown, "The last time I saw the baby it was just eight cells in a test tube. It was beautiful then, and it's still beautiful now" (*Newsweek*, Aug 7, 1978, p 69). That may have been poetic license, but it shows that the value of human beings is linked to our embryonic origin. We also assent to a practical wisdom in the law that allows offspring to bring suit for malpractice against researchers for harm to themselves as embryos.

On the other hand, we acknowledge the value of increased knowledge about earliest human development, such as chromosome constitution of gametes and human infertility. The simplest and most useful way to find out is to experiment, to look through the window that has been opened on early development by in vitro fertilization. Only in this case, our seeing fatally affects the embryo. Such looking may not be done with human beings. We are therefore inclined to exclude the embryo from human status.

This ambiguity growing out of opposing motives was offered to the Ethics Advisory Board by a philosopher who proposed that the status of this being may be judged only in retrospect. If it should be damaged as an embryo and be malformed later, it is fitting to say that the initial harm was an "injury to someone." But if the embryo does not live to term, we may not say that. That ascribes status ("someone") according to what we want to do with the embryo.

Such flexibility is convenient. But historical instances of ascribing human status selectively have not turned out to be our better moments. It is also true that one of the rules of ethics is consistency. If any embryos count as human beings, all do.

It may be a sign of ferment or of poverty in contemporary philosophy, but there is less and less consensus about who counts and why. Handicapped newborns are pushed into the limbo of deferred personhood until we can decide whether they should live. Fetuses are said to have value only when their potentiality is wanted by their progenitors. And a chimpanzee is held to be of more value than a human zygote.

The general trend to restrict humanity to rational and volitional beings may solve a host of medical problems. It cuts the Gordian knot of whether to treat or to protect human beings at the borders of life with a definitional sword that strikes off all who cannot reason. But our medical, humanistic, and religious traditions have been less fierce. We have held and should continue to hold that every human life counts, regardless of capacity. In this more compassionate vision it is fitting to include even the earliest versions of ourselves within the human community....

NO
Clifford Grobstein

COMING TO TERMS WITH TEST-TUBE BABIES

The first baby that was conceived by external (*in vitro*) fertilisation was born in England in 1978. The event created much excitement and some controversy. First reactions died down as additional technology-assisted babies were born, not only in England but in Australia and the US. More than three years later, however, controversy in England is stirring anew—as though people are suddenly seeing the matter in a new light. This "double-take", sometimes exploited by comedians to get a laugh, in this instance has serious significance.

Earlier misgivings in the US were effectively summarised in the hearings and deliberations of the Ethics Advisory Board, charged in 1978 by Joseph Califano, then Secretary of the Department of Health, Education and Welfare, to evaluate external human fertilisation. Central in the board's consideration were questions of the safety and efficacy of the procedure—designed to relieve female infertility due to blockage or loss of the fallopian tubes. Safety referred largely to possible harmful effects on the offspring, efficacy largely to the percentage of attempts that would yield viable offspring. Three years later, with about a score of babies born, all but one appear to have been normal at birth and the several clinics with greatest experience are projecting a one in five chance of success for each attempt. The trend of the growing clinical experience is, therefore, toward safety and success rates close to those for the natural internal process.

While external fertilisation cannot yet be regarded as an established medical procedure, its trials so far suggest that it will prove reasonably safe and efficacious. The new wave of concern, in fact, centres on broader issues—the "open window" on early human development afforded by the procedure and conceivable procedures that can be visualised as ranging along a "slippery slope" toward applications that are unpalatable to many people. The "open window", of course, is the accessibility external fertilisation provides for observation or manipulation of early human developmental stages, previously rarely obtainable and never before able to be maintained alive while undergoing development. The Cambridge physiologist Robert Edwards and obstetrician Patrick Steptoe and their colleagues, whose arduous and dedicated efforts brought the procedure to realisation, have recently reported on the growth of externally cultured human embryos from fertilisation to the blastocyst ("ball of cells") stage, at which time the embryos normally would be implanting in the wall of the uterus. The objective of these observations is to improve further the safety and efficacy of the procedure. However, such entirely reasonable efforts are further widening the open window and heightening concern in some quarters about the presumed slippery slope. This much more consequential matter undoubtedly is providing the major impetus to calls for a second look, and even a moratorium, on continued research to improve and expand the use of the procedure. The concern stems from the fact that manipulations of fertilisation and early stages in development, comparable with those now accessible in humans, are being practised increasingly widely on other mammalian species, both in the laboratory and in commercial animal production. Two objectives of these practices are to gain greater knowledge of hereditary and developmental processes on one hand and to apply this knowledge to achieve economic benefits on the other. The concern is that the very same manipulations, if applied to human eggs or embryos, raise unprecedented moral issues and, in some minds, the possibility of unanticipated or frankly undesirable social impacts.

The possibility of entering upon a slippery slope has come more sharply into focus largely because of two technical innovations in external fertilisation, one already in effect and the other under consideration. The first is the use of hormonal stimulation to increase the number of mature eggs that can be obtained from a given donor. In humans, of course, only a single egg usually matures in each menstrual cycle. Having several eggs mature clearly might increase the success rate for a given procedure for recovering eggs. Edwards and Steptoe in early efforts, however, had poorer success when they obtained multiple eggs by hormonal stimulation than they had with single eggs obtained from a natural cycle. Their first births, in fact, were from eggs obtained in natural cycles. Subsequently, however, other groups using slightly different methods, notably Carl Wood at the Monash University in Australia, have had greater success with multiple eggs hormonally induced from a single donor and are achieving overall improved success rates. The reinsertion of more than one egg has given rise to a few twin pregnancies, and, because up to six mature eggs can be produced hormonally, donors may be stimulated to produce more than the optimal number of eggs for a given cycle.

There are several options for the further fate of such surplus eggs. They might be killed and discarded. They might be used, as the Edwards and Steptoe group has done, to gain more knowledge about these early human stages, in turn perhaps contributing to the safety and efficacy of the procedure. Or they might be frozen and stored for other, later use. Each of the options is controversial, for each raises the knotty issue of the legal and social status of the early human embryo. If one holds, as legislation pending in the US Congress does, that a person exists from conception, then any option other than immediate return to a receptive uterus (and possibly even that) is excluded. If, however, one holds that the early embryo is something other than a person, then the options are admissible, but with a degree of restriction depending upon how close to a person the early embryo is defined to be.

VALUABLE BY-PRODUCTS

Setting aside this question of status for the moment, what do the options offer technically? The first obviously offers nothing other than avoiding the necessity to face the other two. Surplus embryos would be treated as unwanted by-products of the procedure and would be dispatched without further consideration or concern. The second option would assign special value to the early embryos as a source of additional knowledge, not for the benefit of the embryos themselves but possibly to benefit other embryos and humanity in general. The third option is the most complex because it puts the embryos in temporary stasis for purposes that have not been specified. What might some of these purposes be?

The most immediate purpose and the closest to the original rationale of the basic procedure of external fertilisation would be to provide embryos for insertion into the uterus of the donor in later menstrual cycles. One of the concerns about the hormonal induction of multiple eggs is that the hormonal stimulation may not only affect the ovary but might also disturb the cycle of the uterus. Having obtained the embryos it might be advantageous not to return them immediately to the uterus but to wait for a subsequent cycle uncomplicated by the administration of hormones. At the very least, this would allow successive attempts at reinsertion after only a single extraction of eggs. Obtaining the egg is the most uncomfortable step for the patient, involving a small incision through the abdominal wall under light anaesthesia. Moreover, the reinsertion step also has, at the moment, the lowest success rate. If multiple eggs were obtained by a single extraction from the ovary and if all that were not immediately reinserted were frozen, the thawed embryos could later be inserted in successive cycles until success were achieved. This might enhance the success rate while adding as little as possible to the patient's discomfort.

The pertinent question, of course, is the possible harm done to the embryo by freezing and thawing. Here it is important to note that the freezing and thawing of embryos stems from extensive studies over several decades in what is called cryobiology. It is now possible, as the result of research on the processes of freezing and thawing of living tissues in various media and at different temperatures, to freeze and thaw many microbial, plant and animal cells with minimal damage. In the frozen state metabolism is suspended and even genetic change is slowed down to insignificant levels. Mammalian embryos, including those of mice and cattle, have been kept in frozen storage and shown to continue normal development with high frequency on thawing. Scientifically valuable strains of mice are now being stored in frozen embryo banks to eliminate the effort and cost of constant breeding.

The application of the procedure to human embryos would not, therefore, be a shot in the dark. On the other hand, its application to humans is not the same as its application to mice or cattle. Ninety per cent success rates, for example, may be acceptable for laboratory and domestic animals. In humans it is the 10 per cent failure rate that is of concern—particularly if these are partial failures, not detectable until after birth or even later in life. Clearly these are matters for most careful consideration before frozen-thawed human embryos are reinserted for continued development.

If the safety issue were favourably resolved, we can envisage further technical possibilities. Eggs surplus for the original donor might also be inserted into the receptive uterus of a non-donor. Such embryo transfers are commonly done with high rates of success in laboratory animals and cattle. They are done most effectively with frozen-thawed embryos because these can be held until the uterus of the recipient is in the most receptive stage of the cycle. We can imagine two circumstances in which this might be attempted in humans. The first is based upon the original rationale for external human fertilisation; that is, to relieve infertility. The recipient would be a woman whose ovaries do not produce mature and normal eggs but whose uterus is normal. The insertion of an embryo into her uterus would be comparable with an early adoption. She would have the full experience of pregnancy but with an offspring to which she had made no genetic contribution. If, incidentally, she were to receive a surplus egg fertilised by her husband's sperm the offspring would have genetic kinship at least with the father, a situation exactly the converse of artificial insemination by donor to cope with male infertility.

The slippery slope would begin to steepen if the same technical procedure were to be applied to a non-donor who was not sterile but who acted as a surrogate ("foster mother") for the donor. This might still be a measure to overcome sterility if the donor were without a uterus due to an earlier hysterectomy. It might, however, also be done because the donor might expect a pregnancy to be dangerous to her health or merely inconvenient. In the last instance the original motivation to relieve sterility would have been diluted to the vanishing point, replaced by considerations of maternal preference and convenience.

Having reached this point, further options might be seen that would still employ the same basic techniques. For example, there is a trend in the US for women to postpone pregnancy to avoid interrupting their careers. In addition, the incidence of Down's syndrome in offspring rises sharply as maternal age moves into the last decade of fecundity, between 35 and 45. Suppose a young woman were to have eggs removed from her ovaries to be fertilised externally by sperm from her husband (or other male), and the resulting embryos were to be frozen. These embryos could then be inserted into her uterus at convenient times that fit her career needs, and possibly reduce the risk of developmental defect. Incidentally, with a secure supply in the frozen-embryo bank, a couple could submit to sterilisation procedures without losing the capacity to have a family. This comes close to the ultimate in family planning.

This is but one chain of options along an imaginable and not wildly speculative slippery slope. It is the kind of thing that arouses uneasiness and causes many people to say, "Now wait! What are we rushing into? Let's take another look." A prudent position, but what comes next? Do we attempt to prohibit a procedure that is on the way to being safe and efficacious, and able to bring satisfaction to many people? Could or should such a procedure be effectively prohibited? Would it not simply become covert, more expensive and perhaps less well managed? Should we attempt instead to cut off all further advance by limiting research on reproduction, endocrinology and genetics? If this were seriously to be considered could such a draconian measure be enforced worldwide? Can we, should we, cut off the progress of human knowledge?

Better, it would seem, to examine more carefully the kinds of slippery slopes that can reasonably be anticipated to appear on the rising peak of external human fertilisation. All slopes, after all, do not end in precipices and not all are slippery. We live most of our lives on slopes of one kind or another, sometimes using them to advantage, sometimes by exercise of will moving up them instead of down, sometimes enjoying the very slipperiness of slopes or the challenge to overcome them. We do not invariably forgo something that is basically beneficial because it may be abused or may lead toward something malignant. Rather we move to establish sound guidelines and policies that set appropriate boundaries, limits to rates of progression, or otherwise reassure against over-enthusiasm or irresponsibility.

For example, another identifiable slope is arising in the possible combination of external human fertilisation with molecular genetics. Some human genes have been chemically characterised, can be reproduced in bacteria and can be manipulated to yield their normal product. Human insulin has been produced in this way. Moreover, normal genetic material has been inserted into cultured human cells to correct genetic defect in those cells. This is but one step—though possibly a long one—from gene therapy to correct defects in precursor human red cells that give rise to sickle-cell anaemia and B-thalassaemia. Gene transfers also have been made into mouse embryos, leading to genetic modification not only of the resulting adult but of offspring in the next generation. The embryonic stages used in the mouse experiments are precisely the ones in the open window provided by external human fertilisation. The slope thus points toward a distant capability to influence human evolution in limited ways.

We cannot avoid considering the implications of such slopes, even though they may not have to be faced with full responsibility for a generation or two. We cannot avoid this consideration because anxiety over the possibilities produces the reaction mentioned earlier; stop moving ahead until we know where we are going. A reasonable response is to start thinking ahead even as we move ahead, so as to proceed under agreed consensus as to purposes and precautions. The agreed consensus, if it is to be achieved and effective, must be formulated on a broad social base. It must have the character of a future-sensitive tradition that will soundly guide our growing powers to intervene in human reproduction, heredity and development.

IMPROVING THE SPECIES

This is not a task that will be completed in any definable period while all progress is stopped. It is a task to begin now and to intensify as wider options evolve. It might be started by attempting to formulate principles that allow near-term progress but emphasise awareness on the part of all involved that existing concerns and long-term consequences must be carefully considered. For example, many would be reassured to know that the intent of any intervention in human reproduction would be to benefit individuals and not to "improve" the species as a whole. Though these two are linked, in contemporary thinking the first is generally understood and accepted, the second is burdened by suspicion and fraught with uncertainties as to how "improvement" will be defined—and by whom.

It would also be reassuring to know that

defects that *limit* self-realisation and self-satisfaction are the legitimate target; that conservation and fuller fruition of humanity as we know it is the goal, not the "engineering" of new forms of human life. It should be specified most compellingly that no intervention will be countenanced that reduces or limits human potential, regardless of assumed benefits to particular societies, groups or ideologies. On the other hand, interventions to gratify individual desires (for example, to provide offspring of a particular sex) will not be practised without full evaluation of collective consequences (such as distorted sex ratios).

Can such policies be formulated, elevated to the status of social guidelines and implemented? An affirmative answer can be given only if the procedures for establishing such guidelines are soundly formulated. Formulation would have to be by a deliberative body of appropriate integrity, stature and authority. The deliberations must be sufficiently accessible to incorporate all relevant opinion, and yet secluded enough to be free of excessive immediate pressures. The principles must be formulated cogently and emotively, yet simply, so that they can easily gain currency in broad communities. They should not be entangled in statutory legalities but should become matters of individual conscience, of professional ethics and of common law.

This is but a sketch to indicate the nature of the task ahead. The inventiveness of human mind has vastly extended the powers of the human hand; now we are challenged to display equivalent innovativeness in defining human purpose. It is a time for prudence but it is also a time for vision. We must not freeze into immobility but we must step carefully as we move upward to new uncharted ground. At this new level our future will be brought in greater degree into the orbit of our deliberate choice. This will, indeed, take our measure as we move into a new millenium.

POSTSCRIPT

IS IT WRONG TO CREATE
TEST - TUBE BABIES?

In 1986 an in vitro fertilization program was established at United Hospital in Port Chester, New York, in cooperation with IVF Australia (USA) Ltd., a firm headed by specialists from Monash University. This collaboration highlights two trends: the growing use of IVF in this country (this center alone plans to provide more than 1,000 treatments a year, leading to about 200 pregnancies) and the commercialization of the technology.

Two variations of the technology have been announced: gamete intrafallopian transfer (GIFT) and transvaginal oocyte retrieval. Both are intended to improve the success rates and subject women to less trauma. GIFT is a one-step process in which the eggs are removed from the woman, fertilized with the sperm, and immediately inserted into the fallopian tubes. Transvaginal oocyte retrieval involves taking the eggs through the vaginal wall rather than through a surgical procedure. It allows retrieval of eggs that would otherwise be impossible to extract and is cheaper as well.

Although in the U.S. the Ethics Advisory Board's recommendations have never received an official response, internationally there has been a great deal of activity. Commissions have been established in Great Britain, Australia, Canada, France, and elsewhere to examine the issues and to propose legislation. The most often-cited of these works is the British "Warnock Report," chaired by Lady Mary Warnock (published as *A Question of Life* by Basil Blackwell, 1985).

Peter Singer and Deane Wells defend the new technologies in *The Reproduction Revolution: New Ways of Making Babies* (New York: Oxford University Press, 1984).

Clifford Grobstein's views in favor of this technology are amplified in his book *From Chance to Purpose* (Addison-Wesley, 1981), which also contains the text of the Ethics Advisory Board's recommendations. A comprehensive review of varying ethical views is LeRoy Walter's "Human In Vitro Fertilization: A Review of the Ethical Literature" (*Hastings Center Report,* August 1979). Two feminist attacks can be found in Gena Corea's *The Mother Machine* (New York: Harper & Row, 1985) and *Test-Tube Women: What Future for Motherhood?* edited by Rita Arditti, Renate Duelli Klein, and Shelley Minden (Boston: Routledge & Kegan Paul, 1984).

Two classic articles opposing in vitro fertilization and other forms of reproductive technology are: "Making Babies' Revisited" by Leon Kass (*The Public Interest,* Winter 1979); and "Shall We 'Reproduce'?" a two-part series by Paul Ramsey (*Journal of the American Medical Association,* June 5 and June 12, 1972).

ISSUE 3

SHOULD WOMEN BE ALLOWED TO BEAR BABIES FOR A FEE?

YES: John A. Robertson, from "Surrogate Mothers: Not So Novel After All," *Hastings Center Report* 13:5, October 1983

NO: Herbert F. Krimmel, from "The Case Against Surrogate Parenting," *Hastings Center Report* 13:5, October 1983

ISSUE SUMMARY

YES: Professor of law John A. Robertson maintains that infertile couples have a right to arrange for a surrogate mother to bear the husband's child and that the ethical and legal problems that might result are not very different from those that already exist in adoption and artificial insemination by donor.
NO: Professor of law Herbert F. Krimmel takes the position that it is immoral to bear a child for the purpose of giving it up and that surrogate mother arrangements will put additional stress on our society's shared moral values.

The desire to bear a child is a deep and natural one, and for the 3.5 million infertile American couples their inability to reproduce is often a source of sorrow and pain. But adoption is not an easy alternative today. Because of the availability of legal abortion and because an increasing number of unwed teenage mothers are choosing to keep their babies, there are fewer babies available through adoption agencies—particularly the healthy, white newborns that are most in demand. The new reproductive technologies of external fertilization and embryo transfer are available only to a few women who meet the rigid medical and other criteria.

Under these circumstances, it is not surprising that when the wife is infertile, some couples are turning to "surrogate mothers"—women who will bear the husband's baby for a fee and give it up for legal adoption. This is the way it works: A broker (usually a lawyer) puts an infertile couple in contact with potential surrogates who have been recruited (usually through newspaper advertisements) and screened for medical and psychological characteristics. If the couple and the surrogate agree, they sign a contract specifying in detail the fee (usually $10,000), the surrogate's responsibilities to care for her health during pregnancy, the conditions under which she will have an abortion, the transfer of legal custody, and the like. The price tag is high: In addition to the surrogate's fee, the couple will have to pay the broker ($5,000 to $10,000), the doctor who performs the insemination and the one who delivers the baby, and the other medical costs. The total costs can run to $30,000 or more.

In the past such arrangements were almost certainly carried out in secret, and probably without any money changing hands, between friends and relatives. But in 1980 "Elizabeth Kane" (a pseudonym), a married woman with three children, announced publicly that she had borne a baby for a fee. "It's the father's child," she is reported to have said. "I'm only growing it for him." Since then there have been an estimated five hundred to seven hundred babies born by contract, and several firms are now engaged in matching would-be adoptive parents and willing surrogates.

Are these contracts legal? Most states have laws prohibiting "baby-selling": the offering, giving, or receiving anything of value for placing a child for adoption. But whether surrogate mother contracts are "baby-selling" or just another form of private adoption has still to be settled in the courts. At present several states—among them Michigan, California, Maryland, Florida, and Alaska—are considering whether to legalize the practice. Even if the contracts are proven to be legal, serious questions remain about whether they are enforceable—whether, for instance, a mother who decides to keep the baby when it is born can be forced to give it up (in the few cases that have come to court, the mothers have won).

When any unusual social arrangement is introduced, people tend to see it either as a continuation of already existing patterns or as something completely novel, and therefore suspect. Those who support the idea of surrogate mothers see it as similar to other practices in which a child is reared by someone other than its genetic parents. As long as the child is wanted and cared for, they believe, the practice is acceptable—even desirable. That position is expressed in the selection by John Robertson that follows.

Those who oppose the practice point not only to the legal uncertainties but also the psychological and family stresses that will face the children, the surrogate, and the adoptive family. It is unethical, according to the view expressed in the selection by Herbert F. Krimmel, to produce children in order to give them up and to encourage the view of children as commodities.

YES
John A. Robertson

SURROGATE MOTHERS:
NOT SO NOVEL AFTER ALL

All reproduction is collaborative, for no man or woman reproduces alone. Yet the provision of sperm, egg, or uterus through artificial insemination, embryo transfer, and surrogate mothers makes reproduction collaborative in another way. A third person provides a genetic or gestational factor not present in ordinary paired reproduction. As these practices grow, we must confront the ethical issues raised and their implications for public policy.

Collaborative reproduction allows some persons who otherwise might remain childless to produce healthy children. However, its deliberate separation of genetic, gestational, and social parentage is troublesome. The offspring and participants may be harmed, and there is a risk of confusing family lineage and personal identity. In addition, the techniques intentionally manipulate a natural process that many persons want free of technical intervention. Yet many well-accepted practices, including adoption, artificial insemination by donor (AID), and blended families (families where children of different marriages are raised together) intentionally separate biologic and social parenting, and have become an accepted thread in the social fabric. Should all collaborative techniques be similarly treated? When, if ever, are they ethical? Should the law prohibit, encourage, or regulate them, or should the practice be left to private actors? Surrogate motherhood—the controversial practice by which a woman agrees to bear a child conceived by artificial insemination and to relinquish it at birth to others for rearing—illustrates the legal and ethical issues arising in collaborative reproduction generally.

AN ALTERNATIVE TO AGENCY ADOPTIONS

Infertile couples who are seeking surrogates hire attorneys and sign contracts with women recruited through newspaper ads. The practice at present probably involves at most a few hundred persons. But repeated

Reprinted by permission from the *Hastings Center Report,* 13:5, October 1983. Copyright ©1983, the Hastings Center.

attention on *Sixty Minutes* and the *Phil Donahue Show,* and in the popular press is likely to engender more demand, for thousands of infertile couples might find surrogate mothers the answer to their reproductive needs. What began as an enterprise involving a few lawyers and doctors in Michigan, Kentucky, and California is now a national phenomenon. There are surrogate mother centers in Maryland, Arizona, and several other states, and even a surrogate mother newsletter.

Surrogate mother arrangements occur within a tradition of family law that gives the gestational mother (and her spouse, if one exists) rearing rights and obligations. (However, the presumption that the husband is the father can be challenged, and a husband's obligations to his wife's child by AID will usually require his consent.)[1] Although no state has legislation directly on the subject of surrogate motherhood, independently arranged adoptions are lawful in most states. It is no crime to agree to bear a child for another, and then relinquish it for adoption. However, paying the mother a fee for adoption beyond medical expenses is a crime in some states, and in others will prevent the adoption from being approved.[2] Whether termination and transfer of parenting rights will be legally recognized depends on the state. Some states, like Hawaii and Florida, ask few questions and approve independent adoptions very quickly. Others, like Michigan and Kentucky, won't allow surrogate mothers to terminate and assign rearing rights to another if a fee has been paid, or even allow a paternity determination in favor of the sperm donor. The enforcibility of surrogate contracts has also not been tested, and it is safe to assume that some jurisdictions will not enforce them. Legislation clarifying many of these questions has been proposed in several states, but has not yet been enacted.

Even this brief discussion highlights an important fact about surrogate motherhood and other collaborative reproductive techniques. They operate as an alternative to the non-market, agency system of allocating children for adoption, which has contributed to long queues for distributing healthy white babies. This form of independent adoption is controlled by the parties and planned before conception, and enables both the father and mother of the adopted child to be selected in advance.

Understood in these terms, the term "surrogate mother," which means substitute mother, is a misnomer. The natural mother, who contributes egg and uterus, is not so much a substitute mother as a substitute spouse who carries a child for a man whose wife is infertile. Indeed, it is the adoptive mother who is the surrogate mother for the child, since she parents a child borne by another. What, if anything, is wrong with this arrangement? Let us look more closely at its benefits and harms before discussing public policy.

ALL THE PARTIES CAN BENEFIT

Reproduction through surrogate mothering is a deviation from our cultural norms of reproduction, and to many persons it seems immoral or wrong. But surrogate mothering may be good for the parties involved.

Surrogate contracts meet the desire of a husband and wife to rear a healthy child, and more particularly, a child with one partner's genes. The need could arise because the wife has an autosomal dominant or sex-linked genetic disorder, such as hemophilia. More likely, she is infertile and the couple feels a strong need to have children. For many infertile couples the

47

inability to conceive is a major personal problem causing marital conflict and filling both partners with anquish and self-doubt. It may also involve multiple medical work-ups and possibly even surgery. If the husband and wife have sought to adopt a child, they may have been told either that they do not qualify or to join the queue of couples waiting several years for agency adoptions (the wait has grown longer due to birth control, abortion, and the greater willingness of illegitimate mothers to keep their children[3]). For couples exhausted and frustrated by these efforts, the surrogate arrangement seems a Godsend. While the intense desire to have a child often appears selfish, we must not lose sight of the deep-seated psychosocial and biological roots of the desire to generate children.[4]

The arrangement may also benefit the surrogate. Usually women undergo pregnancy and childbirth because they want to rear children. But some women want to have the experience of bearing and birthing a child without the obligation to rear. Phillip Parker, a Michigan psychiatrist who has interviewed over 275 surrogate applicants, finds that the decision to be a surrogate springs from several motives.[5] Most women willing to be surrogates have already had children, and many are married. They choose the surrogate role primarily because the fee provides a better economic opportunity than alternative occupations, but also because they enjoy being pregnant and the respect and attention it draws. The surrogate experience may also be a way to master, through reliving, guilt they feel from past pregnancies that ended in abortion or adoption. Some surrogates may also feel pleased or satisfied, as organ donors do, that they have given the "gift of life" to another couple.[6]

The child born of a surrogate arrangement also benefits. Indeed, but for the surrogate contract, this child would not have been born at all. Unlike the ordinary agency or independent adoption, where a child is already conceived or brought to term, the conception of this child occurs solely as a result of the surrogate agreement. Thus even if the child does suffer identity problems, as adopted children often do, because they are not able to know their mother, this child has benefited, or at least has not been wronged, for without the surrogate arrangement, she would not have been born at all.[7]

BUT PROBLEMS EXIST TOO

Surrogate mothering is also troublesome. Many people think that it is wrong for a woman to conceive and bear a child that she does not intend to raise, particularly if she receives a fee for her services. There are potential costs to the surrogate and her family, the adoptive couple, the child, and even society at large from satisfying the generative needs of infertile couples in this way.

The couple must be willing to spend about $20,000-25,000, depending on lawyers' fees and the supply of and demand for surrogate mothers. (While this price tag makes the surrogate contract a consumption item for the middle classes, it is not unjust to poor couples, for it does not leave them worse off than they were.) The couple must also be prepared to experience, along with the adjustment and demands of becoming parents, the stress and anxiety of participating in a novel social relationship that many still consider immoral or deviant. What do they tell their friends or family? What do they tell the child? Will the child have contact with the mother? What is the couple's relationship with the surrogate and her family during the pregnancy and after? Without established patterns for handling these questions, the parties may experience confusion, frustration, and embarrassment.

A major source of uncertainty and stress is likely to be the surrogate herself. In most cases she will be a stranger, and may never even meet the couple. The lack of a preexisting relation between the couple and surrogate and the possibility that they live far apart enhance the possibility of mistrust. Is the surrogate taking care of herself? Is she having sex with others during her fertile period? Will she contact the child afterwards? What if she demands more money to relinquish the child? To allay these anxieties, the couple could try to establish a relationship of trust with the surrogate, yet such a relationship creates reciprocal rights and duties and might create demands for an undesired relationship after the birth. Even good lawyering that specifies every contingency in the contract is unlikely to allay uncertainty and anxiety about the surrogate's trustworthiness.

The surrogate may also find the experience less satisfying than she envisioned. Conceiving the child may require insemination efforts over several months at inconvenient locations. The pregnancy and birth may entail more pain, unpleasant side effects, and disruption than she expected. The couple may be more intrusive or more aloof than she wishes. As the pregnancy advances and the birth nears, the surrogate may find it increasingly difficult to remain detached by thinking of the child as "theirs" rather than "hers." Relinquishing the baby after birth may be considerably more disheartening and disappointing than she anticipated. Even if informed of this possibility in advance, she may be distressed for several weeks with feelings of loss, depression, and sleep disturbance.[8] She may feel angry at the couple for cutting off all contact with her once the baby is delivered, and guilty at giving up her child. Finally, she will have to face the loss of all contact with "her" child. As the reality of her situation dawns, she may regret not having bargained harder for access to "her baby."

As with the couple, the surrogate's experience will vary with the expectations, needs, and personalities of the parties, the course of the pregnancy, and an advance understanding of the problems that can arise. The surrogate should have a lawyer to protect her interests. Often, however, the couple's lawyer will end up advising the surrogate. Although he has recruited the surrogate, he is paid by and represents the couple. By disclosing his conflicting interest, he satisfies legal ethics, but he may not serve the interests of the surrogate as well as independent counsel.

HARMS TO THE CHILD

Unlike embryo transfer, gene therapy, and other manipulative techniques (some of which are collaborative), surrogate arrangements do not pose the risk of physical harm to the offspring. But there is the risk of psychosocial harm. Surrogate mothering, like adoption and artificial insemination by donor (AID), deliberately separates genetic and gestational from social parentage. The mother who begets, bears, and births does not parent. This separation can pose a problem for the child who discovers it. Like adopted and AID children, the child may be strongly motivated to learn the absent parent's identity and to establish a relationship, in this case with the mother and her family. Inability to make that connection, especially inability to learn who the mother is, may affect the child's self-esteem, create feelings of rootlessness, and leave the child thinking that she had been rejected due to some personal fault.[9] While this is a serious concern, the situation is tolerated when it arises with AID and adoptive children. Intentional conception for adoption—the essence of surrogate mothering—poses no different issue.

The child can also be harmed if the adoptive couple are not fit parents. After all, a willingness to spend substantial money to fulfill a desire to rear children is no guarantee of good parenting. But then neither is reproduction by paired mates who wish intensely to have a child. The nonbiologic parent may resent or reject the child, but the same possibility exists with adoption, AID, or ordinary reproduction.

There is also the fear, articulated by such commentators as Leon Kass and Paul Ramsey,[10] that collaborative reproduction confuses the lineage of children and destroys the meaning of family as we know it. In surrogate mothering, as with sperm or ovum or womb donors, the genetic and gestational mother does not rear the child, though the biologic father does. What implications does this hold for the family and the child's lineage?

The separation of the child from the genetic or biologic parent in surrogate mothering is hardly unique. It arises with adoption, but surrogate arrangments are more closely akin to AID or blended families, where at least one parent has a bloodtie to the child and the child will know at least one genetic parent. He may, as adopted children often do, have intense desires to learn his biologic mother's identity and seek contact with her and her family. Failure to connect with biologic roots may cause suffering. But the fact that adoption through surrogate mother contracts is planned before conception does not increase the chance of identity confusion, lowered self esteem, or the blurring of lineage that occurs with adoption or AID.

The greatest chance of confusing family lines arises if the child and couple establish relations with the surrogate and the surrogate's family. If that unlikely event occurs, questions about the child's relations with the surrogate's spouse, parents, and other children can arise. But these issues are not unique. Indeed, they are increasingly common with the growth of blended families. Surrogate mothering in a few instances may lead to a new variation on blended families, but its threat to the family is trivial compared to the rapid changes in family structure now occurring for social, economic, and demographic reasons.

In many cases surrogate motherhood and other forms of collaborative reproduction may shore up, rather than undermine, the traditional family by enabling couples who would otherwise be childless to have children. The practice of employing others to assist in child rearing—including wet-nurses, neonatal ICU nurses, day-care workers, and babysitters—is widely accepted. We also tolerate assistance in the form of sperm sales and donation of egg and gestation (adoption). Surrogate mothering is another method of assisting people to undertake childrearing, and thus serves the purposes of the marital union. It is hard to see how its planned nature obstructs that contribution.

USING BIRTH FOR SELFISH ENDS

A basic fear about the new reproductive technologies is that they manipulate a natural physiologic process involved in the creation of human life. When one considers the potential power that resides in our ability to manipulate the genes of embryos, the charges of playing God or arrogantly tampering with nature, and the dark Huxleyian vision of genetically engineered babies decanted from bottles are not surprising. While *Brave New World* is the standard text for this fear, the 1982 film *Bladerunner* also evokes it. Trycorp., a genetic engineering corporation, manufactures "replicants," who resemble human beings in most respects, including their ability to remember their childhoods, but who are programmed to die in four years. In portraying the replicants' struggle for a long life and full human status, the film raises a host of ethical issues relevant to the issue of gene manipulation, from the meaning of personhood to the duties we have in "fabricating" people to make them as whole and healthy as possible.

Such fears, however, are not a sufficient reason to stop splicing genes or relieving infertility through external fertilization.[11] In any event they have no application to surrogate mothering, which does not alter genes or even manipulate the embryo. The only technological aid is a syringe to inseminate and a thermometer to determine when ovulation occurs. Although embryo manipulation would occur if the surrogate received the fertilized egg of another woman, the qualms about surrogate mothering stem less from its potential for technical manipulation, and more from the attitude that it reflects toward the body and mother-child relations. Mothers bear and give up children for adoption rather frequently when the conception is unplanned. But here the mother conceives the child for that purpose, deliberately using her body for a fee to serve the needs of others. It is the cold willingness to use her body as a baby-making machine and deny the mother-child gestational bond that bothers. (Ironically, the natural bond may turn out to be deeper and stronger than the surrogate imagined.)

Since the transfer of rearing duties from the natural gestational mother to others is widely accepted, the unwillingness of the surrogate mother to rear her child cannot in itself be wrong. As long as she transfers rearing responsibility to capable parents, she is not acting irresponsibly. Still, some persons take a deontological position that it is wrong to use the reproductive process for ends other than the good of the child.[12] But the mere presence of selfish motives does not render reproduction immoral, as long as it is carried out in a way that respects the child's interests. Otherwise most pregnancies and births would be immoral, for people have children to serve individual ends as well as the good of the child. In terms of instrumentalism, surrogate mothering cannot be distinguished from most other reproductive situations, whether AID, adoption, or simply planning a child to experience the pleasures of parenthood.

In this vein the problems that can arise when a defective child is born are cited as proof of the immorality of surrogate mothering. The fear is that neither the contracting couple nor the surrogate will want the defective child. In one recent case (*New York Times*, January 28, 1983, p. 18) a dispute arose when none of the parties wanted to take a child born with microcephaly, a condition related to mental retardation. The contracting man claimed on the basis of blood typing that the baby was not his, and thus was not obligated under the contract to take it, or to pay the surrogate's fee. It turned out that surrogate had borne her husband's child, for she had unwittingly become pregnant by him before being artificially inseminated by the contracting man. The surrogate and her husband eventually assumed responsibility for the child.

An excessively instrumental and callous approach to reproduction when a less than perfect baby is born is not unique to surrogate mothering. Similar reactions can occur whenever married couples have a defective child, as the Baby Doe controversy, which involved the passive euthanasia of a child with Down syndrome, indicates. All surrogate mothering is not wrong because in some instances a defective newborn will be rejected. Nor is it clear that this reaction is more likely in surrogate mothering than in conventional births for it reflects common attitudes toward handicapped newborns more than alienation inherent in the surrogate arrangement.

As with most situations, "how" something is done is more important than the mere fact of doing it. The morality of surrogate mothering thus depends on how the duties and responsibilities of the role are carried out, rather than on the mere fact that a couple produces a child with the aid of a collaborator. . . .

NOTES

The author gratefully acknowledges the comments of Rebecca Dresser, Mark Frankel, Inga Markovits, Phillip Parker, Bruce Russell, John Sampson, and Ted Schneyer on earlier drafts.

1 People v. Sorenson, 68 Cal. 2d 280, 437 P.2d 495; Walter Wadlington. "Artificial Insemination: The Dangers of a Poorly Kept Secret," *Northwestern Law Review* 64 (1970), 777.

2 See, for example, Michigan Statutes Annotated, 27.3178 (555.54)(555.69).

3 William Landes and Eleanor Posner, "The Economics of the Baby Shortage," *Journal of Legal Studies* 7 (1978), 323.

4 See Erik Erikson, *The Life Cycle Completed* (New York: Norton, 1980), pp. 122-124.

5 Phillip Parker, "Surrogate Mother's Motivations: Initial Findings," *American Journal of Psychiatry* 140:1 (January 1983), 117-118; Phillip Parker, "The Psychology of Surrogate Motherhood: A Preliminary Report of a Longitudinal Pilot Study" (unpublished). See also Dava Sobel, "Surrogate Mothers: Why Women Volunteer," *New York Times*, June 25, 1981, p. 18.

6 Mark Frankel, "Surrogate Motherhood: An Ethical Perspective," pp. 1-2. (Paper presented at Wayne State Symposium on Surrogate Motherhood, Nov. 20, 1982.)

7 See John Robertson, "In Vitro Conception and Harm to the Unborn," 8 *Hastings Center Report* 8 (October 1978), 13-14; Michael Bayles, "Harm to the Unconceived," *Philosophy and Public Affairs* 5 (1976), 295.

8 A small, uncontrolled study found these effects to last some 4-6 weeks. Statement of Nancy Reame, R.N. at Wayne State University, Symposium on Surrogate Motherhood, Nov. 20, 1982.

9 Betty Jane Lifton, *Twice Born: Memoirs of an Adopted Daughter* (New York: Penguin, 1977); L. Dusky, "Brave New Babies," *Newsweek*, Dec. 6, 1982, p. 30.

10 Leon Kass, "Making Babies—the New Biology and the Old Morality," *The Public Interest* 26 (1972), 18; "Making Babies Revisited," *The Public Interest* 54 (1979), 32; Paul Ramsey, *Fabricated Man: The Ethics of Genetic Control* (New Haven: Yale University Press, 1970).

11 The President's Commission for the Study of Ethical Problems in Medicine and Biomedical and Behavioral Research, *Splicing Life: The Social and Ethical Issues of Genetic Engineering with Human Beings* (Washington, D.C., 1982), pp. 53-60.

12 Herbert Krimmel, Testimony before California Assembly Committee on Judiciary, Surrogate Parenting Contracts (November 14, 1982), pp. 89-96.

NO

Herbert T. Krimmel

THE CASE AGAINST
SURROGATE PARENTING

Is it ethical for someone to create a human life with the intention of giving it up? This seems to be the primary question for both surrogate mother arrangements and artificial insemination by donor (AID), since in both situations a person who is providing germinal material does so only upon the assurance that someone else will assume full responsibility for the child they help to create.

THE ETHICAL ISSUE

In analyzing the ethics of surrogate mother arrangements, it is helpful to begin by examining the roles the surrogate mother performs. First, she acts as a procreator in providing an ovum to be fertilized. Second, after her ovum has been fertilized by the sperm of the man who wishes to parent the child, she acts as host to the fetus, providing nurture and protection while the newly conceived individual develops.

In this second role as host I see no insurmountable moral objections to the functions she performs. Her actions are analogous to those of a foster mother or of a wet-nurse who cares for a child when the natural mother cannot or does not do so. Using a surrogate mother as a host for the fetus when the biological mother cannot bear the child is no more morally objectionable than employing others to help educate, train or otherwise care for a child. Except in extremes, where the parent abdicates or delegates responsibilities for a child for trivial reasons, the practice would not seem to raise a serious moral issue.

I would argue, however that the first role that the surrogate mother performs—providing germinal material to be fertilized—does pose a major ethical problem. The surrogate mother provides her ovum, and enters into a surrogate mother arrangement, with the clear understanding that she is to avoid responsibility for the life she creates. Surrogate mother arrangements

Reprinted by permission from the *Hastings Center Report*, 13:5, October 1983. Copyright © 1983, the Hastings Center.

are designed to separate in the mind of the surrogate mother the decision to have and raise that child. The cause of this disassociation is some other benefit she will receive, most often money.[1] In other words, her desire to create a child is born of some motive other than the desire to be a parent. This separation of the decision to create a child from the decision to parent it is ethically suspect. The child is conceived not because he is wanted by his biological mother, but because he can be useful to someone else. He is conceived in order to be given away.

At their deepest level, surrogate mother arrangements involve a change in motive for creating children: from a desire to have them for their own sake, to a desire to have them because they can provide her some other benefit. The surrogate mother creates a child with the intention to abdicate parental responsibilities. Can we view this as ethical? My answer is no. I will try to explain why by analyzing various situations in which surrogate mother arrangements might be used.

WHY MOTIVE MATTERS

Let's begin with the single parent. A single woman might use AID, or a single man might use a surrogate mother arrangement, if she or he wanted a child but did not want to be burdened with a spouse.[2] Either practice would intentionally deprive the child of a mother or a father. This, I assert, is fundamentally unfair to the child.

Those who disagree might point to divorce or to the death of a parent as situations in which a child is deprived of one parent and must rely solely or primarily upon the other. The comparison, however, is inapt. After divorce or the death of a parent, a child may find herself with a single parent due to circumstances that were unfortunate, unintended, and undesired. But when surrogate mother arrangements are used by a single parent, depriving the child of a second parent is one of the intended and desired effects. It is one thing to ask how to make the best of a bad situation when it is thrust upon a person. It is different altogether to ask whether one may intentionally set out to achieve the same result. The morality of identical results (for example, killings) will often times differ depending upon whether the situation is invited by, or involuntarily thrust upon, the actor. Legal distinctions following and based upon this ethical distinction are abundant. The law of self-defense provides a notable example.[3]

Since a woman can get pregnant if she wishes whether or not she is married, and since there is little that society can do to prevent women from creating children even if their intention is to deprive them of a father, why should we be so concerned with single men using surrogate mother arrangements if they too want a child but not a spouse? To say that women can intentionally plan to be unwed mothers is not to condone the practice. Besides, society will hold the father liable in a paternity action if he can be found and identified, which indicates some social concern that people should not be able to abdicate the responsibilities that they incur in generating children. Otherwise, why do we condemn the proverbial sailor with a pregnant girl in every port?

In many surrogate mother arrangements, of course, the surrogate mother will not be transferring custody of the child to a single man, but to a couple: the child's biological father and a stepmother, his wife. What are the ethics of surrogate mother arrangements when the child is taken into a two-parent family? Again, surrogate mother arrangements and AID pose similar ethical questions: The surrogate mother transfers her parental responsibilities to the wife of the biological father, while with AID the sperm donor relinquishes his interest in the child to the husband of the biological mother. In both cases the child is created with the intention of transferring the responsibility for its care to a new set of parents. The surrogate mother situation is more dramatic than AID since the transfer occurs after the child is born, while in the case of AID the transfer takes place at the time of the insemination even before the child is yet in being. Nevertheless, the ethical point is the same: creating children for the purpose of transferring them. For a surrogate mother the question remains: is it ethical to create a child for the purpose of transferring it to the wife of the biological father?

At first blush this looks to be little different from the typical adoption, for what is an adoption other than a transfer of responsibility from one set of parents to another? The analogy is misleading, however, for two reasons. First, it is difficult to imagine anyone conceiving children for the purpose of putting them up for adoption. And, if such a bizarre event were to occur, I doubt if we would look upon it with moral approval. Most adoptions arise either because an undesired conception is brought to term, or because the parents wanted to have the child, but find that they are unable to provide for it because of some unfortunate circumstances that develop after conception.

Second, even if surrogate mother arrangements were to be classified as a type of adoption, not all offerings of children for adoption are necessarily moral. For example, would it be moral for parents to offer their three-year old for adoption because they are bored with the child? Would it be moral for a couple to offer for adoption their newborn female baby because they wanted a boy?

Therefore, even though surrogate mother arrangements may in some superficial ways be likened to adoption, one must still ask whether it is ethical to separate the decision to create children from the desire to have them. I would answer no. The procreator should desire the child for its own sake, and not as a means of attaining some other end. Even though one of the ends may be stated altruistically as an attempt to bring happiness to an infertile couple, the child is still being used by the surrogate. She creates it not because she desires it, but because she desires to get something from it.

To sanction the use and treatment of human beings as means to the achievement of other goals instead of as ends in themselves is to accept an ethic with a tragic past, and to establish a precedent with a dangerous future. Already the press has reported the decision of one couple to conceive a child for the purpose of using it as a bone marrow donor for its sibling (*Los Angeles Times,* April 17, 1979, p. 1-2). And the bioethics literature contains articles seriously considering whether we should clone human beings to serve as an inventory of spare parts for organ transplants[4] and articles that foresee the use of comatose human beings as self-replenishing blood banks and manufacturing plants for human hormones.[5] How far our society is willing to proceed down this road is uncertain, but it is clear that the first step to all these practices is the acceptance of the same principle that the Nazis attempted to use to justify their medical experiments at the Nuremberg War Crimes Trials: that human beings may be used as means to the achievement of other worthy goals, and need not be treated solely as ends in themselves.[6]

3. SHOULD WOMEN BE ALLOWED TO BEAR BABIES FOR A FEE?

But why, it might be asked, is it so terrible if the surrogate mother does not desire the child for its own sake, when under the proposed surrogate mother arrangements there will be a couple eagerly desiring to have the child and to be its parents? That this argument may not be entirely accurate will be illustrated in the following section, but the basic reply is that creating a child without desiring it fundamentally changes the way we look at children—instead of viewing them as unique individual personalities to be desired in their own right, we may come to view them as commodities or items of manufacture to be desired because of their utility. A recent newspaper account describes the business of an agency that matches surrogate mothers with barren couples as follows:

Its first product is due for delivery today. Twelve others are on the way and an additional 20 have been ordered. The "company" is Surrogate Mothering Ltd. and the "product" is babies.[7]

The dangers of this view are best illustrated by examining what might go wrong in a surrogate mother arrangement, and most important, by viewing how the various parties to the contract may react to the disappointment of their expectations.

WHAT MIGHT GO WRONG

Ninety-nine percent of the surrogate mother arrangements may work out just fine; the child will be born normal, and the adopting parents (that is, the biological father and his wife) will want it. But, what happens when, unforeseeably, the child is born deformed? Since many defects cannot be discovered prenatally by amniocentesis or other means, the situation is bound to arise.[8] Similarly, consider what would happen if the biological father were

to die before the birth of the child. Or if the "child" turns out to be twins or triplets. Each of these instances poses an inevitable situation where the adopting parents may be unhappy with the prospect of getting the child or children. Although legislation can mandate that the adopting parents take the child or children in whatever condition they come or whatever the situation, provided the surrogate mother has abided by all the contractual provisions of the surrogate mother arrangement, the important point for our discussion is the attitude that the surrogate mother or the adopting parent might have. Consider the example of the deformed child.

When I participated in the Surrogate Parent Foundation's inaugural symposium in November 1981, I was struck by the attitude of both the surrogate mothers and the adopting parents to these problems. The adopting parents worried, "Do we have to take such a child?" and the surrogate mothers said in response, "Well, we don't want to be stuck with it." Clearly, both groups were anxious not to be responsible for the "undesirable child" born of the surrogate mother arrangement. What does this portend?

It is human nature that when one pays money, one expects value. Things that one pays for have a way of becoming viewed as commodities. Unavoidable in surrogate mother arrangements are questions such as: "Did I get a good one?" We see similar behavior with respect to the adoption of children: comparatively speaking, there is no shortage of black, Mexican-American, mentally retarded, or older children seeking homes; the shortage is in attractive, intelligent-looking Caucasian babies.[9] Similarly, surrogate mother arrangements involve more than just the desire to have a child. The desire is for a certain type of child.

But, it may be objected, don't all parents voice these same concerns in the normal course of having children? Not exactly. No one doubts or minimizes the pain and disappointment parents feel when they learn that their child is born with some genetic or congenital birth defect. But this is different from the surrogate mother situation, where neither the surrogate mother nor the adopting parents may feel responsible, and both sides may feel that they have a legitimate excuse not to assume responsibility for the child. The surrogate mother might blame the biological father for having "defective sperm," as the adopting parents might blame the surrogate mother for a "defective ovum" or for improper care of the fetus during pregnancy. The point is that the adopting parents desire a normal child, not *this* child in any condition, and the surrogate mother doesn't want it in any event. So both sides will feel threatened by the birth of an "undesirable child." Like bruised fruit in the produce bin of a supermarket, this child is more likely to become an object of avoidance than one of desire.

Certainly, in the natural course of having children a mother may doubt whether she wants a child if the father has died before its birth; parents may shy away from a defective infant, or be distressed at the thought of multiple births. Nevertheless, I believe they are more likely to accept these contingencies as a matter of fate. I do not think this is the case with surrogate mother arrangements. After all, in the surrogate mother arrangement the adopting parents can blame someone outside the marital relationship. The surrogate mother has been hosting this child all along, and she is delivering it. It certainly *looks* far more like a commodity than the child which arrives in the natural course within the family unit.

A DANGEROUS AGENDA

Another social problem, which arises out of the first, is the fear that surrogate mother arrangements will fall prey to eugenic concerns.[10] Surrogate mother contracts typically have clauses requiring genetic tests of the fetus and stating that the surrogate mother must have an abortion (or keep the child herself) if the child does not meet these tests.[11]

In the last decade we have witnessed a renaissance of interest in eugenics. This, coupled with advances in biomedical technology, has created a host of abuses and new moral problems. For example, genetic counseling clinics now face a dilemma: amniocentesis, the same procedure that identifies whether a fetus suffers from certain genetic defects, also discloses the sex of a fetus. Genetic counseling clinics have reported that even when the fetus is normal, a disproportionate number of mothers abort female children.[12] Aborting normal fetuses simply because the prospective parents desire children of a certain sex is one result of viewing children as commodities. The recent scandal at the Repository for Germinal Choice, the so called "Nobel Sperm Bank," provides another chilling example. Their first "customer" was, inbeknownest to them, a woman who "had lost custody of two other children because they were abused in an effort to 'make them smart.'"[13] Of course, these and similar evils may occur whether or not surrogate mother arrangements are allowed by law. But to the extent that these arrangements are part of the milieu that promotes the view of children as commodities, they contribute to these problems. There is nothing wrong with striving for betterment, as long as it does not result in intolerance to that which is not perfect. But I fear that the latter attitude will become prevalent.

Sanctioning surrogate mother arrangements can also exert pressures upon the family structure. First, as was noted earlier, there is nothing technically to prevent the use of surrogate mother arrangements by single males desiring to become parents and, indeed, single females can already do this with AID or even without it. But even if legislation were to limit the use of the surrogate mother arrangement to infertile couples, other pressures would make themselves felt: namely the intrusion of a third adult into the marital community.[14] I do not think that society is ready to accept either single parenting or quasi-adulterous arrangements as normal.

Another stress on the family structure arises within the family of the surrogate mother. When the child is surrendered to the adopting parents it is removed not only from the surrogate mother, but also from her family. They too have interests to be considered. Do not the siblings of that child have an interest in the fact that their little baby brother has been "given" away?[15] One woman, the mother of a medical student who had often donated sperm for artificial insemination, expressed her feelings to me eloquently. She asked, "I wonder how many grandchildren I have that I have never seen and never been able to hold or cuddle."

Intrafamily tensions can also be expected to result in the family of the adopting parents due to the asymmetry of relationship the adopting parents will have toward the child. The adopting mother has no biological relationship to the child, whereas the adopting father is also the child's biological father. Won't this unequal biological claim on the child be used as a wedge in child-rearing arguments? Can't we imagine the father saying, "Well, he is my son, not yours"? What if the couple eventually gets divorced? Should custody in a subsequent divorce between the adopting mother and the biological father be treated simply as a normal child custody dispute in any other divorce? Or should the biological relationship between father and child weigh more heavily? These questions do not arise in typical adoption situations since both parents are equally unrelated biologically to the child. Indeed, in adoption there is symmetry. The surrogate mother situation is more analogous to second marriages, where the children of one party by a prior marriage are adopted by the new spouse. Since asymmetry in second marriage situations causes problems, we can anticipate similar difficulties arising from surrogate mother arrangements.

There is also the worry the offspring of a surrogate mother arrangement will be deprived of important information about his or her heritage. This also happens with adopted children or children conceived by AID,[16] who lack information about their biological parents, which could be important to them medically. Another less popularly recognized problem is the danger of half-sibling marriages,[17] where the child of the surrogate mother unwittingly falls in love with a half sister or brother. The only way to avoid these problems is to dispense with the confidentiality of parental records; however, the natural parents may not always want their identity disclosed.

The legalization of surrogate mother arrangements may also put undue pressure upon poor women to use their bodies in this way to support themselves and their families. Analogous problems have arisen in the past with the use of paid blood donors.[18] And occasionally the press reports someone desperate enough to offer to sell an eye or some other organ.[19] I believe that certain things should be viewed as too important to be sold as commodities, and I hope that we have advanced from the time when parents raised children for profitable labor, or found themselves forced to sell their children.

While many of the social problems I have outlined here have their analogies in other present-day occurrences such as divorced families or in adoption, every addition is hurtful. Legalizing surrogate mother arrangements will increase the frequency of these problems, and due to its dramatic nature is more likely to put stress on our society's shared moral values.[20] . . .

NOTES

1   Phillip J. Parker, "Motivation of Surrogate Mothers: Initial Findings," *American Journal of Psychiatry* 140:1 (January 1983), 117-18; see also Doe v. Kelley, Circuit Court of Wayne County Michigan (1980) reported in 1980 Rep. on Human Reproduction and Law II-A-1.

2   See. e.g., C.M. v. C.C., 152 N.J. Supp. 160, 377 A.2d 821 (1977); "Why She Went to 'Nobel Sperm Bank' for Child," *Los Angeles Herald Examiner*, Aug. 6, 1982, p. A9; "Womb for Rent," *Los Angeles Herald Examiner*, Sept. 21, 1981, p. A3.

3   See also Richard McCormick, "Reproductive Technologies: Ethical Issues" in *Encyclopedia of Bioethics*. edited by Walter Reich, Vol. 4 (New York: The Free Press, 1978) pp. 1454, 1459; Robert Snowden and G.D. Mitchell, *The Artificial Family* (London: George Allen & Unwin, 1981), p. 71.

4   See, e.g., Alexander Peters, "The Brave New World: Can the Law Bring Order Within Traditional Concepts of Due Process?" *Suffolk Law Review* 4 (1970), 894. 901-02; Roderic Gorney, "The New Biology and the Future of Man," *UCLA Law Review* 15 (1968), 273, 302; J.G. Castel, "Legal Implications of Biomedical Science and Technology in the Twenty-First Century," *Canadian Bar Review* 51 (1973), 119, 127.

5   See Harry Nelson, "Maintaining Dead to Serve as Blood Makers Proposed: Logical, Sociologist Says," *Los Angeles Times*, February 26, 1974; Hans Jonas, "Against the Stream: Comments on the Definition and Redefinition of Death," in *Philosophical Essays: From Ancient Creed to Technological Man* (Chicago: University of Chicago Press, 1974), pp. 132-40.

6   See Leo Alexander, "Medical Science under Dictatorship," *New England Journal of Medicine* 241:2 (1949), 39; United States v. Brandt, Trial of the Major War Criminals, International Military Tribunal: Nuremberg, 14 November 1945-1 October 1946.

7   Bob Dvorchak, "Surrogate Mothers: Pregnant Idea Now a Pregnant Business," *Los Angeles Herald Examiner*, December 27, 1983, p. A1.

8   "Surrogate's Baby Born with Deformities Rejected by All," *Los Angeles Times*, January 22, 1983, p. 1-17; "Man Who Hired Surrogate Did Not Father Ailing Baby," *Los Angeles Herald Examiner*, February 3, 1983, p. A-6.

9   See, e.g., Adoption in America, Hearing before the Subcommittee on Aging, Family and Human Services of the Senate Committee on Labor and Human Resources, 97th Congress. 1st Session (1981), p. 3 (comments of Senator Jeremiah Denton and p. 3 (statement of Warren Master, Acting Commissioner of Administration for Children, Youth and Families, HHS.

10   Cf. "Discussion: Moral, Social and Ethical Issues," in *Law and Ethics of A.I.D. and Embryo Transfer* (1973) (comments of Himmelweit); reprinted in Michael Shapiro and Roy Spece, *Bioethics and Law* (St. Paul: West Publishing Company, 1981), p. 548.

11   See, e.g., Lane (Newsday), "Womb for Rent," *Tucson Citizen* (Weekender), June 7, 1980, p. 3; Susan Lewis, "Baby Bartering? Surrogate Mothers Pose Issues for Lawyers, Courts," *The Los Angeles Daily Journal*, April 20, 1981; see also Elaine Markoutsas, "Women Who Have Babies for Other Women," *Good Housekeeping* 96 (April 1981), 104.

12   See Morton A. Stenchever, "An Abuse of Prenatal Diagnosis," *Journal of the American Medical Association* 221 (1972), 408; Charles Westoff and Ronald R. Rindfus, "Sex Preselection in the United States: Some Implications," *Science* 184 (1974), 633, 636; see also Phyllis Battelle, "Is It a Boy or a Girl"? *Los Angeles Herald Examiner*, Oct. 8, 1981, p. A17.

3. SHOULD WOMEN BE ALLOWED TO BEAR BABIES FOR A FEE?

13 "2 Children Taken from Sperm Bank Mother," *Los Angeles Times,* July 14, 1982; p. I-3; "The Sperm-Bank Scandal," *Newsweek* 24 (July 26, 1982).

14 See Helmut Thielicke, *The Ethics of Sex,* John W. Doberstein, trans. (New York: Harper & Row, 1964).

15 According to one newspaper account, when a surrogate mother informed her nine-year-old daughter that the new baby would be given away, the daughter replied: "Oh, good. If it's a girl we can keep it and give Jeffrey [her two-year-old half brother] away." "Womb for Rent," *Los Angeles Herald Examiner,* Sept. 21, 1981, p. A3.

16 See, e.g., Lorraine Dusky, "Brave New Babies"? *Newsweek* 30 (December 6, 1982). Also testimony of Suzanne Rubin before the California Assembly Committee on Judiciary, Surrogate Parenting Contracts, Assembly Publication No. 962, pp. 72-75 (November 19, 1982).

17 Regarding how this has posed an accelerating problem for children conceived through AID, see, e.g., Martin Curie-Cohen, et al., "Current Practice of Artificial Insemination by Donor in the United States," *New England Journal of Medicine* 300 (1979), 585-89.

18 See Richard M. Titmuss, *The Gift Relationship: From Human Blood to Social Policy* (New York: Random House, 1971).

19 See, e.g., "Man Desperate for Funds: Eye for Sale at $35,000," *Los Angeles Times,* February 1, 1975; "100 Answer Man's Ad for New Kidney," *Los Angeles Times,* September 12, 1974.

20 See generally Guido Calabresi, "Reflections on Medical Experimentation in Humans," *Daedalus* 98 (1969), 387-93; also see Michael Shapiro and Roy Spece, "On Being 'Unprincipled on Principle': The Limits of Decision Making 'On the Merits,' " in *Bioethics and Law,* pp. 67-71.

POSTSCRIPT

SHOULD WOMEN BE ALLOWED TO BEAR BABIES FOR A FEE?

Two legal cases in 1986 supported some aspects of the legality of surrogate parenting. Kentucky's Supreme Court ruled that Surrogate Parenting Associates did not violate the state's law against baby-selling because the fee for surrogate mothers was agreed to before conception and the mother retained the right to cancel the contract up to the point of relinquishing her parental rights. In a case involving the implantation of an embryo created from the egg of one woman and her husband's sperm into another woman, a lower court in Michigan ruled that the genetic mother, not the gestational one, was the legal parent. In Great Britain, the practice has had a rockier course. Legislation making surrogacy illegal was passed in 1986.

Concerned by the growth of the practice, the American College of Obstetricians and Gynecologists has issued the first ethical guidelines for its members. The organization cautions physicians to avoid any surrogate mother arrangement that is likely to lead to any financial exploitation of any of the parties and acknowledges that many physicians may not wish to take part in such arrangements. One particularly troubling issue for physicians is: Who shall give the consent for treatment: the surrogate or the adoptive parents who are going to be responsible for the baby?

A persuasive argument for surrogate mothering contracts is *The Surrogate Mother* (Everest House, 1981), by Noel P. Keane with Dennis L. Breo. Keane is a lawyer who handled the first surrogate mother cases. A journalistic account is Elaine Markoutsas, "Women Who Have Babies for Other Women," *Good Housekeeping* (April 1981).

A number of articles have appeared in law journals, including Barbara Cohen, "Surrogate Mothers: Whose Baby Is It?" *American Journal of Law and Medicine* (Fall 1984); and M. Louise Graham, "Surrogate Gestation and the Protection of Choice," *Santa Clara Law Review* (Spring 1982). While these articles focus on the legal uncertainties, they also bring up many ethical problems. George J. Annas, in his article "The Baby Broker Boom" (*Hastings Center Report,* April 1986), warns against commercialism. See also Sherman Elias and George J. Annas, "Social Policy Considerations in Noncoital Reproduction," *Journal of the American Medical Association* (January 3, 1986, pp. 62-68). In *New Conceptions* (New York: St. Martin's Press, 1984), attorney Lori B. Andrews guides prospective parents through the new reproductive technologies, including surrogacy.

PART II
DECISIONS
ABOUT DEATH

What are the ethical responsibilities associated with death? Doctors are sworn "to do no harm" but this proscription is open to many different interpretations. Death is a natural event that can in some instances put an end to suffering. Is it then ethically necessary to prolong life at all times under all circumstances? If not, is the quality of life a valid criterion for determining when life must be prolonged? Medical personnel often must face these agonizing questions and decide matters of literal life and death. Even the question of whether or not to tell terminally ill patients the truth of their condition has great ethical implications. The right of humans to decide their own fate conflicts with society's interest in maintaining the value of human life in regard to suicide and the right of parents to decide the fate of critically ill newborns. This section examines some of these anguishing questions.

Should Doctors Withhold the Truth From Dying Patients?

Is Killing the Same as Letting Die?

Must Fluids and Nutrition Always Be Given to Dying Patients?

Should Parents be Allowed to Decide to Withhold Treatment From Newborns with Birth Defects?

EPA Documerica photo.

63

ISSUE 4

IS IT ETHICAL TO WITHHOLD THE TRUTH FROM DYING PATIENTS?

YES: Bernard C. Meyer, from "Truth and the Physician," in *Ethical Issues in Medicine,* E. Fuller Torrey, editor (Boston: Little, Brown, 1968)

NO: Sissela Bok, from *Lying: Moral Choice in Public and Private Life* (New York: Pantheon Books, 1978)

ISSUE SUMMARY

YES: Physician Bernard C. Meyer argues that physicians must use discretion in communicating bad news to patients. Adherence to a rigid formula of truthtelling fails to appreciate the differences in patients' readiness to hear and understand the information.

NO: Philosopher Sissela Bok challenges the traditional physician's view by arguing that the harm resulting from disclosure is less than they think and is outweighed by the benefits, including the important one of giving the patient the right to choose among treatments.

In his powerful short story, "The Death of Ivan Ilych," Leo Tolstoy graphically portrayed the physical agony and the social isolation of a dying man. But, he wrote, "What tormented Ivan Ilych most was the deception, the lie, which for some reason they all accepted, that he was not dying but was simply ill, and that he only need keep quiet and undergo a treatment and then something very good would result." Instrumental in setting up the deception is Ilych's doctor, who reassures him to the very end that all will be well. Hearing the banal news once again, "Ivan Ilych looks at him as much as to say: 'Are you really never ashamed of lying?' But the doctor does not wish to understand this question. . . ."

Unlike many of the ethical issues discussed in this volume, which have arisen as a result of modern scientific knowledge and technology, the question of whether to tell dying patients the truth is an old and persistent one. However, it has been given a new urgency because medical practice today is so complex that it is often difficult to know just what the "truth" really is. A dying patient's life can often be prolonged, although at great financial and personal cost, and many people differ over the definition of a "terminal" illness.

What must be balanced in this decision are two significant principles of ethical conduct: the obligation to tell the truth and the obligation not to harm others. Moral philosophers, beginning with Aristotle, have regarded truth as either an absolute value or one that, at the very least, is preferable to deception. The great German philosopher Immanuel Kant argued in the nineteenth century that there is no justification for lying (although some later commentators feel that his absolutist position has been overstated). Other philosophers have argued that deception is sometimes justified: For example, Henry Sidgwick, an early twentieth-century British philosopher, believed that it was entirely acceptable to lie to invalids and children to protect them from the shock of the truth. Although the question has been debated for centuries, no clear-cut answer has been reached. In fact, the case of a benevolent lie to a dying patient is often given as the prime example of an excusable deception.

If moral philosophers cannot agree, what guidance is there for the physician torn between his desire for truth and his desire to protect his patient from harm (and his admittedly paternalistic conviction that he knows best what will harm the patient)? None of the early medical codes and oaths offered any advice to physicians on what to tell patients, although they were quite explicit about the physicians' obligations to keep confidential what patients told them. The American Medical Association's 1847 "Code of Ethics" did endorse some forms of deception by noting that the physician has a sacred duty "to avoid all things which have a tendency to discourage the patient and to depress his spirits." The most recent (1980) AMA "Principles of Medical Ethics" says only that "A physician shall deal honestly with patients and colleagues. . . ." However, the American Hospital Association's "Patient's Bill of Rights," adopted in 1972, is more specific: "The patient has the right to obtain from his physician complete current information concerning his diagnosis, treatment, and prognosis in terms the patient can reasonably be expected to understand. When it is not medically advisable to give such information to the patient, the information should be made available to an appropriate person in his behalf."

In the following selections, Bernard C. Meyer argues for an ethic that transcends the virtue of uttering truth for truth's sake. He believes that the physician's prime responsibility is contained in the Hippocratic Oath—"So far as possible, do no harm." Sissela Bok counters with evidence that physicians often misread patients' wishes and that withholding the truth can often harm them more than disclosure.

YES
Bernard C. Meyer

TRUTH AND THE PHYSICIAN

Truth does not do so much good in this world as the semblance of it does harm.
La Rochefoucauld

Among the reminiscences of his Alsatian boyhood, my father related the story of the local functionary who was berated for the crude and blunt manner in which he went from house to house announcing to wives and mothers news of battle casualties befalling men from the village. On the next occasion, mindful of the injunctions to be more tactful and to soften the impact of his doleful message, he rapped gently on the door and, when it opened, inquired, "Is the widow Schmidt at home?"

Insofar as this essay is concerned with the subject of truth it is only proper to add that when I told this story to a colleague, he already knew it and claimed that it concerned a woman named Braun who lived in a small town in Austria. By this time it would not surprise me to learn that the episode is a well-known vignette in the folklore of Tennessee where it is attributed to a woman named Smith or Brown whose husband was killed at the battle of Shiloh. Ultimately, we may find that all three versions are plagiarized accounts of an occurrence during the Trojan War.

COMMUNICATION BETWEEN PHYSICIAN AND PATIENT

Apocryphal or not, the story illustrates a few of the vexing aspects of the problem of conveying unpalatable news, notably the difficulty of doing so in a manner that causes a minimum amount of pain, and also the realization that not everyone is capable of learning how to do it. Both aspects find their application in the field of medicine where the imparting of the grim facts of diagnosis and prognosis is a constant and recurring issue. Nor does it seem likely that for all our learning we doctors are particularly endowed with superior talents and techniques for coping with these problems. On the contrary, for reasons to be given later, there is cause to believe that in not a few

From, "Truth and the Physician," by Bernard Meyer in *Ethical Issues in Medicine: The Role of the Physician in Today's Society,* E. Fuller Torrey, editor. Copyright © 1968. Reprinted by permission of Little, Brown and Company, Inc., publishers.

instances, elements in his own psychological makeup may cause the physician to be singularly ill-equipped to be the bearer of bad tidings. It should be observed, moreover, that until comparatively recent times, the subject of communication between physician and patient received little attention in medical curriculum and medical literature.

Within the past decade or so, coincident with an expanded recognition of the significance of emotional factors in all medical practice, an impressive number of books and articles by physicians, paramedical personnel, and others have been published, attesting to both the growing awareness of the importance of the subject and an apparent willingness to face it. An especially noteworthy example of this trend was provided by a three-day meeting in February, 1967, sponsored by the New York Academy of Sciences, on the subject of *The Care of Patients with Fatal Illness*. The problem of communicating with such patients and their families was a recurring theme in most of the papers presented.

Both at this conference and in the literature, particular emphasis has been focused on the patient with cancer, which is hardly surprising in light of its frequency and of the extraordinary emotional reactions that it unleashes not only in the patient and in his kinsmen but in the physician himself. At the same time, it should be noted that the accent on the cancer patient or the dying patient may foster the impression that in less grave conditions this dialogue between patient and physician hardly warrants much concern or discussion. Such a view is unfounded, however, and could only be espoused by someone who has had the good fortune to escape the experience of being ill and hospitalized. Those less fortunate will recall the emo-

tional stresses induced by hospitalization, even when the condition requiring it is relatively banal.

A striking example of such stress may sometimes be seen when the patient who is hospitalized, say, for repair of an inguinal hernia, happens to be a physician. All the usual anxieties confronting a prospective surgical subject tend to become greatly amplified and garnished with a generous sprinkling of hypochondriasis in the physician-turned-patient. Wavering unsteadily between these two roles, he conjures up visions of all the complications of anesthesia, of wound dehiscence or infection, of embolization, cardiac arrest, and whatnot that he has ever heard or read about. To him, lying between hospital sheets, clad in impersonal hospital clothes, divested of his watch and the keys to his car, the hospital suddenly takes on a different appearance from the place he may have known in a professional capacity. Even his colleagues—the anesthetist who will put him to sleep or cause a temporary motor and sensory paralysis of the lower half of his body, and the surgeon who will incise it—appear different. He would like to have a little talk with them, a very professional talk to be sure, although in his heart he may know that the talk will also be different. And if they are in tune with the situation, they too know that it will be different, that beneath the restrained tones of sober and factual conversation is the thumping anxiety of a man who seeks words of reassurance. With some embarrassment he may introduce his anxieties with the phrase, "I suppose this is going to seem a little silly, but . . ."; and from this point on he may sound like any other individual confronted by the ordeal of surgical experience.[1] Indeed, it would appear that under these circumstances, to say nothing of more ominous ones, most people, regardless of their experience, knowledge, maturity or sophistication, are assailed by more or less similar psychological pressures, from which they seek relief not through pharmacological sedation, but through the more calming influence of the spoken word.

Seen in this light the question of what to tell the patient about his illness is but one facet of the practice of medicine as an art, a particular example of that spoken and mute dialogue between patient and physician which has always been and will always be an indispensable ingredient in the therapeutic process. How to carry on this dialogue, what to say and when to say it, and what not to say, are questions not unlike those posed by an awkward suitor; like him, those not naturally versed in this art may find themselves discomfited and needful of the promptings of some Cyrano who will whisper those words and phrases that ultimately will wing their way to soothe an anguished heart.

EMOTIONAL REACTIONS OF PHYSICIAN

The difficulties besetting the physician under these circumstances, however, cannot be ascribed simply to his mere lack of experience or innate eloquence. For like the stammering suitor, the doctor seeking to communicate with his patient may have an emotional stake in his message. When that message contains an ominous significance, he may find himself too troubled to use words wisely, too ridden with anxiety to be kind, and too depressed to convey hope. An understanding of such reactions touches upon a recognition of some of the several psychological motivations that have led some individuals to choose a medical career. There is evidence that at times that choice has been dictat-

ed by what might be viewed as counter-phobic forces. Having in childhood experienced recurring brushes with illness and having encountered a deep and abiding fear of death and dying, such persons may embrace a medical career as if it will confer upon them a magical immunity from a repetition of those dreaded eventualities; for them the letters M.D. constitute a talisman bestowing upon the wearer a sense of invulnerability and a pass of safe conduct through the perilous frontiers of life. There are others for whom the choice of a career dedicated to helping and healing appears to have arisen as a reaction formation against earlier impulses to wound and to destroy.[2] For still others among us, the practice of medicine serves as the professional enactment of a long-standing rescue fantasy.

It is readily apparent in these examples (which by no means exhaust the catalogue of motives leading to the choice of a medical career) that confrontation by the failure of one's efforts and by the need to announce it may unloose a variety of inner psychological disturbances: faced by the gravely ill or dying patient the "counter-phobic" doctor may feel personally vulnerable again; the "reaction-formation" doctor, evil and guilty; and the "rescuer," worthless and impotent. For such as these, words cannot come readily in their discourse with the seriously or perilously ill. Indeed, they may curtail their communications; and, what is no less meaningful to their patients, withdraw their physical presence. Thus the patient with inoperable cancer and his family may discover that the physician, who at a more hopeful moment in the course of the illness had been both articulate and supportive, has become remote both in his speech and in his behavior. Nor is the patient uncomprehending of the significance of the change in his doctor's attitude. Observers have recorded the verbal expressions of patients who sensed the feelings of futility and depression in their physicians. Seeking to account for their own reluctance to ask questions (a reluctance based partly upon their own disinclination to face a grim reality), one such patient said, "He looked so tired." Another stated, "I don't want to upset him because he has tried so hard to help me"; and another, "I know he feels so badly already and is doing his best" (Abrams, 1966). To paraphrase a celebrated utterance, one might suppose that these remarks were dictated by the maxim: "Ask not what your doctor can do for you; ask what you can do for your doctor."[3]

ADHERENCE TO A FORMULA

In the dilemma created both by a natural disinclination to be a bearer of bad news and by those other considerations already cited, many a physician is tempted to abandon personal judgment and authorship in his discourse with his patients, and to rely instead upon a set formula which he employs with dogged and indiscriminate consistency. Thus, in determining what to say to patients with cancer, there are exponents of standard policies that are applied routinely in seeming disregard of the overall clinical picture and of the personality or psychological makeup of the patient. In general, two such schools of thought prevail; i.e., those that always tell and those that never do. Each of these is amply supplied with statistical anecdotal evidence proving the correctness of the policy. Yet even if the figures were accurate—and not infrequently they are obtained via a questionnaire, itself a rather opaque window to the human mind—all they demonstrate is that more rather than

less of a given proportion of the cancer population profited by the policy employed. This would provide small comfort, one might suppose, to the patients and their families that constitute the minority of the sample.

TRUTH AS ABSTRACT PRINCIPLE

At times adherence to such a rigid formula is dressed up in the vestments of slick and facile morality. Thus a theologian has insisted that the physician has a moral obligation to tell the truth and that his withholding it constitutes a deprivation of the patient's right; therefore it is "theft, therefore unjust, therefore immoral" (Fletcher, 1954). "Can it be," he asks, "that doctors who practice professional deception would, if the roles were reversed, want to be coddled or deceived?" To which, as many physicians can assert, the answer is distinctly yes. Indeed so adamant is this writer upon the right of the patient to know the facts of his illness that in the event he refuses to hear what the doctor is trying to say, the latter should "ask leave to withdraw from the case, urging that another physician be called in his place."[4] (Once there were three boy scouts who were sent away from a campfire and told not to return until each had done his good turn for the day. In 20 minutes all three had returned, and curiously each one reported that he had helped a little old lady to cross a street. The scoutmaster's surprise was even greater when he learned that in each case it was the same little old lady, prompting him to inquire why it took the three of them to perform this one simple good deed. "Well, sir," replied one of the boys, "you see she really didn't want to cross the street at all.")

In this casuistry wherein so much attention is focused upon abstract principle and so little upon humanity, one is reminded of the no less specious arguments of those who assert that the thwarting of suicide and the involuntary hospitalization of the mentally deranged constitute violations of personal freedom and human right.[5] It is surely irregular for a fire engine to travel in the wrong direction on a one-way street, but if one is not averse to putting out fires and saving lives, the traffic violation looms as a conspicuous irrelevancy. No less irrelevant is the obsessional concern with meticulous definitions of truth in an enterprise where kindness, charity, and the relief of human suffering are the ethical verities. "The letter killeth," say the Scriptures, "but the spirit giveth life."

Problem of Definition

Nor should it be forgotten that in the healing arts, the matter of truth is not always susceptible to easy definition. Consider for a moment the question of the hopeless diagnosis. It was not so long ago that such a designation was appropriate for subacute bacterial endocarditis, pneumococcal meningitis, pernicious anemia, and a number of other conditions which today are no longer incurable, while those diseases which today are deemed hopeless may cease to be so by tomorrow. Experience has proved, too, the unreliability of obdurate opinions concerning prognosis even in those conditions where all the clinical evidence and the known behavior of a given disease should leave no room for doubt. To paraphrase Clemenceau, to insist that a patient is hopelessly ill may at times be worse than a crime; it may be a mistake.

Problem of Determining
Patient's Desires

There are other pitfalls, moreover, that complicate the problem of telling patients the truth about their illness. There is the naive notion, for example, that when the patient asserts that what he is seeking is the plain truth he means just that. But as more than one observer has noted, this is sometimes the last thing the patient really wants. Such assertions may be voiced with particular emphasis by patients who happen to be physicians and who strive to display a professional and scientifically objective attitude toward their own condition. Yet to accept such assertions at their face value may sometimes lead to tragic consequences, as in the following incident.

> A distinguished urological surgeon was hospitalized for a hypernephroma, which diagnosis had been withheld from him. One day he summoned the intern into his room, and after appealing to the latter on the basis of we're-both-doctors-and-grown-up-men, succeeded in getting the unwary younger man to divulge the facts. Not long afterward, while the nurse was momentarily absent from the room, the patient opened a window and leaped to his death.

Role of Secrecy in Creating Anxiety

Another common error is the assumption that until someone has been formally told the truth he doesn't know it. Such self-deception is often present when parents feel moved to supply their pubertal children with the sexual facts of life. With much embarrassment and a good deal of backing and filling on the subjects of eggs, bees, and babies, sexual information is imparted to a child who often not only already knows it but is uncomfortable in hearing it from that particular source. There is indeed a general tendency to underestimate the perceptiveness of children not only about such matters but where graver issues, notably illness and death, are concerned. As a consequence, attitudes of secrecy and overprotection designed to shield children from painful realities may result paradoxically in creating an atmosphere that is saturated with suspicion, distrust, perplexity, and intolerable anxiety. Caught between trust in their own intuitive perceptions and the deceptions practiced by the adults about them, such children may suffer greatly from a lack of opportunity of coming to terms emotionally with some of the vicissitudes of existence that in the end are inescapable. A refreshing contrast to this approach has been presented in a paper entitled "Who's Afraid of Death on a Leukemia Ward" (Vernick and Karon, 1965). Recognizing that most of the children afflicted with this disease had some knowledge of its seriousness, and that all were worried about it, the hospital staff abandoned the traditional custom of protection and secrecy, providing instead an atmosphere in which the children could feel free to express their fears and their concerns and could openly acknowledge the fact of death when one of the group passed away. The result of this measure was immensely salutary.

Similar miscalculations of the accuracy of inner perceptions may be noted in dealing with adults. Thus, in a study entitled "Mongolism: When Should Parents Be Told?" (Drillien and Wilkinson, 1964), it was found that in nearly half the cases the mothers declared they had realized before being told that something was seriously wrong with the child's development, a figure which obviously excludes the mothers who refused consciously to acknowledge their suspicions. On the basis of their findings the authors concluded that a full explanation given in the early months, coupled with regular support thereafter, appeared to facilitate the mother's acceptance of and adjustment to her child's handicap.

A pointless and sometimes deleterious withholding of truth is a common practice in dealing with elderly people. "Don't tell Mother" often seems to be an almost reflex maxim among some adults in the face of any misfortune, large or small. Here, too, elaborate efforts at camouflage may backfire, for, sensing that he is being shielded from some ostensibly intolerable secret, not only is the elderly one deprived of the opportunity of reacting appropriately to it, but he is being tacitly encouraged to conjure up something in his imagination that may be infinitely worse.

Discussion of Known Truth

Still another misconception is the belief that if it is certain that the truth is known it is all right to discuss it. How mistaken such an assumption may be was illustrated by the violent rage which a recent widow continued to harbor toward a friend for having alluded to cancer in the presence of her late husband. Hearing her outburst one would have concluded that until the ominous word had been uttered, her husband had been ignorant of the nature of his condition. The facts, however, were different, as the unhappy woman knew, for it had been her husband who originally had told the friend what the diagnosis was.

DENIAL AND REPRESSION

The psychological devices that make such seeming inconsistencies of thought and knowledge possible are the mechanisms of repression and denial. It is indeed the remarkable capacity to bury or conceal more or less transparent truth that makes the problem of telling it so sticky and difficult a matter, and one that is so unsusceptible to simple rule-of-thumb formulas. For while in some instances the maintenance of denial may lead to severe emotional distress, in others it may serve as a merciful shield. For example,

A physician with a reputation for considerable diagnostic acumen developed a painless jaundice. When, not surprisingly, a laparotomy revealed a carcinoma of the head of the pancreas, the surgeon relocated the biliary outflow so that postoperatively the jaundice subsided. This seeming improvement was consistent with the surgeon's explanation to the patient that the operation had revealed a hepatitis. Immensely relieved, the patient chided himself for not having anticipated the "correct" diagnosis. "What a fool I was!" he declared, obviously alluding to an earlier, albeit unspoken, fear of cancer.

Among less sophisticated persons the play of denial may assume a more primitive expression. Thus a woman who had ignored the growth of a breast cancer to a point where it had produced spinal metastases and paraplegia, attributed the latter to "arthritis" and asked whether the breast would grow back again. The same mental mechanism allowed another woman to ignore dangerous rectal bleeding by ascribing it to menstruation, although she was well beyond the menopause.

In contrast to these examples is a case reported by Winkelstein and Blacher of a man who, awaiting the report of a cervical node biopsy, asserted that if it showed cancer he wouldn't want to live, and that if it didn't he wouldn't believe it (Winkelstein and Blacher, 1967). Yet despite this seemingly unambiguous willingness to deal with raw reality, when the chips were down, as will be described later, this man too was able to protect himself throuugh the use of denial.

From the foregoing it should be self-evident that what is imparted to a patient about his illness should be planned with the same care and executed with the same skill that are demanded by any potentially therapeutic measure. Like the transfusion of blood, the dispensing of certain information must be distinctly indicated, the amount given consonant with the needs of the recipient, and the type chosen with the view of avoiding untoward reactions. This means that only in selected instances is there any justification for telling a patient the precise figures of his blood pressure, and that the question of revealing interesting but asymptomatic congenital anomalies should be considered in light of the possibility of evoking either hypochondriacal ruminations or narcissistic gratification.

Under graver circumstances the choices of confronting the physician rest upon more crucial psychological issues. In principle, we should strive to make the patient sufficiently aware of the facts of his condition to facilitate his participation in the treatment without at the same time giving him cause to believe that such participation is futile. "The indispensable ingredient of this therapeutic approach," write Stehlin and Beach, "is free communication between [physician] and patient, in which the latter is sustained by hope within a framework of reality" (Stehlin and Beach, 1966). What this may mean in many instances is neither outright truth nor outright falsehood but a carefully modulated formulation that neither overtaxes human credulity nor invites despair. Thus a sophisticated woman might be expected to reject with complete disbelief the notion that she has had to undergo mastectomy for a benign cyst, but she may at the same time accept postoperative radiation as a prophylactic measure rather than as evidence of metastasis.

A doctor's wife was found to have ovarian carcinoma with widespread metastases. Although the surgeon was convinced she would not survive for more than three or four months, he wished to try the effects of radiotherapy and chemotherapy. After some discussion of the problem with a psychiatrist, he addressed himself to the patient as follows: to his surprise, when examined under the microscope the tumor in her abdomen proved to be cancerous; he fully believed he had removed it entirely; to feel perfectly safe, however, he intended to give her radiation and chemical therapies over an indeterminate period of time. The patient was highly gratified by his frankness and proceeded to live for nearly three more *years*, during which time she enjoyed an active and a productive life.

A rather similar approach was utilized in the case of Winkelstein and Blacher previously mentioned (Winkelstein and Blacher, 1967). In the presence of his wife the patient was told by the resident surgeon, upon the advice of the psychiatrist, that the biopsy of the cervical node showed cancer; that he had a cancerous growth in the abdomen; that it was the type of cancer that responds well to chemotherapy; that if the latter produced any discomfort he would receive medication for its relief; and finally that the doctors were very hopeful for a successful outcome. The patient, who, it will be recalled, had declared he wouldn't want to live if the doctors found cancer, was obviously gratified. Immediately he telephoned members of his family to tell them the news, gratuitously adding that the tumor was of low-grade malignancy. That night he slept well for the first time since entering the hospital and he continued to do so during the balance of his stay. Just before leaving he confessed that he had known all along about the existence of the abdominal mass but that he had concealed his knowledge to see what the doctors would tell him. Upon arriving home he wrote a warm letter of thanks and admiration to the resident surgeon.

It should be emphasized that although in both of these instances the advice of a psychiatrist was instrumental in formulating the discussion of the facts of the illness, it was the surgeon, not the psychiatrist, who did the talking. The importance of ths point cannot be exaggerated, for since it is the surgeon who plays the central and crucial role in such cases, it is to him, and not to some substitute mouthpiece, that the patient looks for enlightenment and for hope. As noted earlier, it is not every surgeon who can bring himself to speak in this fashion to his patient; and for some there may be a strong temptation to take refuge in a sterotyped formula, or to pass the buck altogether. The surgical resident, in the last case cited, for example, was both appalled and distressed when he was advised what to do. Yet he steeled himself, looked the patient straight in the eye and spoke with conviction. When he saw the result, he was both relieved and gratified. Indeed, he emerged from the experience a far wiser man and a better physician.

THE DYING PATIENT

The general point of view expressed in the foregoing pages has been espoused by others in considering the problem of communicating with the dying patient. Aldrich stresses the importance of providing such persons with an appropriately timed opportunity of selecting acceptance or denial of the truth in their efforts to cope with their plight (Aldrich, 1963). Weisman and Hackett believe that for the majority of patients it is likely that there is neither complete acceptance nor total repudiation of the imminence of death (Weismann and Hackett, 1961). "To deny this 'middle knowledge' of approaching death," they assert,

. . . is to deny the responsiveness of the mind to both internal perceptions and external information. There is always a psychological sampling of the physiological stream; fever, weakness, anorexia, weight loss and pain are subjective counterparts of homeostatic alteration. . . . If to this are added changes in those close to the patient, the knowledge of approaching death is confirmed.

Other observers agree that a patient who is sick enough to die often knows it without being told, and that what he seeks from his physician are no longer statements concerning diagnosis and prognosis, but earnest manifestations of his unwavering concern and devotion. As noted earlier, it is at such times that for reason of their own psychological makeup some physicians becomme deeply troubled and are most prone to drift away, thereby adding, to the dying patient's physical suffering, the suffering that is caused by a sense of abandonment, isolation, and emotional deprivation.

In contrast, it should be stressed that no less potent than morphine nor less effective than an array of tranquilizers is the steadfast and serious concern of the physician for those often numerous and relatively minor complaints of the dying patient. To this beneficent manifestation of psychological denial, which may at times attain hypochondriacal proportions, the physician ideally should respond in kind, shifting his gaze from the lethal process he is now helpless to arrest to the living being whose discomfort and distress he is still able to assuage. In these, the final measures of the dance of life, it may then appear as if both partners had reached a tacit and a mutual understanding, an unspoken pledge to ignore the dark shadow of impending death and to resume those turns and rhythms that were familiar figures in a more felicitious past. If in this he is possessed of enough grace and elegance to play his part the doctor may well succeed in fulfilling the assertion of

Oliver Wendell Holmes that if one of the functions of the physician is to assist at the coming in, another is to assist at the going out.

If what has been set down here should prove uncongenial to some strict moralists, one can only observe that there is a hierarchy of morality, and that ours is a profession which traditionally has been guided by a precept that transends the virtue of uttering truth for truth's sake; that is, "So far as possible, do no harm." Where it concerns the communication between the physician and his patient, the attainment of this goal demands an ear that is sensitive to both what is said and what is not said, a mind that is capable of understanding what has been heard, and a heart that can respond to what has been understood. Here, as in many difficult human enterprises, it may prove easier to learn the words than to sing the tune.

> We did not dare to breathe a prayer
> Or give our anguish scope!
> Something was dead in each of us,
> And what was dead was Hope!
>
> Oscar Wilde,
> *The Ballad of Reading Gaol*

NOTES

1. It should be observed, however, that while the emotional conflicts of the sick doctor may contribute to the ambiguity of his position, that ambiguity may be abetted by the treating physician, who in turn may experience difficulty in assigning to his ailing colleague the unequivocal status of patient. Indeed the latter may be more or less tacitly invited to share the responsibility in the diagnosis and care of his own illness to a degree that in some instances he is virtually a consultant on his own case.

A similar lack of a clear-cut definition of role is not uncommon when members of a doctor's family are ill. Here a further muddying of the waters may be caused by the time-honored practice of extending so-called courtesy—i.e., free care—to physicians and their families, a custom which, however well intentioned, may place its presumed beneficiaries in a moral straitjacket that discourages them from making rather ordinary demands on the treating physician, to say nothing of discharging him. It is not surprising that the care of physicians and their families occasionally evokes an atmosphere of bitterness and rancor.

2. The notion that at heart some doctors are killers is a common theme in literature. It is claimed that when in a fit of despondency Napoleon Bonaparte declared he should have been a physician, Talleyrand commented: *"Toujours assassin."*

3. This aspect of the patient-doctor relationship has not received the attention it deserves. Moreover, aside from being a therapeutic success, there are other ways in which his patients may support the doctor's psychological needs. His self-esteem, no less than his economic well-being, may be nourished by an ever-growing roster of devoted patients, particularly when the latter include celebrities and other persons of prominence. How important this can be may be judged by the not too uncommon indiscretions perpetrated by some physicians (and sometimes by their wives) in leaking confidential matters pertaining to their practice, notably the identity of their patients.

4. The same writer relaxes his position when it concerns psychiatric patients. Here he would sanction the withholding of knowledge "precisely because he may prevent the patient's recovery by revealing it." But in this, too, the writer is in error, in double error, it would seem, for, first, it is artificial and inexact to make a sharp distinction between psychiatric and nonpsychiatric patterns—the seriously sick and the dying are not infrequently conspicuously emotionally disturbed: and second, because it may at times be therapeutically advisable to acquaint the psychiatric patient with the facts of his illness.

5. Proponents of these views have seemingly overlooked the unconscious elements in human behavior and thought. Paradoxical though it may seem, the would-be suicide may wish to live: what he seeks to destroy may be restricted to that part of the self that has become burdensome or hateful. By the same token, despite his manifest combativeness, a psychotic individual is often inwardly grateful for the restraints imposed upon his dangerous aggression. There can be no logical objection to designating such persons as "prisoners," as Szasz would have it, provided we apply the same term to breathless individuals who are "incarcerated" in oxygen tents.

REFERENCES

Abrams, R.D.   The patient with cancer—His changing pattern of communication. *New Eng. J. Med.* 274:317, 1966.

Aldrich, C.K.   The dying patient's grief. *J.A.M.A.* 184:329, 1963.

Drillien, C.M., and Wilkinson, E.M.   Mongolism: When should parents be told? *Brit. Med. J. 2:*1306, 1964.

Fletcher, J.   *Morals and Medicine.* Princeton: Princeton University Press, 1954.

Stehlin, J.S., and Beach, K.A.   Psychological aspects of cancer therapy. *J.A.M.A. 197:*100, 1966.

Vernick, J., and Karon, M.   Who's afraid of death on a leukemia ward? *Amer. J. Dis. Child, 109:*393, 1965.

Weisman, A.D., and Hackett, T.   Predilection to death: Death and dying as a psychiatric problem. *Psychosom. Med. 23:*232, 1961.

Winkelstein, C., and Blacher, R.   Personal communication, 1967.

NO

Sissela Bok

LIES TO THE
SICK AND DYING

DECEPTION AS THERAPY

... A forty-six-year-old man, coming to a clinic for a routine physical check-up needed for insurance purposes, is diagnosed as having a form of cancer likely to cause him to die within six months. No known cure exists for it. Chemotherapy may prolong life by a few extra months, but will have side effects the physician does not think warranted in this case. In addition, he believes that such therapy should be reserved for patients with a chance for recovery or remission. The patient has no symptoms giving him any reason to believe that he is not perfectly healthy. He expects to take a short vacation in a week.

For the physician, there are now several choices involving truthfulness. Ought he to tell the patient what he has learned, or conceal it? If asked, should he deny it? If he decides to reveal the diagnosis, should he delay doing so until after the patient returns from his vacation? Finally, even if he does reveal the serious nature of the diagnosis, should he mention the possibility of chemotherapy and his reasons for not recommending it in this case? Or should he encourage every last effort to postpone death?

In this particular case, the physician chose to inform the patient of his diagnosis right away. He did not, however, mention the possibility of chemotherapy. A medical student working under him disagreed; several nurses also thought that the patient should have been informed of his possibility. They tried, unsuccessfully, to persuade the physician that this was the patient's right. When persuasion had failed, the student elected to disobey the doctor by informing the patient of the alternative of chemotherapy. After consultation with family members, the patient chose to ask for the treatment.

Doctors confront such choices often and urgently. What they reveal, hold back, or distort will matter profoundly to their patients. Doctors stress with corresponding vehemence their reasons for the distortion or concealment: not to confuse a sick person needlessly, or cause what may well be unnecessary pain or discomfort, as in the case of the cancer patient; not to leave a patient without hope, as in those many cases where the dying are not told the truth about their condition; or to improve the chances of cure, as where unwarranted optimism is expressed about some form of therapy. Doctors use information as part of the therapeutic regimen; it is given out in amounts, in admixtures, and according to timing believed best for patients. Accuracy, by comparison, matters far less.

Lying to patients has, therefore, seemed an especially excusable act. Some would argue that doctors, and *only* doctors, should be granted the right to manipulate the truth in ways so undesirable for politicians, lawyers, and others. Doctors are trained to help patients; their relationship to patients carries special obligations, and they know much more than laymen about what helps and hinders recovery and survival.

Even the most conscientious doctors, then, who hold themselves at a distance from the quacks and the purveyors of false remedies, hesitate to forswear all lying. Lying is usually wrong, they argue, but less so than allowing the truth to harm patients. B.C. Meyer echoes this very common view:

> [O]urs is a profession which traditionally has been guided by a precept that transcends the virtue of uttering truth for truth's sake, and that is, "so far as possible, do no harm."

Truth, for Meyer, may be important, but not when it endangers the health and well-being of patients. This has seemed self-evident to many physicians in the past—so much so that we find very few mentions of veracity in the codes and oaths and writings by physicians through the centuries. This absence is all the more striking as other principles of ethics have been consistently and movingly expressed in the same documents. . . .

Given such freedom, a physician can decide to tell as much or as little as he wants the patient to know, so long as he breaks no law. In the case of the man mentioned at the beginning of this chapter, some physicians might feel justified in lying for the good of the patient, others might be truthful. Some may conceal alternatives to the treatment they recommend; others not. In each case, they could appeal to the A.M.A. Principles of Ethics. A great many would choose to be able to lie. They would claim that not only can a lie avoid harm for the patient, but that it is also hard to know whether they have been right in the first place in making their pessimistic diagnosis; a "truthful" statement could therefore turn out to hurt patients unnecessarily. The concern for curing and for supporting those who cannot be cured then runs counter to the desire to be completely open. This concern is especially strong where the prognosis is bleak; even more so when patients are so affected by their illness or their medication that they are more dependent than usual, perhaps more easily depressed or irrational.

Physicians know only too well how uncertain a diagnosis or prognosis can be. They know how hard it is to give meaningful and correct answers regarding health and illness. They also know that disclosing their own uncertainty or fears can reduce those benefits that depend upon faith in recovery. They fear, too, that revealing grave risks, no matter how unlikely it is that these will come about, may exercise the pull of the "self-fulfilling prophecy." They dislike being the bearers of uncertain or bad news as much as anyone else. And last, but not least, sitting down to discuss an illness truthfully and sensitively may take much-needed time away from other patients.

These reasons help explain why nurses

and physicians and relatives of the sick and dying prefer not to be bound by rules that might limit their ability to suppress, delay, or distort information. This is not to say that they necessarily plan to lie much of the time. They merely want to have the freedom to do so when they believe it wise. And the reluctance to see lying prohibited explains, in turn, the failure of the codes and oaths to come to grips with the problems of truth-telling and lying.

But sharp conflicts are now arising. Doctors no longer work alone with patients. They have to consult with others much more than before; it they choose to lie, the choice may not be met with approval by all who take part in the care of the patient. A nurse expresses the difficulty which results as follows:

> From personal experience I would say that the patients who aren't told about their terminal illness have so many verbal and mental questions unanswered that many will begin to realize that their illness is more serious than they're being told. ...

The doctor's choice to lie increasingly involves coworkers in acting a part they find neither humane nor wise. The fact that these problems have not been carefully thought through within the medical profession, nor seriously addressed in medical education, merely serves to intensify the conflicts. Different doctors then respond very differently to patients in exactly similar predicaments. The friction is increased by the fact that relatives often disagree even where those giving medical care to a patient are in accord on how to approach the patient. Here again, because physicians have not worked out to common satisfaction the question of whether relatives have the right to make such requests, the problems are allowed to be haphazardly resolved by each physician as he sees fit.

THE PATIENT'S PERSPECTIVE

The turmoil in the medical profession regarding truth-telling is further augmented by the pressures that patients themselves now bring to bear and by empirical data coming to light. Challenges are growing to the three major arguments for lying to patients: that truthfulness is impossible; that patients do not want bad news; and that truthful information harms them.

The first of these arguments ... confuses "truth" and "truthfulness" so as to clear the way for occasional lying on grounds supported by the second and third arguments. At this point, we can see more clearly that it is a strategic move intended to discourage the question of truthfulness from carrying much weight in the first place, and thus to leave the choice of what to say and how to say it up to the physician. To claim that "since telling the truth is impossible, there can be no sharp distinction between what is true and what is false" is to try to defeat objections to lying before even discussing them. One need only imagine how such an argument would be received, were it made by a car salesman or a real estate dealer, to see how fallacious it is.

In medicine, however, the argument is supported by a subsidiary point: even if people might ordinarily understand what is spoken to them, patients are often not in a position to do so. This is where paternalism enters in. When we buy cars or houses, the paternalist will argue, we need to have all our wits about us; but when we are ill, we cannot always do so. We need help in making choices, even if help can be given only by keeping us in the dark. And the physician is trained and willing to provide such help.

It is certainly true that some patients cannot make the best choices for themselves when weakened by illness or drugs. But most still can. And even those who are incompetent have a right to have someone—their guardian or spouse perhaps—receive the correct information.

The paternalistic assumption of superiority to patients also carries great dangers for physicians themselves—it risks turning to contempt. The following view was recently expressed in a letter to a medical journal:

> As a radiologist who has been sued, I have reflected earnestly on advice to obtain Informed Consent but have decided to "take the risks without informing the patient" and trust to "God, judge, and jury" rather than evade responsibility through a legal gimmick....
>
> [I]n a general radiologic practice many of our patients are uninformable and we would never get through the day if we had to obtain their consent to every potentially harmful study....

The argument which rejects informing patients because adequate truthful information is impossible in itself or because patients are lacking in understanding, must itself be rejected when looked at from the point of view of patients. They know that liberties granted to the most conscientious and altruistic doctors will be exercised also in the "Medicaid Mills"; that the choices thus kept from patients will be exercised by not only competent but incompetent physicians; and that even the best doctors can make choices patients would want to make differently for themselves.

The second argument for deceiving patients refers specifically to giving them news of a frightening or depressing kind. It holds that patients do not, in fact, generally want such information, that they prefer not to have to face up to serious illness and death. On the basis of such a belief, most doctors in a number of surveys stated that they do not, as a rule, inform patients that they have an illness such as cancer.

When studies are made of what patients desire to know, on the other hand, a large majority say that they *would* like to be told of such a diagnosis. All these studies need updating and should be done with larger numbers of patients and non-patients. But they do show that there is generally a dramatic divergence between physicians and patients on the factual question of whether patients want to know what ails them in cases of serious illness such as cancer. In most of the studies, over 80 percent of the persons asked indicated that they would want to be told.

Sometimes this discrepancy is set aside by doctors who want to retain the view that patients do not want unhappy news. In reality, they claim, the fact that patients say they want it has to be discounted. The more someone asks to know, the more he suffers from fear which will lead to the denial of the information even if it is given. Informing patients is, therefore, useless; they resist and deny having been told what they cannot assimilate. According to this view, empirical studies of what patients say they want are worthless since they do not probe deeply enough to uncover this universal resistance to the contemplation of one's own death.

This view is only partially correct. For some patients, denial is indeed well established in medical experience. A number of patients (estimated at between 15 percent and 25 percent) will give evidence of denial of having been told about their illness, even when they repeatedly ask and are repeatedly informed. And nearly everyone experiences a period of denial at some point in the course of approaching death. Elisabeth Kubler-Ross sees denial as resulting often from premature and abrupt information by a stranger who goes through the process quickly to "get it over with." She holds that denial functions as a buffer after unexpected shocking news, permitting individuals to collect themselves and to mobilize other defenses. She describes prolonged denial in one patient as follows:

> She was convinced that the X-rays were "mixed up"; she asked for reassurance that her pathology report could not possibly be back so soon and that another patient's report must have been marked with her name. When none of this could be confirmed, she quickly asked to leave the hospital, looking for another physician in the vain hope "to get a better explanation for my troubles." This patient went "shopping around" for many doctors, some of whom gave her reassuring answers, others of whom confirmed the previous suspicion. Whether confirmed or not, she reacted in the same manner; she asked for examination and reexamination. . . .

But to say that denial is universal flies in the face of all evidence. And to take any claim to the contrary as "symptomatic" of deeper denial leaves no room for reasoned discourse. There is no way that such universal denial can be proved true or false. To believe in it is a metaphysical belief about man's condition, not a statement about what patients do and do not want. It is true that we can never completely understand the possibility of our own death, any more than being alive in the first place. But people certainly differ in the degree to which they can approach such knowledge, take it into account in their plans, and make their peace with it.

Montaigne claimed that in order to learn both to live and to die, men have to think about death and be prepared to accept it. To stick one's head in the sand, or to be prevented by lies from trying to discern what is to come, hampers freedom—freedom to consider one's life as a whole, with a beginning, a duration, an end. Some may request to be deceived rather than to see their lives as thus finite; others reject the information which would require them to do so; but most say that they want to know. Their concern for knowing about their condition goes far beyond mere curiosity or the wish to make isolated personal choices in the short time left to them; their stance toward the entire life they have lived, and their ability to give it meaning and completion, are at stake. In lying or withholding the facts which permit such discernment, doctors may reflect their own fears (which, according to one study, are much stronger than those of laymen) of facing questions about the meaning of one's life and the inevitability of death.

Beyond the fundamental deprivation that can result from deception, we are also becoming increasingly aware of all that can befall patients in the course of their illness when information is denied or distorted. Lies place them in a position where they no longer participate in choices concerning their own health, including the choice of whether to be a "patient" in the first place. A terminally ill person who is not informed that his illness is incurable and that he is near death cannot make decisions about the end of his life: about whether or not to enter a hospital, or to have surgery; where and with whom to spend his last days; how to put his affairs in order—these most personal choices cannot be made if he is kept in the dark, or given contradictory hints and clues.

It has always been especially easy to keep knowledge from terminally ill patients. They are most vulnerable, least able to take action to learn what they need to know, or to protect their autonomy. The very fact of being so ill greatly increases the likelihood of control by others. And the fear of being helpless in the face of such control is growing. At the same time, the period of dependency and slow deterioration of health and strength that people undergo has lengthened. There has been a dramatic shift toward institutionalization of the aged and those near death. (Over 80 percent of Americans now die in a hospital or other institution.)

Patients who are severely ill often suffer a further distancing and loss of control over their most basic functions. Electrical wiring, machines, intravenous administration of liquids, all create new dependency and at the same time new distance between the patient and all who come near. Curable patients are often willing to undergo such procedures; but when no cure is possible, these procedures merely intensify the sense of distance and uncertainty and can even become a substitute for comforting human acts. Yet those who suffer in this way often fear to seem troublesome by complaining. Lying to them, perhaps for the most charitable of purposes, can then cause them to slip unwittingly into subjection to new procedures, perhaps new surgery, where death is held at bay through transfusions, respirators, even resuscitation far beyond what most would wish.

Seeing relatives in such predicaments has caused a great upsurge of worrying about death and dying. At the root of this fear is not a growing terror of the *moment* of death, or even the instants before it. Nor is there greater fear of *being* dead. In contrast to the centuries of lives lived in dread of the punishments to be inflicted after death, many would now accept the view expressed by Epicurus, who died in 270 B.C.:

> Death, therefore, the most awful of evils, is nothing to us, seeing that, when we are, death is not come, and, when death is come, we are not.

The growing fear, if it is not of the moment of dying nor of being dead, is of all that which now precedes dying for so many: the possibility of prolonged pain, the increasing weakness, the uncertainty, the loss of powers and chance of senility, the sense of being a burden. This fear is further nourished by the loss of trust in health professionals. In part, the loss of trust results from the abuses which have been exposed—the Medicaid scandals, the old-age home profiteering, the commercial exploitation of those who seek remedies for their ailments;   in part also because of the deceptive practices patients suspect, having seen how friends and relatives were kept in the dark; in part, finally, because of the sheer numbers of persons, often strangers, participating in the care of any one patient. Trust which might have gone to a doctor long known to the patient goes less easily to a team of strangers, no matter how expert or well-meaning.

It is with the working out of all that *informed consent** implies and the information it presupposes that truth-telling is coming to be discussed in a serious way for the first time in the health professions. Informed consent is a farce if the information provided is distorted or withheld. And even complete information regarding sur-

*The law requires that inroads made upon a person's body take place only with the informed voluntary consent of that person. The term "informed consent" came into common use only after 1960, when it was used by the Kansas Supreme Court in Nathanson vs. Kline, 186 Kan. 393, 350, p. 2d, 1093 (1960). The patient is now entitled to full disclosure of risks, benefits, and alternative treatments to any proposed procedure, both in therapy and in medical experimentation, except in emergencies or when the patient is incompetent, in which case proxy consent is required.

gical procedures or medication is obviously useless unless the patient also knows what the condition is that these are supposed to correct.

Bills of rights for patients, similarly stressing the right to be informed, are now gaining acceptance. This right is not new, but the effort to implement it is. Nevertheless, even where patients are handed the most elegantly phrased Bill of Rights, their right to a truthful diagnosis and prognosis is by no means always respected.

The reason why even doctors who recognize a patient's right to have information might still not provide it brings us to the third argument against telling all patients the truth. It holds that the information given might hurt the patient and that the concern for the right to such information is therefore a threat to proper health care. A patient, these doctors argue, may wish to commit suicide after being given discouraging news, or suffer a cardiac arrest, or simply cease to struggle, and thus not grasp the small remaining chance for recovery. And even where the outlook for a patient is very good, the disclosure of a minute risk can shock some patients or cause them to reject needed protection such as a vaccination or antibiotics.

The factual basis for this argument has been challenged from two points of view. The damages associated with the disclosure of sad news or risks are rarer than physicians believe; and the *benefits* which result from being informed are more substantial, even measurably so. Pain is tolerated more easily, recovery from surgery is quicker, and cooperation with therapy is greatly improved. The attitude that "what you don't know won't hurt you" is proving unrealistic; it is what patients do not know but vaguely suspect that causes them corrosive worry.

It is certain that no answers to this question of harm from information are the same for all patients. If we look, first, at the fear expressed by physicians that informing patients of even remote or unlikely risks connected with a drug prescription or operation might shock some and make others refuse the treatment that would have been best for them, it appears to be unfounded for the great majority of patients. Studies show that very few patients respond to being told of such risks by withdrawing their consent to the procedure and that those who do withdraw are the very ones who might well have been upset enough to sue the physician had they not been asked to consent before hand. It is possible that on even rarer occasions especially susceptible persons might manifest physical deterioration from shock; some physicians have even asked whether patients who die after giving informed consent to an operation, but before it actually takes place, somehow expire because of the information given to them. While such questions are unanswerable in any one case, they certainly argue in favor of caution, a real concern for the person to whom one is recounting the risks he or she will face, and sensitivity to all signs of distress.

The situation is quite different when persons who are already ill, perhaps already quite weak and discouraged, are told of a very serious prognosis. Physicians fear that such knowledge may cause the patients to commit suicide, or to be frightened or depressed to the point that their illness takes a downward turn. The fear that great numbers of patients will commit suicide appears to be unfounded. And if some do, is that a response so unreasonable, so much against the patient's best interest that physicians ought to make it a reason for concealment or lies? Many societies have allowed suicide in the past; our own has decriminalized it; and some are coming to make distinctions among the many suicides which ought to be prevented if at all possible, and those which ought to be respected.

Another possible response to very bleak news is the triggering of physiological mechanisms which allow death to come more quickly—a form of giving up or of preparing for the inevitable, depending on one's outlook. Lewis Thomas, studying responses in humans and animals, holds it not unlikely that:

> . . . there is a pivotal movement at some stage in the body's reaction to injury or disease, maybe in aging as well, when the organism concedes that it is finished and the time for dying is at hand, and at this moment the events that lead to death are launched, as a coordinated mechanism. Functions are then shut off, in sequence, irreversibly, and, while this is going on, a neural mechanism, held ready for this occasion, is switched on. . . .

Such a response may be appropriate, in which case it makes the moments of dying as peaceful as those who have died and been resuscitated so often testify. But it may also be brought on inappropriately, when the organism could have lived on, perhaps even induced malevolently, by external acts intended to kill. Thomas speculates that some of the deaths resulting from "hexing" are due to such responses. Levi-Strauss describes deaths from exorcism and the casting of spells in ways which suggest that the same process may then be brought on by the community.

It is not inconceivable that unhappy news abruptly conveyed, or a great shock given to someone unable to tolerate it, could also bring on such a "dying response," quite unintended by the speaker. There is

every reason to be cautious and to try to know ahead of time how susceptible a patient might be to the accidental triggering—however rare—of such a response. One has to assume, however, that most of those who have survived long enough to be in a situation where their informed consent is asked have a very robust resistance to such accidental triggering of processes leading to death.

When, on the other hand, one considers those who are already near death, the "dying response" may be much less inappropriate, much less accidental, much less unreasonable. In most societies, long before the advent of modern medicine, human beings have made themselves ready for death once they felt its approach. Philippe Aries describes how many in the Middle Ages prepared themselves for death when they "felt the end approach." They awaited death lying down, surrounded by friends and relatives. They recollected all they had lived through and done, pardoning all who stood near their deathbed, calling on God to bless them, and finally praying. "After the final prayer all that remained was to wait for death, and there was no reason for death to tarry."

Modern medicine, in its valiant efforts to defeat disease and to save lives, may be dislocating the conscious as well as the purely organic responses allowing death to come when it is inevitable, thus denying those who are dying the benefits of the traditional approach to death. In lying to them, and in pressing medical efforts to cure them long past the point of possible recovery, physicians may thus rob individuals of an autonomy few would choose to give up.

Sometimes, then, the "dying response" is a natural organic reaction at the time when the body has no further defense. Sometimes it is inappropriately brought on

83

by news too shocking or given in too abrupt a manner. We need to learn a great deal more about this last category, no matter how small. But there is no evidence that patients in general will be debilitated by truthful information about their condition.

Apart from the possible harm from information, we are coming to learn much more about the benefits it can bring patients. People follow instructions more carefully if they know what their disease is and why they are asked to take medication; any benefits from those procedures are therefore much more likely to come about.* Similarly, people recover faster from surgery and tolerate pain with less medication if they understand what ails them and what can be done for them.**

RESPECT AND TRUTHFULNESS

Taken all together, the three arguments defending lies to patients stand on much shakier ground as a counterweight to the right to be informed than is often thought. The common view that many patients cannot understand, do not want, and may be harmed by, knowledge of their condi-

---

*Barbara S. Hulka, J.C. Cassel, et al. "Communication, Compliance, and Concordance between Physicians and Patients with Prescribed Medications," *American Journal of Public Health,* Sept. 1976, pp. 847-53. The study shows that of the nearly half of all patients who do not follow the prescriptions of the doctors (thus foregoing the intended effect of these prescriptions), many will follow them if adequately informed about the nature of their illness and what the proposed medication will do.

**See Lawrence D. Egbert, George E. Batitt, et al., "Reduction of Postoperative Pain by Encouragement and Instruction of Patients," *New England Journal of Medicine,* 270, pp. 825-827, 1964.
See also: Howard Waitzskin and John D. Stoeckle, "The Communication of Information about Illness," *Advances in Psychosomatic Medicine,* Vol. 8, 1972, pp. 185-215.

tion, and that lying to them is either morally neutral or even to be recommended, must be set aside. Instead, we have to make a more complex comparison. Over against the right of patients to knowledge concerning themselves, the medical and psychological benefits to them from this knowledge, the unnecessary and sometimes harmful treatment to which they can be subjected if ignorant, and the harm to physicians, their profession, and other patients from deceptive practices, we have to set a severely restricted and narrowed paternalistic view—that *some* patients cannot understand, *some* do not want, and *some* may be harmed by, knowledge of their condition, and that they ought not to have to be treated like everyone else if this is not in their best interest.

Such a view is persuasive. A few patients openly request not to be given bad news. Others give clear signals to that effect, or are demonstrably vulnerable to the shock or anguish such news might call forth. Can one not in such cases infer implied consent to being deceived?

Concealment, evasion, withholding of information may at times be necessary. But if someone contemplates lying to a patient or concealing the truth, the burden of proof must shift. It must rest, here, as with all deception, on those who advocate it in any one instance. They must show why they fear a patient may be harmed or how they know that another cannot cope with the truthful knowledge. A decision to deceive must be seen as a very unusual step, to be talked over with colleagues and others who participate in the care of the patient. Reasons must be set forth and debated, alternatives weighed carefully. At all times, the correct information must go to *someone* closely related to the patient. . . .

POSTSCRIPT

IS IT ETHICAL TO WITHHOLD THE TRUTH FROM DYING PATIENTS?

In its 1983 report, *Making Health Care Decisions,* the President's Commission for the Study of Ethical Problems in Medicine and Biomedical and Behavioral Research cited evidence from a survey it conducted indicating that ninety-four percent of the public would "want to know everything" about a diagnosis and prognosis, and ninety-six percent would want to know specifically about a diagnosis of cancer. To the question, "If you had a type of cancer that usually leads to death in less than a year, would you want your doctor to give you a realistic estimate of how long you had to live, or would you prefer that he not tell you?" Eighty-five percent said that they would want the realistic estimate. However, when physicians were asked a similar question about what they would disclose to a patient, only thirteen percent would give a "straight, statistical prognosis," and a third said that they would not give a definite time period but would stress that it wouldn't be a long one. Physicians, it appears, are more reluctant to tell the truth than the public (at least when faced with a hypothetical choice) is to hear it.

For a strong defense of the patient's right to know the truth, see Robert M. Veatch, *Death, Dying, and the Biological Revolution* (Yale, 1976), chapter 6. A philosophical argument with a different view is Donald Vandeveer's article, "The Contractual Argument for Withholding Information," *Philosophy and Public Affairs* (Winter 1980). See also Mark Sheldon, "Truth Telling in Medicine," *Journal of the American Medical Association* (February 5, 1982), and Thurstan B. Brewin, "Truth, Trust, and Paternalism," *The Lancet,* August 31, 1985.

Two books that stress the importance of communication in the doctor-patient relationship are Jay Katz, *The Silent World of Doctor and Patient* (New York: The Free Press, 1984) and Eric J. Cassell, *Talking with Patients,* 2 vols. (Cambridge: MIT Press, 1985).

ISSUE 5

IS KILLING THE SAME
AS LETTING DIE?

YES: James Rachels, from "Active and Passive Euthanasia," *New England Journal of Medicine,* 292:2, January 9, 1975

NO: Tom L. Beauchamp and James F. Childress, from *Principles of Biomedical Ethics,* Second edition (New York: Oxford University Press, 1983)

ISSUE SUMMARY

YES: Philosopher James Rachels argues that the conventional distinction between active euthanasia (killing) and passive euthanasia (letting die) has no moral importance, and that active euthanasia can be more humane and justifiable than passive euthanasia.
NO: Philosophers Tom L. Beauchamp and James F. Childress, in rebutting Rachels' arguments, hold that the distinction is not only valid morally (it upholds certain principles such as "do no harm") but also practically (it avoids certain harmful consequences such as loss of trust by patients in physicians).

Like truth-telling, euthanasia is an old problem given new dimensions by the ability of modern medical technology to prolong life. The word itself is Greek (literally, "happy death") and the Greeks wrestled with the question of whether, in some cases, people would be better off dead. But the Hippocratic Oath in this instance was clear: "I will neither give a deadly drug to anybody if asked for it, nor will I make a suggestion to that effect." On the other hand, if the goal of medicine is not simply to prolong life but to reduce suffering, at some point the question of what measures should be taken or withdrawn will inevitably arise. The problem is: When death is inevitable, how far should one go in hastening it?

Cases of "mercy killing" often make headlines. These are usually cases in which distraught relatives, unable to bear the suffering of their loved ones (or their own suffering), kill the patient outright. Sometimes these people are charged with murder, and if the case comes to trial the defendant is most often acquitted or put on probation, for juries are reluctant to convict a person acting out of what appear to be benevolent motives. As dramatic as these cases may be, they are relatively unproblematic in a moral sense. No moral philosopher has constructed a justification for these acts of violence, as understandable as they may be on psychological grounds.

But the majority of cases in which euthanasia is raised as a possibility are among the most difficult ethical issues to resolve, for they involve the conflict between a physician's duty to preserve life and the burden on the patient and the family that is created by fulfilling that duty. One common distinction is between "active" euthanasia (that is, some positive act such as administering a lethal injection) and "passive" euthanasia (that is, an inaction such as deciding not to administer antibiotics when the patient has a severe infection). Another common distinction is between "voluntary" euthanasia (that is, the patient wishes to die and consents to the action that will make it happen) and "involuntary"—or better, "nonvoluntary"—euthanasia (that is, the patient is unable to consent, perhaps because he or she is in a coma).

There are varying views on whether euthanasia, in any form, can ever be permissible. Some philosophers and theologians, such as Arthur Dyck, believe that although it can be moral to withdraw life-prolonging treatments when they are futile, it can never be moral to take another's life, which is sacred. Others, such as law professor Yale Kamisar, agree on nonreligious grounds, believing that there is a danger that "legal machinery initially designed to kill those who are a nuisance to themselves may someday engulf those who are a nuisance to others." On the other hand, some philosophers, such as Peter Singer, defend voluntary euthanasia, claiming that a policy of permitting people to choose to die does not violate anyone's rights or autonomy and will not lead inevitably to genocide. (The Nazi example is often invoked in this argument, since involuntary euthanasia of the sick and mentally defective preceded the wholesale destruction of Jews and other non-Aryan groups.)

The two selections that follow take up one aspect of this large issue: the question of whether there is a moral distinction between killing and letting die. Such a distinction is at the basis of the American Medical Society's policy: "The intentional termination of the life of one human being by another—mercy killing—is contrary to that for which the medical profession stands. . . ." James Rachels attacks that distinction, asserting that our moral evaluation of such acts depends more on other factors, such as motivation and consequences. Tom L. Beauchamp and James F. Childress defend both the distinction and the AMA's policy, pointing out that since "the current practice of prohibiting killing while accepting some 'allowed deaths' has served us well, if not perfectly, it should be altered only with the utmost caution."

YES

James Rachels

ACTIVE AND PASSIVE EUTHANASIA

The distinction between active and passive euthanasia is thought to be crucial for medical ethics. The idea is that it is permissible, at least in some cases, to withhold treatment and allow a patient to die, but it is never permissible to take any direct action designed to kill the patient. This doctrine seems to be accepted by most doctors, and it is endorsed in a statement adopted by the House of Delegates of the American Medical Association on December 4, 1973:

> The intentional termination of the life of one human being by another—mercy killing—is contrary to that for which the medical profession stands and is contrary to the policy of the American Medical Association.
>
> The cessation of the employment of extraordinary means to prolong the life of the body when there is irrefutable evidence that biological death is imminent is the decision of the patient and/or his immediate family. The advice and judgment of the physician should be freely available to the patient and/or his immediate family.

However, a strong case can be made against this doctrine. In what follows I will set out some of the relevant arguments, and urge doctors to reconsider their views on this matter.

To begin with a familiar type of situation, a patient who is dying of incurable cancer of the throat is in terrible pain, which can no longer be satisfactorily alleviated. He is certain to die within a few days, even if present treatment is

Reprinted by permission from the *New England Journal of Medicine,* Vol. 292, January 9, 1975. Copyright °1975.

continued, but he does not want to go on living for those days since the pain is unbearable. So he asks the doctor for an end to it, and his family joins in the request.

Suppose the doctor agrees to withhold treatment, as the conventional doctrine says he may. The justification for his doing so is that the patient is in terrible agony, and since he is going to die anyway, it would be wrong to prolong his suffering needlessly. But now notice this. If one simply withholds treatment, it may take the patient longer to die, and so he may suffer more than he would if more direct action were taken and a lethal injection given. This fact provides strong reason for thinking that, once the initial decision not to prolong his agony has been made, active euthanasia is actually preferable to passive euthanasia, rather than the reverse. To say otherwise is to endorse the option that leads to more suffering rather than less, and is contrary to the humanitarian impulse that prompts the decision not to prolong his life in the first place.

Part of my point is that the process of being "allowed to die" can be relatively slow and painful, whereas being given a lethal injection is relatively quick and painless. Let me give a different sort of example. In the United States about one in 600 babies is born with Down's syndrome. Most of these babies are otherwise healthy—that is, with only the usual pediatric care, they will proceed to an otherwise normal infancy. Some, however, are born with congenital defects such as intestinal obstructions that require operations if they are to live. Sometimes, the parents and the doctor will decide not to operate, and let the infant die. Anthony Shaw describes what happens then:

> ... When surgery is denied [the doctor] must try to keep the infant from suffering while natural forces sap the baby's life away. As a surgeon whose natural inclination is to use the scalpel to fight off death, standing by and watching a salvageable baby die is the most emotionally exhausting experience I know. It is easy at a conference, in a theoretical discussion, to decide that such infants should be allowed to die. It is altogether different to stand by in the nursery and watch as dehydration and infection wither a tiny being over hours and days. This is a terrible ordeal for me and the hospital staff—much more so than for the parents who never set foot in the nursery.[1]

I can understand why some people are opposed to all euthanasia, and insist that such infants must be allowed to live. I think I can also understand why other people favor destroying these babies quickly and painlessly. But why should anyone favor letting "dehydration and infection wither a tiny being over hours and days"? The doctrine that says that a baby may be allowed to dehydrate and wither, but may not be given an injection that would end its life without suffering, seems so patently cruel as to require no further refutation. The strong language is not intended to offend, but only to put the point in the clearest possible way.

My second argument is that the conventional doctrine leads to decisions concerning life and death made on irrelevant grounds.

Consider again the case of the infants with Down's syndrome who need operations for congenital defects unrelated to the syndrome to live. Sometimes, there is no operation, and the baby dies, but when there is no such defect, the baby lives on. Now, an operation such as that to remove an intestinal obstruction is not prohibitively difficult. The reason why such operations are not performed in these cases is, clearly, that the child has Down's syndrome and the parents and the doctor judge that because of that fact it is better for the child to die.

But notice that this situation is absurd, no matter what view one takes of the lives and potentials of such babies. If the life of such an infant is worth preserving, what does it matter if it needs a simple operation? Or, if one thinks it better that such a baby should not live on, what difference does it make that it happens to have an obstructed intestinal tract? In either case, the matter of life and death is being decided on irrelevant grounds. It is the Down's syndrome, and not the intestines, that is the issue. The matter should be decided, if at all, on that basis, and not be allowed to depend on the essentially irrelevant question of whether the intestinal tract is blocked.

What makes this situation possible, of course, is the idea that when there is an intestinal blockage, one can "let the baby die," but when there is no such defect there is nothing that can be done, for one must not "kill" it. The fact that this idea leads to such results as deciding life or death on irrelevant grounds is another good reason why the doctrine should be rejected.

One reason why so many people think that there is an important moral difference between active and passive euthanasia is that they think killing someone is morally worse than letting someone die. But is it? Is killing, in itself, worse than letting die? To investigate this issue, two cases may be considered that are exactly alike except that one involves killing whereas the other involves letting someone die. Then, it can be asked whether this difference makes any difference to the moral assessments. It is important that the cases be exactly alike, except for this one difference, since otherwise one cannot be confident that it is this difference and not some other that accounts for any variation in the assessment of the two cases. So, let us consider this pair of cases:

In the first, Smith stands to gain a large inheritance if anything should happen to his six-year-old cousin. One evening while the child is taking his bath, Smith sneaks into the bathroom and drowns the child, and then arranges things so that it will look like an accident.

In the second, Jones also stands to gain if anything should happen to his six-year-old cousin. Like Smith, Jones sneaks in planning to drown the child in his bath. However, just as he enters the bathroom Jones sees the child slip and hit his head, and fall face down in the water. Jones is delighted; he stands by, ready to push the child's head back under if it is necessary, but it is not necessary. With only a little thrashing about, the child drowns all by himself, "accidentally," as Jones watches and does nothing.

Now Smith killed the child, whereas Jones "merely" let the child die. That is the only difference between them. Did either man behave better, from a moral point of view? If the difference between killing and letting die were in itself a morally important matter, one should say that Jones's behavior was less reprehensible than Smith's. But does one really want to say that? I think not. In the first place, both men acted from the same motive, personal gain, and both had exactly the same end in view when they acted. It may be inferred from Smith's conduct that he is a bad man, although that judgment may be withdrawn or modified if certain further facts are learned about him—for example, that he is mentally deranged. But would not the very same thing be inferred about Jones from his conduct? And would not the same further considerations also be relevant to any modification of this judgment? Moreover, suppose Jones pleaded, in his own defense, "After all, I didn't do anything except just stand there and watch the child drown. I didn't kill him; I only let him die." Again, if letting die were in itself less bad than killing, this defense should have at least some weight. But it does not. Such a "defense" can only be regarded as a grotesque perversion of moral reasoning. Morally speaking, it is no defense at all.

Now, it may be pointed out, quite properly, that the cases of euthanasia with which doctors are concerned are not like this at all. They do not involve personal gain or the destruction of normal healthy children. Doctors are concerned only with cases in which the patient's life is of no further use to him, or in which the patient's life has become or will soon become a terrible burden. However, the point is the same in these cases: the bare difference between killing and letting die does not, in itself, make a moral difference. If a doctor lets a patient die, for humane reasons, he is in the same moral position as if he had given the patient a lethal injection for humane reasons. If his decision was wrong—if, for example, the patient's illness was in fact curable—the decision would be equally regrettable no matter which method was used to carry it out. And if the doctor's decision was the right one, the method used is not in itself important.

The AMA policy statement isolates the crucial issue very well: the crucial issue is "the intentional termination of the life of one human being by another." But after identifying this issue, and forbidding "mercy killing," the statement goes on to deny that the cessation of treatment is the intentional termination of life. This is where the mistake comes in, for what is the cessation of treatment, in these circumstances, if it is not "the intentional termination of the life

of one human being by another"? Of course it is exactly that, and if it were not, there would be no point to it.

Many people will find this judgment hard to accept. One reason, I think, is that it is very easy to conflate the question of whether killing is, in itself, worse than letting die, with the very different question of whether most actual cases of killing are more reprehensible than most actual cases of letting die. Most actual cases of killing are clearly terrible (think, for example, of all the murders reported in the newspapers), and one hears of such cases every day. On the other hand, one hardly ever hears of a case of letting die, except for the action of doctors who are motivated by humanitarian reasons. So one learns to think of killing in a much worse light than of letting die. But this does not mean that there is something about killing that makes it in itself worse than letting die, for it is not the bare difference between killing and letting die that makes the difference in these cases. Rather, the other factors—the murderer's motive of personal gain, for example, contrasted with the doctor's humanitarian motivation—account for different reactions to the different cases.

I have argued that killing is not in itself any worse than letting die; if my contention is right, it follows that active euthanasia is not any worse than passive euthanasia. What arguments can be given on the other side? The most common, I believe, is the following:

"The important difference between active and passive euthanasia is that, in passive euthanasia, the doctor does not do anything to bring about the patient's death. The doctor does nothing, and the patient dies of whatever ills already afflict him. In active euthanasia, however, the doctor does something to bring about the patient's death: he kills him. The doctor who gives the patient with cancer a lethal injection has himself caused his patient's death; whereas if he merely ceases treatment, the cancer is the cause of the death."

A number of points need to be made here. The first is that it is not exactly correct to say that in passive euthanasia the doctor does nothing, for he does do one thing that is very important: he lets the patient die. "Letting someone die" is certainly different, in some respects, from other types of action—mainly in that it is a kind of action that one may perform by way of not performing certain other actions. For example, one may let a patient die by way of not giving medication, just as one may insult someone by way of not shaking his hand. But for any purpose of moral assessment, it is a type of action nonetheless. The decision to let a patient die is subject to moral appraisal in the same way that a decision to kill him would be subject to moral appraisal: it may be assessed as wise or unwise, compassionate or sadistic, right or wrong. If a doctor deliberately let a patient die who was suffering from a routinely curable illness, the doctor would certainly be to blame for what he had done, just as he would be to blame if he had needlessly killed the patient. Charges against him would then be appropriate. If so, it would be no defense at all for him to insist that he didn't "do anything." He would have done something very serious indeed, for he let his patient die.

Fixing the cause of death may be very important from a legal point of view, for it may determine whether criminal charges are brought against the doctor. But I do not think that this notion can be used to show a moral difference between active and passive euthanasia. The reason why it is considered bad to be the cause of some-

one's death is that death is regarded as a great evil—and so it is. However, if it has been decided that euthanasia—even passive euthanasia—is desirable in a given case, it has also been decided that in this instance death is no greater an evil than the patient's continued existence. And if this is true, the usual reason for not wanting to be the cause of someone's death simply does not apply.

Finally, doctors may think that all of this is only of academic interest—the sort of thing that philosophers may worry about but that has no practical bearing on their own work. After all, doctors must be concerned about the legal consequences of what they do, and active euthanasia is clearly forbidden by the law. But even so, doctors should also be concerned with the fact that the law is forcing upon them a moral doctrine that may well be indefensible, and has a considerable effect on their practices. Of course, most doctors are not now in the position of being coerced in this matter, for they do not regard themselves as merely going along with what the law requires. Rather, in statements such as the AMA policy statement that I have quoted, they are endorsing this doctrine as a central point of medical ethics. In that statement, active euthanasia is condemned not merely as illegal but as "contrary to that for which the medical profession stands," whereas passive euthanasia is approved. However, the preceding considerations suggest that there is really no moral difference between the two, considered in themselves (there may be important moral differences in some cases in their consequences, but as I pointed out, these differences may make active euthanasia, and not passive euthanasia, the morally preferable option). So, whereas doctors may have to discriminate between active and passive euthanasia to satisfy the law, they should not do any more than that. In particular, they should not give the distinction any added authority and weight by writing it into official statements of medical ethics.

NOTE

1   A. Shaw, "Doctor, Do We Have a Choice?" *The New York Times Magazine,* January 30, 1972, p. 59.

NO

Tom L. Beauchamp and James F. Childress

PRINCIPLES OF BIOMEDICAL ETHICS

KILLING AND LETTING DIE

... [A] sixty-eight-year-old doctor, who suffered severely from terminal carcinoma of the stomach, collapsed with a massive pulmonary embolism. He survived because one of his young colleagues performed a pulmonary embolectomy. Upon recovery the doctor-patient requested that no steps should be taken to prolong his life if he suffered another cardiovascular collapse. He even wrote an authorization to this effect for the hospital records. He reasoned that his pain was too much to bear given his dismal prospects. He thus asked to be *allowed to die* under certain conditions, but he did not ask to be *killed*. In [another] case ... a defective infant needed an operation to correct a tracheoesophogeal fistula. The parents and physicians determined that survival was not in this infant's best interests and decided to allow the infant to die rather than to perform an operation. In both cases, we need to ask whether certain actions, such as intentionally not trying to overcome a cardiovascular collapse and not performing an operation, can legitimately be described as "allowing to die" rather than "killing," and whether such actions are justifiable.

For many people, it is important to distinguish killing and letting die, and to prohibit the former while authorizing the latter in some range of cases. For example, after prohibiting "mercy killing" or the "intentional termination of the life of one human being by another,"[1] the AMA House of Delegates held that cessation of treatment is morally justified when the patient and/or the patient's immediate family, with the advice and judgment of the physician, decide to withhold or stop the use of "extraordinary means to prolong life when there is irrefutable evidence that biological death is imminent." Although several terms in this statement—such as "extraordinary," "irrefut-

Excerpted from *Principles of Biomedical Ethics*, Second Edition by Tom L. Beauchamp and James F. Childress. Copyright ©1979, 1983 by Oxford University Press, Inc. Reprinted by permission of the publisher.

able," and "imminent"—need careful examination, it is clear that the statement authorizes some instances of allowing to die by withholding or stopping treatment, while it excludes killing. Whether letting particular patients die—such as the sixty-eight-year-old man suffering from terminal carcinoma of the stomach and the defective infant needing an operation—is morally acceptable would depend on several conditions. But if their deaths involve killing rather than being merely "allowed deaths," they are not justifiable according to the AMA House of Delegates' statement.

In recent years, the distinction between killing and letting die has come under frequent attack. Some critics focus on developments in biomedical technology that appear to make it difficult to classify acts as instances either of killing or of letting die. Unplugging the respirator is now a standard example of this problem. Other critics dismiss the distinction itself, holding that it is a "moral quibble" without any "moral bite." As we explore the arguments for and against this distinction, it is important to emphasize that acceptance or rejection of the *distinction* does not necessarily determine *moral conclusions* about particular cases. For instance, it is possible to reject the distinction and to hold that some cases of what have been called "killing" and "letting die" are morally permissible, or that all cases are morally prohibited; and it is also possible to affirm the distinction and yet to hold that most cases of letting die and all cases of killing are morally wrong. Even if the distinction is morally significant, the label "killing" or the label "letting die" should not dictate a conclusion about a particular case. For example, it would be absurd to affirm the moral significance of the distinction and then to accept *all* cases of letting die as morally fitting. Even instances of letting die must meet other criteria such as the detriment-benefit calculation, and some cases of allowed death involve egregious negligence.

In a widely discussed argument for rejecting both the distinction between active and passive euthanasia and the AMA's policy statement, James Rachels contends that killing is not, in itself, worse than letting die.[2] That is, the "bare difference" between acts of killing and acts of letting die is not in itself a morally relevant difference. Part of his strategy is to sketch two cases that differ only in that one involves killing, while the other involves allowing to die. He contends that if there is no morally relevant difference between these cases, the "bare difference" between killing and allowing to die is demonstrated to be morally irrelevant. In his two cases, two young men want their six-year-old cousins dead so that they can gain large inheritances. Smith drowns his cousin while the boy is taking a bath. Jones plans to drown his cousin, but as he enters the bathroom he sees the boy slip and hit his head; Jones stands by, doing nothing, while the boy drowns. Smith killed his cousin; Jones merely allowed his cousin to die.

While we agree with Rachels that both acts are equally reprehensible because of the motives, ends, and actions, we do not accept his conclusion that these examples show that the distinction between killing and letting die is morally irrelevant. Several rejoinders to Rachels are in order. First, Rachels's cases and the cessations of treatment envisioned by the AMA are so markedly disanalogous that it is not clear what Rachels's argument shows. In some cases of unjustified acts, including both of Rachels's examples, we are not interested in moral distinctions per se. As Richard Trammell points out, some examples have a "masking" or "sledgehammer" effect; the fact that "one cannot distinguish the taste of two wines when both are mixed with green persimmon juice, does not imply that there is no distinction between the wines."[3] Since Rachel's examples involve two morally justified acts by agents whose motives and intentions are despicable, it is not surprising that some *other* features of their situations, such as killing and letting die, do not strike us as morally compelling considerations.

Second, while Rachels's cases involve two *unjustified* actions, one of killing and the other of letting die, the AMA statement distinguished cases of *unjustified killing* from cases of *justified letting die*. The AMA statement does not, however, claim that the moral difference is identical to the distinction between killing and letting die. It does not even imply that the "bare difference" between (passive) letting die and (active) killing is the only difference or even a morally sufficient difference between the justified and unjustified cases. Its point is rather that the justified actions in medicine are confined to (passive) letting die. While the AMA statement holds that "mercy killing" in medicine is unjustified in all circumstances, it does not hold that letting die is right in all circumstances or that killing outside medicine is always wrong. For an act that results in an earlier death for the patient to be justified, it is necessary that it be describable as an act of "letting die," but this description is not sufficient to justify the act; nor is the bare description of killing sufficient to make *all* acts of killing wrong. This AMA pronouncement is meant to hold only in the context of the physician-patient relationship.

Third, in Rachels's cases Smith and Jones are *morally* responsible and *morally* blameworthy for the deaths of their respective cousins, even if Jones, who allowed his cousin to drown, is not *causally* respon-

sible. The law might find only Smith who killed his cousin, guilty of homicide (because of the law's theory of proximate cause), but morality condemns both actions because of the agents' motives and their commissions and omissions. While we would not condemn a nonswimmer for failing to jump into deep water to try to rescue a drowning child, we find Jones's actions reprehensible because he (morally) should have rescued the child. Even if he had no other special duties to the child, the duty of beneficence . . . requires affirmative action. The point of the cases envisioned by the AMA is that the physician is always morally prohibited from killing patients but is not morally bound to preserve life in *all* cases. According to the AMA, the physician has a right—and perhaps a duty—to stop treatment if and only if three conditions are met: (1) the life of the body is being preserved by extraordinary means, (2) there is irrefutable evidence that biological death is imminent, and (3) the patient and/or the family consents.

Fourth, even if the distinction between killing and letting die is morally irrelevant in some contexts, it does not follow that it is always morally irrelevant. The fact that the distinction does not show up in every sort of case does not mean that it is morally unimportant under all circumstances. Rachels does effectively undermine any attempt to rest judgments about ending life on the "bare difference" between killing and letting die, but his target may be a straw man. Many philosophers and theologians have argued that there are *independent* moral, religious, and other reasons for defending the distinction and for prohibiting killing while authorizing allowing to die in some circumstances.

One theologian has argued, for example, that we can discern the moral significance of the distinction between killing and letting die only by "placing it in the religious context out of which it grew."[4] That context is the Biblical story of God's actions toward his creatures. In that context it makes *sense* to talk about "placing patients in God's hands," just as it is important not to usurp God's prerogatives by desperately struggling to prolong life when the patient is irreversibly dying. But even if the distinction between killing and letting die originated within a religious context, and even if it makes more sense in that context than in some others, it can be defended on nontheological grounds without being reduced to a claim about a "bare difference." However important the religious context was for the origin of the distinction, religious doctrines are not presupposed by the distinction and independent moral grounds are sufficient to support it.

Some nontheological arguments in favor of the distinction between killing and allowing to die invoke both moral and practical considerations. They hold that the distinction enables us to express and maintain certain principles such as nonmaleficence and to avoid certain harmful consequences. Probably no single reason by itself is sufficient to support the moral relevance of the distinction and thus to prohibit killing while permitting some intentionally allowed deaths. But several reasons together indicate that the distinction is worth retaining or, in effect, that our current practices should be maintained with some clarifications and modifications. We now turn to this set of reasons.

The most important arguments for the distinction between killing and letting die depend on a distinction between *acts* and *practices*.[5] It is one thing to justify an act, i.e., to hold that it is right; it is another to justify a general practice. [M]any beliefs about principles and consequences are applied to practices or rules rather than directly to acts. For example, we might justify a rule of confidentiality because it encourages people to seek therapy and because it promotes respect for persons and their privacy. Such a rule might, however, lead to undesirable results in *particular* cases. Likewise, a rule that prohibits "active killing," while permitting some "allowed deaths," may be justifiable, even though it excludes some acts of killing that in and of themselves might appear to be justifiable. Such a rule would not permit us to kill a patient who suffers from terrible pain, who rationally asks for "mercy," i.e., to be killed, and who will probably die within three weeks. According to the rule of double effect, we should, of course, use measures to alleviate the patient's pain even though these would hasten death; we should allow the patient to die, but not kill the patient. It may be necessary to prohibit by rule and policy some acts that do not appear to be wrong in some circumstances in order to maintain a viable practice that, for the most part, expresses our principles and avoids seriously undesirable consequences. Thus, although particular acts of killing may not violate the duty of nonmaleficence and may even be humane and compassionate, a policy of authorizing killing would probably violate the duty of nonmaleficence by creating a grave risk of harm in many cases.

According to one line of argument, the prohibition of killing even for "mercy" expresses principles and values that provide a basis of trust between patients and health care professionals. Trust involves the expectation that others will respect moral limits. When we trust medical practitioners, we expect them to promote our welfare and, at least, to do us no harm without a corresponding prospect of benefit. The prohibition of killing in medical contexts is a basic expression of the ethos of care for the patient's life and health as well as the duty of maleficence. Some claim that it is instrumentally as well as symbolically important, for its removal would weaken a "climate, both moral and legal, which we are not able to do without."[6] David Louisell, for example, contends that "Euthanasia would threaten the patient-physician relationship: confidence might give way to suspicion. . . . Can the physician, historic battler for life, become an affirmative agent of death without jeopardizing the trust of his dependents?"[7] . . .

If rules permitting active killing were introduced into a society, it is not implausible to suppose that the society over time would move increasingly in the direction of involuntary euthanasia—e.g., in the form of killing defective newborns for such reasons as the avoidance of social burdens. There could be a general reduction of respect for human life as a result of the official removal of some barriers to killing. Rules against killing in a moral code are not isolated; they are threads in a fabric of rules, based in part on nonmaleficence, that support respect for human life. The more threads we remove, the weaker the fabric becomes. If we focus on attitudes and not merely rules, the general attitude of respect for life may be eroded by shifts in particular areas. Determination of the probability of such an erosion depends not only on the connectedness of rules and attitudes, but also on various forces in the society. . . .

In addition to fears of abuse, including abuse of the mentally disturbed and others who cannot consent, there are other legitimate fears. First, easy resort to killing to relieve pain and suffering may divert attention and resources from other strategies that may be effective, such as the hospice movement. Second, consider the following two types of wrongly diagnosed patients.[8]

1. Patients wrongly diagnosed as hopeless, and who will survive even if a treatment *is* ceased (in order to allow a natural death).
2. Patients wrongly diagnosed as hopeless, and who will survive only if the treatment is *not ceased* (in order to allow a natural death).

If a social rule of allowing some patients to die were in effect, doctors and families who followed it would only lose patients in the second category. But if killing were permitted, at least some of the patients in the first category would be needlessly lost. Thus, a rule prohibiting killing would save some lives that would be lost if *both* killing and allowing to die were permitted. Of course, such a consequence is not a decisive reason for a policy of (only) allowing to die, for the numbers in categories (1) and (2) are likely to be small and other reasons for killing, such as extreme pain and autonomous choice, might be weighty. But it is certainly *a* morally relevant reason.

Proponents of the practice of killing some patients appeal to a range of exceptional cases to show the utility of the practice. Among the strongest reasons for killing some patients is to relieve unbearable and uncontrollable pain and suffering. No one would deny that pain and suffering can so ravage and dehumanize patients that death appears to be in their best interests. Prolonging life and refusing to kill in such circumstances may appear to be cruel and even to violate the duty of nonmaleficence. Often proponents of "mercy killing" appeal to nonmedical situations to show that killing may be more humane and compassionate than letting die—as, for example, in the case of a truck driver inextricably trapped in a burning wreck who cries out for "mercy" and asks to be killed. In such tragic situations we are reluctant to say that those who kill at the behest of the victim act wrongly. Furthermore, juries often find persons who have killed a suffering relative not guilty by reason of temporary insanity.

There are, nevertheless, serious objections to building into *medical practice* an explicit exception licensing physicians to kill their patients in order to relieve uncontrollable pain and suffering. One objection is that it is not clear that many, if any, cases in medical practice are really parallel to the person trapped in a burning wreck. The physician may be able to relieve pain and suffering short of killing—even if death is hastened—by means that are not available to a bystander at the scene of an accident. A second objection holds that we should not construct a social or professional ethic on borderline situations and emergency cases, even if medical practitioners confront some cases of unmanageable pain and suffering. It is dangerous to generalize from emergencies, for hard cases may make bad social and professional ethics as well as bad law. As Charles Fried writes,

> The concept of emergency is only a tolerable moral concept if somehow we can truly think of it as exceptional, if we can truly think of it as a circumstance that, far from defying our usual moral universe, suspends it for a limited time and thus suspends usual moral principles. It is when emergencies become usual that we are threatened with moral disintegration, dehumanization.[9]

Third, there are ways to "accept" acts of killing in exceptional circumstances with-

out altering the rules of practice in order to accomodate them. As mentioned earlier, juries often find those who kill their suffering relatives not guilty by reason of temporary insanity, as occurred in the Zygmaniak case in New Jersey.[10] In June 1973, George Zygmaniak was in a motorcycle accident that left him paralyzed from the neck down. This paralysis was considered to be irreversible, and Zygmaniak begged his brother, Lester, to kill him. Three days later, Lester brought a sawed-off shotgun into the hospital and shot his brother in the head, after having told him, "Close your eyes now, I'm going to shoot you." Verdicts like "not guilty by reason of temporary insanity" do not *justify* the act of killing a suffering relative. They differ from a verdict of not guilty on grounds of self-defense, for self-defense does justify killing, at least in some circumstances. Verdicts like not guilty by reason of temporary insanity thus function to *excuse* the agent by finding that he or she lacked the conditions of responsibility necessary to be legally guilty.

Others have proposed that we maintain the legal rule against killing even if physicians and others sometime have to engage in justified conscientious or civil disobedience. Concurring with Robert Veatch, Paul Ramsey holds that "civil disobedience—the courage to go against the rules when morally warranted—may be better than to allow for exceptions in a rule of general practice."[11] But what conditions might justify conscientious refusals in medical practice to follow the rule against killing patients? According to Ramsey, when dying patients are totally inaccessible to our care, when our care is a matter of indifference to them because of intractable pain or a deep coma, "there is no longer any morally significant distinction between omission and commission, between standing aside and directly dispatching them."[12] "Total inaccessibility" is a limit of care itself; for care can become totally useless. It is not clear, however, that Ramsey's distinction between dying and nondying patients can carry his argument. Nor is it clear whether he considers someone in a deep and prolonged state of unconsciousness as dying, and if so, whether such a view is justifiable. In addition, it is necessary to ask whether Ramsey's exception can be limited to the cases that he endorses; it too may be the thin edge of the wedge. Nevertheless, even if pain and suffering of a certain magnitude can in principle justify active killing, as long as other conditions are met, they may only justify acts of conscientious refusal to follow the rule of practice, not basic changes in the rule itself.

Finally, which side in the debate has the burden of proof—the proponents or the opponents of a practice of selective killing? Anthony Flew has argued that supporters of the current practice of prohibiting killing must bear the burden of proof because the prohibition of *voluntary* euthanasia violates the principle of liberty by refusing to respect individual autonomy.[13] However, a policy of voluntary euthanasia, based on either a negative right to die (a right to noninterference) or a positive right to die (a right to be killed), would involve such a change in society's vision of the medical profession and medical attitudes that a shift in the burden of proof to the proponents of change is inevitable. The prohibition of killing is not arbitrary even when cases of voluntary request are factored in. It expresses some important moral principles, values, and attitudes whose loss, or serious alteration, could have major negative consequences. Because the current practice of prohibiting killing while accepting some "allowed deaths" has served us well, if not perfectly, it should be altered only with the utmost caution. Lines are not easy to draw and maintain, but in general we have been able to follow the line between killing and letting die in medical practice. Before we undertake any major changes, we need strong evidence that these changes are really needed in order to avoid important harms or secure important benefits, and that the good effects will outweigh the bad effects. . . .

NOTES

1   It is a mistake to view these expressions as synonymous, though the present statement appears to.
2   James Rachels, "Active and Passive Euthanasia," *New England Journal of Medicine* 292 (January a9, 1975): 78-80. For valuable discussions of the distinction between killing and letting die, see Bonnie Steinbock, ed., *Killing and Letting Die*; and John Ladd, ed., *Ethical Issues Relating to Life and Death* (New York: Oxford University Press, 1979).
3   Richard L. Trammell, "Saving and Taking Life," *Journal of Philosophy* 72 (1975): 131-37
4   Gilbert Meilaender, "The Distinction Between Killing and Allowing to Die," *Theological Studies* 37 (1976): 467-70.
5   See John Rawls, "Two Concepts of Rules," *Philosphical Review* 64 (1955): 3-32.
6   G.J. Hughes, S.J., "Killing and Letting Die," *The Month* 236 (1975):42-45.
7   David Louisell, "Euthanasia and Biothanasia: On Dying and Killing," *Linacre Quarterly* 40 (1973): 234-58.
8   We owe most of this argument to James Rachels.
9   Charles Fried, "Rights and Health Care—Beyond Equity and Efficiency," *New England Journal of Medicine* 293 (July 31, 1975): 245.
10   For a discussion of this case, see Paige Mitchell, *Act of Love: The Killing of George Zygmaniak* (New York: Knopf, 1976).
11   See Paul Ramsey, *Ethics at the Edges of Life*, p. 217; Robert Veatch, *Death, Dying, and the Biological Revolution* (New Haven, Conn.: Yale University Press, 1976) p. 97.
12   Ramsey, *Ethics at the Edges of Life*, pp. 195, 214, 216; cf. Ramsey, *The Patient as Person*, pp. 161-64.
13   Antony Flew, "The Principle of Euthanasia," *Euthanasia and the Right to Death: The Case of Voluntary Euthanasia*, ed. A.B. Downing (London: Peter Owen, 1969), pp. 30-48.

POSTSCRIPT

IS KILLING THE SAME AS LETTING DIE?

In 1982 the American Medical Association reaffirmed its stand on euthanasia. An opinion from its Judicial Council declared: "For humane reasons, with informed consent a physician may do what is medically necessary to alleviate severe pain, or cease or omit treatment to let a terminally ill patient die, but he should not intentionally cause death." The Catholic view on euthanasia was forcefully stated in a Vatican declaration of May 5, 1980: ". . . (N)othing and no one can in any way permit the killing of an innocent human being, whether a fetus or an embryo, an infant or an adult, an old person, or one suffering from an incurable disease, or a person who is dying. Furthermore, no one is permitted to ask for this act of killing, either for himself or herself or for another person entrusted to his or her care, nor can he or she consent to it. . . ."

However, the competent patient's right to refuse treatment is well established in law and ethics. Several states have "right to die" laws, although they do not all work equally well in achieving their aims. For a recent proposal see "The Right to Refuse Treatment: A Model Act," by the Legal Advisors Committee of Concern for Dying (*American Journal of Public Health,* August 1983).

The most comprehensive review of all issues concerned with treatment of dying patients is *Deciding to Forego Life-Sustaining Treatment,* a report of the President's Commission for the Study of Ethical Problems in Medicine and Biomedical and Behavioral Research (Government Printing Office, 1983). *Death, Dying, and Euthanasia,* edited by Dennis J. Horan and David Mall, is a collection of articles from various points of view (University Publications of America, 1980). Also see Bonnie Steinbock, editor, *Killing and Letting Die* (Prentice-Hall, 1980); Marvin Kohl, editor, *Beneficient Euthanasia* (Prometheus Books, 1975); John Behnke and Sissela Bok, editors, *The Dilemmas of Euthanasia* (Doubleday, 1975); and Derek Humphrey and Ann Wickett, *The Right to Die: Understanding Euthanasia* (New York: Harper & Row, 1986).

James Rachels has amplified the views expressed in the selection here in *The End of Life: Euthanasia and Morality* (New York: Oxford University Press, 1986). He concludes with a proposal to accept mercy killing as a defense against charges of homicide as a way of legalizing euthanasia without cumbersome laws.

ISSUE 6

MUST FLUIDS AND NUTRITION ALWAYS BE GIVEN TO DYING PATIENTS?

YES: Gilbert Meilaender, from "On Removing Food and Water: Against the Stream," *Hastings Center Report,* 14:6, December 1984

NO: Joanne Lynn and James F. Childress, from "Must Patients Always Be Given Food and Water?" *Hastings Center Report,* 13:5, October 1983

ISSUE SUMMARY

YES: Professor of religion Gilbert Meilaender maintains that food and water are ordinary care, not medical treatment. Removing them constitutes "aiming to kill" rather than "allowing to die."
NO: Physician Joanne Lynn and professor of religious studies James F. Childress claim that nutrition and hydration by medical means are not morally different from other life-sustaining medical treatments that may on occasion be withheld or withdrawn. The patient's best interests should be the deciding factor.

The landmark *Quinlan* decision in 1976 affirmed the right of a patient to refuse life-sustaining treatment and the right of a parent or guardian to make that same decision for an incompetent patient. But Karen Ann Quinlan's parents wanted only to remove her from a respirator; they did not even consider the removal of a nasogastric tube through which she was artificially fed for the next ten years until her death.

The question of whether food and water must always be provided reached the public arena in a series of legal cases that began in 1981. In that year Robert Nejdl and Neil Barber, two Los Angeles physicians, were charged with murder for taking Clarence Herbert, their patient who had suffered severe brain damage after an operation, off a respirator and then, when he continued to breathe, removing all artificial nutrition. The charges were dropped, and the court ruled in 1983 that artificial feeding was like any other medical treatment and could be withheld with consent of the patient or family.

Also in 1981 in Danville, Illinois, the parents and physician of newborn conjoined twins (often called "Siamese twins") decided not to feed the infants. The courts disagreed and feeding and other treatments were given. But in 1982, in Bloomington, Indiana, another newborn—with Down syndrome, a genetic disease that results in mild to severe mental retardation—was not given surgery to correct a defect of his esophagus and was not fed. The baby's death led to a series of governmental regulations [see Issue 7].

In a series of other cases, the courts have grappled with the same problem. But they have come up with different answers. In New Jersey, in the 1983 case of Claire Conroy, the court ruled, after her death, that food and nutrition could be withheld from a nursing home patient as long as a series of complicated procedures were followed to prevent abuse. In Massachusetts, in the 1986 case of Paul Brophy, a firefighter in a persistent vegetative state, the court ruled that feeding could not be withdrawn, despite the unanimous wishes of the family and the judgment of several physicians that he would never recover.

The ethical question centers on whether artificial nutrition and hydration is ordinary care, which must be provided for every patient, or a medical treatment like antibiotics or a respirator, which can be withheld if it is not in the patient's best interests. The symbolic value of feeding a dying patient must be weighed against the likely benefit to the patient.

In the following selections, Gilbert Meilaender sees a willingness to provide food and drink "even when the struggle against death has been lost" as "the last evidence we can offer that . . . we are willing to love to the very point of death." Joanne Lynn and James Childress set out three circumstances when, in their view, it would be ethical to withhold fluids and nutrition: when the procedures would be futile in achieving improved nutritional and fluid levels; when the improvement, though achievable, would not benefit the patient; and when the burden of receiving the treatment outweighs the benefits.

YES
Gilbert Meilaender

ON REMOVING FOOD AND WATER: AGAINST THE STREAM

As infants we were given food and drink when we were too helpless to nourish ourselves. And for many of us a day will come before we die when we are once again too helpless to feed ourselves. If there is any way in which the living can stand by those who are not yet dead, it would seem to be through the continued provision of food and drink even when the struggle against disease has been lost. To continue to nourish the life of one who has been defeated in that battle is the last evidence we can offer that we are more than frontrunners, that we are willing to love to the very point of death.

Today this intuitive reaction is being challenged. The President's Commission for the Study of Ethical Problems in Medicine and Biomedical and Behavioral Research has suggested that for patients with permanent loss of consciousness artificial feeding interventions need not be continued.[1] A group of physicians writing in the *New England Journal of Medicine* has counseled doctors that for irreversibly ill patients whose condition warrants nothing more aggressive than general nursing care, "naturally or artificially administered hydration and nutrition may be given or withheld, depending on the patient's comfort."[2]

Court decisions in cases like those of Claire Conroy in New Jersey or Clarence Herbert in California or Mary Hier in Massachusetts are contradictory,[3] but a consensus is gradually building toward the day when what we have already done in the case of some nondying infants with birth defects who were "allowed to die" by not being fed will become standard "treatment" for all patients who are permanently unconscious or suffering from severe and irreversible dementia. Those who defend this view stand ready with ethical arguments that nutrition and hydration are not "in the best interests" of such patients, but Daniel Callahan may have isolated the energizing force that is driving this consensus: "A denial of nutrition," he says, "may in the long run become the only effective way to make certain that a large number of biologically tenacious patients actually die."[4]

Reprinted by permission from the *Hastings Center Report*, 14:6, December 1984. Copyright © 1984 by the Hastings Center.

To the degree that this is true, however, the policy toward which we are moving is not merely one of "allowing to die": it is one of aiming to kill. *If we are in fact heading in this direction, we should turn back* before this policy corrupts our intellect and emotions and our capacity for moral reasoning. That stance I take to be a given, for which I shall not attempt to argue. Here I will consider only whether removal of artificial nutrition and hydration really does amount to no more than "allowing to die."

WHY FEEDING
IS NOT MEDICAL CARE

The argument for ceasing to feed seems strongest in cases of people suffering from a "persistent vegetative state," those (like Karen Quinlan) who have suffered an irreversible loss of consciousness. Sidney Wanzer and his physician colleagues suggest that in such circumstances "it is morally justifiable to withhold antibiotics and artificial nutrition and hydration, as well as other forms of life-sustaining treatment, allowing the patient to die." The President's Commission advises: "Since permanently unconscious patients will never be aware of nutrition, the only benefit to the patient of providing such increasingly burdensome interventions is sustaining the body to allow for a remote possibility of recovery. The sensitivities of the family and of care giving professionals ought to determine whether such interventions are made." Joanne Lynn, a physician at George Washington University, and James Childress, a professor of religious studies at the University of Virginia, believe that "in these cases, it is very difficult to discern how any medical intervention can benefit or harm the patient."[5] But we need to ask whether the physicians are right to suggest that they seek only to allow the patient to die;

whether the President's Commission has used language carefully enough in saying that nutrition and hydration of such persons is merely sustaining a *body;* whether Lynn and Childress may too readily have assumed that providing food and drink is *medical* treatment.

Should the provision of food and drink be regarded as *medical* care? It seems, rather, to be the sort of care that all human beings owe each other. All living beings need food and water in order to live, but such nourishment does not itself heal or cure disease. When we stop feeding the permanently unconscious patient, we are not withdrawing from the battle against any illness or disease; we are withholding the nourishment that sustains all life.

The President's Commission does suggest that certain kinds of care remain mandatory for the permanently unconscious patient: "The awkward posture and lack of motion of unconscious patients often lead to pressure sores, and skin lesions are a major complication. Treatment and prevention of these problems is standard nursing care and should be provided." Yet it is hard to see why such services (turning the person regularly, giving alcohol rubs, and the like) are standard nursing care when feeding is not. Moreover, if feeding cannot benefit these patients, it is far from clear how they could experience bed sores as harm.

If this is true, we may have good reason to question whether the withdrawal of nutrition and hydration in such cases is properly characterized as stopping medical treatment in order to allow a patient to die. There are circumstances in which a plausible and helpful distinction can be made between killing and allowing to die, between an aim and a foreseen but unintended consequence. And sometimes it may make excellent moral sense to hold that we should cease to provide a now useless treatment, foreseeing but not intending that death will result. Such reasoning is also useful in the ethics of warfare, but there its use must be strictly controlled lest we simply unleash the bombs while "directing our intention" to a military target that could be attacked with far less firepower. Careful use of language is also necessary lest we talk about unconscious patients in ways that obscure our true aim.

Challenging those who have argued that it is no longer possible to distinguish between combatants and noncombatants in war, Michael Walzer has pointed out that "the relevant distinction is not between those who work for the war effort and those who do not, but between those who make what soldiers need to fight and those who make what they need to live, like the rest of us."[6]

Hence, farmers are not legitimate targets in war simply because they grow the food that soldiers need to live (and then to fight). The soldiers would need the food to live, even if there were no war. Thus, as Paul Ramsey has observed, though an army may march upon its belly, bellies are not the target. It is an abuse of double-effect reasoning to justify cutting off the food supply of a nation as a way of stopping its soldiers. We could not properly say that we were aiming at the soldiers while merely foreseeing the deaths of the civilian population.

Nor can we, when withdrawing food from the permanently unconsious person, properly claim that our intention is to cease useless treatment for a dying patient. These patients are not dying, and we cease no treatment aimed at disease; rather, we withdraw the nourishment that sustains all human beings whether healthy or ill, and we do so when the only result

of our action can be death. At what, other than that death, could we be aiming?

One might argue that the same could be said of turning off a respirator, but the situations are somewhat different. Remove a person from a respirator and he may die—but, then, he may also surprise us and continue to breathe spontaneously. We test to see if the patient can breathe. If he does, it is not our task—unless we are aiming at his death—now to smother him (or to stop feeding him). But deprive a person of food and water and she will die as surely as if we had administered a lethal drug, and it is hard to claim that we did not aim at her death.

I am unable—and this is a lack of insight, not of space—to say more about the analogy between eating and breathing. Clearly, air is as essential to life as food. We might wonder, therefore, whether provision of air is not also more than medical treatment. What justification could there be, then, for turning off a respirator? If the person's death, due to the progress of a disease, is irreversibly and imminently at hand, then continued assistance with respiration may now be useless. But if the person is not going to die from any disease but, instead, simply needs assistance with breathing because of some injury, it is less clear to me why such assistance should not be given. More than this I am unable to say. I repeat, however, that to remove a respirator is not necessarily to aim at death; one will not go on to kill the patient who manages to breathe spontaneously. But it is difficult for me to construe removal of nutrition for permanently unconscious patients in any other way. Perhaps we only wish them dead or think they would be better off dead. There are circumstances in which such a thought is understandable. But it would still be wrong to enact that wish by aiming at their death.

SEPARATING PERSONHOOD AND BODY

Suppose that we accept the view that provision of food and water is properly termed medical treatment. Is there good reason to withhold this treatment from permanently unconscious patients? A treatment refusal needs to be justified either on the ground that the treatment is (or has now become) useless, or that the treatment (though perhaps still useful) is excessively burdensome for the patient. Still taking as our focus the permanently unconscious patient, we can consider, first, whether feeding is useless. There could be occasions on which artificial feeding would be futile. Lynn and Childress offer instances of patients who simply cannot be fed effectively, but they are not cases of permanently unconscious patients.

Yet for many people the uselessness of feeding the permanently unconscious seems self-evident. Why? Probably because they suppose that the nourishment we provide is, in the words of the President's Commission, doing no more than "sustaining the body." But we should pause before separating personhood and body so decisively. When considering other topics (care of the environment, for example) we are eager to criticize a dualism that divorces human reason and consciousness from the larger world of nature. Why not here? We can know people—of all ranges of cognitive capacity—only as they are embodied; there is no other "person" for whom we might care. Such care is not useless if it "only" preserves bodily life but does not restore cognitive capacities. Even if it is less than we wish could be accomplished, it remains care for the embodied person.

Some will object to characterizing as persons those who lack the capacity or, even, the potential for self-awareness, for envisioning a future for themselves, for relating to other selves. I am not fully persuaded that speaking of "persons" in such contexts is mistaken, but the point can be made without using that language. Human nature has a capacity to know, to be self-aware, and to relate to others. We can share in that human nature even though we may not yet or no longer exercise all the functions of which it is capable. We share in it simply by virtue of being born into the human species. We could describe as persons all individuals sharing our common nature, all members of the species. Or we could ascribe personhood only to those human beings presently capable of exercising the characteristic human functions.

I think it better—primarily because it is far less dualistic—to understand personhood as an endowment that comes with our nature, even if at some stages of life we are unable to exercise characteristic human capacities. But the point can be made, if anyone wishes, by talking of embodied human beings rather than embodied persons. To be a human being one need not presently be exercising or be capable of exercising the functions characteristic of consciousness. Those are capacities of human nature; they are not functions that all human beings exercise. It is human beings, not just persons in that more restricted sense, whose death should not be our aim. And if this view is characterized as an objectionable "speciesism," I can only reply that at least it is not one more way by which the strong and gifted in our world rid themselves of the weak, and it does not fall prey to that abstraction by which we reify consciousness and separate it from the body.

The permanently unconscious are not dying subjects who should simply be allowed to die. But they will, of course, die if we aim at their death by ceasing to feed them. If we are not going to feed them because that would be nothing more than sustaining a body, why not bury them at once? No one, I think, recommends that. But if, then, they are still living beings who ought not be buried, the nourishment that all human beings need to live ought not be denied them. When we permit ourselves to think that care is useless if it preserves the life of the embodied human being without restoring cognitive capacity, we fall victim to the old delusion that we have failed if we cannot *cure* and that there is, then, little point to continued *care*. David Smith, a professor of religious studies at the University of Indiana, has suggested that I might be mistaken in describing the comatose person as a "nondying" patient. At least in some cases, he believes lapsing into permanent coma might be a sign that a person is trying to die. Thus, though a comatose state would not itself be sufficient reason to characterize someone as dying, it might be one of several conditions which, taken together, would be sufficient. This is a reasonable suggestion, and it might enable us to distinguish different sorts of comatose patients—the dying, for whom feeding might be useless; the nondying, for whom it would not. Even then, however, I would still be troubled by the worry I raised earlier: whether food and drink are really medical treatment that should be withdrawn when it becomes useless.

Even when care is not useless it may be so burdensome that it should be dispensed with. When that is the case, we can honestly say—and it makes good moral sense to say—that our aim is to relieve the person of a burden, with the foreseen but unintended effect of a hastened death. We should note, however, that this line of argument *cannot* be applied to the cases of the permanently unconscious. Other patients—those, for example, with fairly severe dementia—may be made afraid and uncomfortable by artificial nutrition and hydration. But this can hardly be true of the permanently unconscious. It seems unlikely that they experience the care involved in feeding them as burdensome.

Even for severely demented patients who retain some consciousness, we should be certain that we are considering the burden of the treatment, not the burden of continued existence itself. In the case of Claire Conroy, for example, the trial judge suggested that her life (not simply the intervention needed to feed her) had become "impossibly and permanently burdensome." That is a judgment, I think, that no one should make for another; indeed, it is hard to know exactly how one would do so. Besides, it seems evident that if the burden involved is her continued life, the point of ceasing to feed is that we aim at relieving her of that burden—that is, we aim to kill.

Having said that, I am quite ready to grant that the burden of the feeding itself may sometimes be so excessive that it is not warranted. Lynn and Childress offer examples, some of which seem persuasive. If, however, we want to assess the burden of the treatment, we should certainly not dispense with nutrition and hydration until a reasonable trial period has demonstrated that the person truly finds such care excessively burdensome.

In short, if we focus our attention on irreversibly ill adults for whom general nursing care but no more seems appropriate, we can say the following: First, when the person is permanently unconscious, the care involved in feeding can hardly be experienced as burdensome. Neither can such care be described as useless, since it preserves the life of the embodied human being (who is not a dying patient). Second, when the person is conscious but severely and irreversibly demented, the care involved in feeding, though not useless, *may* be so burdensome that it should cease. This requires demonstration during a trial period, however, and the judgment is quite different from concluding that the person's life has become too burdensome to preserve. Third, for both sorts of patients the care involved in feeding is not, in any strict sense, medical treatment, even if provided in a hospital. It gives what all need to live; it is treatment of no particular disease; and its cessation means certain death, a death at which we can only be said to aim, whatever our motive.

That we should continue to feed the permanently unconscious still seems obvious to some people, even as it was to Karen Quinlan's father at the time he sought removal of her respirator. It has not always seemed so to me, but it does now. For the permanently unconscious person, feeding is neither useless nor excessively burdensome. It is ordinary human care and is not given as treatment for any life-threatening disease. Since this is true, a decision not to offer such care can enact only one intention: to take the life of the unconscious person.

I have offered no arguments here to prove that such a life-taking intention and aim would be morally wrong, though I believe it is and that to embrace such an aim would be corrupting. If we can face the fact that withdrawing the nourishment of such persons is, indeed, aiming to kill, I am hopeful (though not altogether confident) that the more fundamental principle will not need to be argued. Let us hope that this is the case, since that more basic principle is not one that can be argued *to;* rather, all useful moral argument must proceed *from* the conviction that it is wrong to aim to kill the innocent.

REFERENCES

1. The President's Commission for the Study of Ethical Problems in Medicine and Biomedical and Behavioral Research, *Deciding to Forego Life-Sustaining Treatment* (Washington, DC: Government Printing Office, 1982), p. 190.

2. Sidney H. Wanzer, M.D., et al., "The Physician's Responsibility Toward Hopelessly Ill Patients," *New England Journal of Medicine,* 310 (April 12, 1984) 958.

3. See a discussion of the first two cases in Bonnie Steinbock, "The Removal of Mr. Herbert's Feeding Tube," *Hastings Center Report,* 13 (October 1983) 13-16; also see George J. Annas, "The Case of Mary Hier: When Substituted Judgment Becomes Sleight of Hand," *Hastings Center Report* 14 (August 1984), 23-25.

4. Daniel Callahan, "On Feeding the Dying," *Hastings Center Report,* 13 (October 1983) 22.

5. Joanne Lynn and James Childress, "Must Patients Always Be Given Food and Water?" *Hastings Center Report,* 13 (October 1983) 18.

6. Michael Walzer, *Just and Unjust Wars* (New York: Basic Books, Inc., 1977), p. 146.

NO
Joanne Lynne and
James F. Childress

MUST PATIENTS ALWAYS BE GIVEN FOOD AND WATER?

Many people die from the lack of food or water. For some, this lack is the result of poverty or famine, but for others it is the result of disease or deliberate decision. In the past, malnutrition and dehydration must have accompanied nearly every death that followed an illness of more than a few days. Most dying patients do not eat much on their own, and nothing could be done for them until the first flexible tubing for instilling food or other liquid into the stomach was developed about a hundred years ago. Even then, the procedure was so scarce, so costly in physician and nursing time, and so poorly tolerated that it was used only for patients who clearly could benefit. With the advent of more reliable and efficient procedures in the past few decades, these conditions can be corrected or ameliorated in nearly every patient who would otherwise be malnourished or dehydrated. In fact, intravenous lines and nasogastric tubes have become common images of hospital care.

Providing adequate nutrition and fluids is a high priority for most patients, both because they suffer directly from inadequacies and because these deficiencies hinder their ability to overcome other diseases. But are there some patients who need not receive these treatments? . . .

The answer in any real case should acknowledge the psychological contiguity between feeding and loving and between nutritional satisfaction and emotional satisfaction. Yet this acknowledgement does not resolve the core question. . . .

Reprinted by permission from the *Hastings Center Report,* 13:5, October 1983. Copyright © 1983 by the Hastings Center.

[W]e will concentrate upon the care of patients who are incompetent to make choices for themselves. Patients who are competent to determine the course of their therapy may refuse any and all interventions proposed by others, as long as their refusals do not seriously harm or impose unfair burdens upon others.[1] A competent patient's decision regarding whether or not to accept the provision of food and water by medical means such as tube feeding or intravenous alimentation is unlikely to raise questions of harm or burden to others.

What then should guide those who must decide about nutrition for a patient who cannot decide? As a start, consider the standard by which other medical decisions are made: one should decide as the incompetent person would have if he or she were competent, when that is possible to determine, and advance that person's interests in a more generalized sense when individual preferences cannot be known.

THE MEDICAL PROCEDURES

There is no reason to apply a different standard to feeding and hydration. Surely, when one inserts a feeding tube, or creates a gastrostomy opening, or inserts a needle into a vein, one intends to benefit the patient. Ideally, one should provide what the patient believes to be of benefit, but at least the effect should be beneficial in the opinions of surrogates and caregivers.

Thus, the question becomes: is it ever in the patient's interest to become malnourished and dehydrated, rather than to receive treatment? Posing the question so starkly points to our need to know what is entailed in treating these conditions and what benefits the treatments offer.

The medical interventions that provide food and fluids are of two basic types. First,

liquids can be delivered by a tube that is inserted into a functioning gastrointestinal tract, most commonly through the nose and esophagus into the stomach or through a surgical incision in the abdominal wall and directly into the stomach. The liquids used can be specially prepared solutions of nutrients or a blenderized version of an ordinary diet. The nasogastric tube is cheap; it may lead to pneumonia and often annoys the patient and family, sometimes even requiring that the patient be restrained to prevent its removal.

Creating a gastrostomy is usually a simple surgical procedure, and, once the wound is healed, care is very simple. Since it is out of sight, it is aesthetically more acceptable and restraints are needed less often. Also, the gastrostomy creates no additional risk of pneumonia. However, while elimination of a nasogastric tube requires only removing the tube, a gastrostomy is fairly permanent, and can be closed only by surgery.

The second type of medical intervention is intravenous feeding and hydration, which also has two major forms. The ordinary hospital or peripheral IV, in which fluid is delivered directly to the bloodstream through a small needle, is useful only for temporary efforts to improve hydration and electrolyte concentrations. One cannot provide a balanced diet through the veins in the limbs: to do that requires a central line, or a special catheter placed into one of the major veins in the chest. The latter procedure is much more risky and vulnerable to infections and technical errors, and it is much more costly than any of the other procedures. Both forms of intravenous nutrition and hydration commonly require restraining the patient, cause minor infections and other ill effects, and are costly, especially since they ordinarily require the patient to be in a hospital.

None of these procedures, then, is ideal; each entails some distress, some medical limitations, and some costs. When may a procedure be foregone that might improve nutrition and hydration for a given patient? Only when the procedure and the resulting improvement in nutrition and hydration do not offer the patient a net benefit over what he or she would otherwise have faced.

Are there such circumstances? We believe that there are; but they are few and limited to the following three kinds of situations: 1. The procedures that would be required are so unlikely to achieve improved nutritional and fluid levels that they could be correctly considered futile; 2. The improvement in nutritional and fluid balance, though achievable, could be of no benefit to the patient; 3. The burdens of receiving the treatment may outweigh the benefit.

WHEN FOOD AND WATER MAY BE WITHHELD

Futile Treatment. Sometimes even providing "food and water" to a patient becomes a monumental task. Consider a patient with a severe clotting deficiency and a nearly total body burn. Gaining access to the central veins is likely to cause hemorrhage or infection, nasogastric tube placement may be quite painful, and there may be no skin to which to suture the stomach for a gastrostomy tube. Or consider a patient with severe congestive heart failure who develops cancer of the stomach with a fistula that delivers foods from the stomach to the colon without passing through the intestine and being absorbed. Feeding the patient may be possible, but little is absorbed. Intravenous feeding cannot be tolerated because the fluid would be too much for the weakened heart. Or consider the infant with infarction of all but a short segment of bowel. Again, the infant can be fed, but little if anything is absorbed. Intravenous methods can be used, but only for a short time (weeks or months) until their complications, including thrombosis, hemorrhage, infections, and malnutrition, cause death.

In these circumstances, the patient is going to die soon, no matter what is done. The ineffective efforts to provide nutrition and hydration may well directly cause suffering that offers no counterbalancing benefit for the patient. Although the procedures might be tried, especially if the competent patient wanted them or the incompetent patient's surrogate had reason to believe that this incompetent patient would have wanted them, they cannot be considered obligatory. To hold that a patient must be subjected to this predictably futile sort of intervention just because protein balance is negative or the blood serum is concentrated is to lose sight of the moral warrant for medical care and to reduce the patient to an array of measurable variables.

No Possibility of Benefit. Some patients can be reliably diagnosed to have permanently lost consciousness. This unusual group of patients includes those with anencephaly, persistent vegetative state, and some preterminal comas. In these cases, it is very difficult to discern how any medical intervention can benefit or harm the patient. These patients cannot and never will be able to experience any of the events occurring in the world or in their bodies. When the diagnosis is exceedingly clear, we sustain their lives vigorously mainly for their loved ones and the community at large.

While these considerations probably indicate that continued artificial feeding is best in most cases, there may be some cases in which the family and the caregivers are convinced that artificial feeding is offensive and unreasonable. In such cases, there seems to be no adequate reason to claim that withholding food and water violates any obligations that these parties or the general society have with regard to permanently unconscious patients. Thus, if the parents of an anencephalic infant or of a patient like Karen Quinlan in a persistent vegetative state feel strongly that no medical procedures should be applied to provide nutrition and hydration, and the caregivers are willing to comply, there should be no barrier in law or public policy to thwart the plan.[2]

Disproportionate Burden. The most difficult cases are those in which normal nutritional status or fluid blance could be restored, but only with a severe burden for the patient. In these cases, the treatment is futile in a broader sense—the patient will not actually benefit from the improved nutrition and hydration. A patient who is competent can decide the relative merits of the treatment being provided, knowing the probable consequences, and weighing the merits of life under various sets of constrained circumstances. But a surrogate decision maker for a patient who is incompetent to decide will have a difficult task. When the situation is irremediably ambiguous, erring on the side of continued life and improved nutrition and hydration seems the less grievous error. But are there situations that would warrant a determination that this patient, whose nutrition and hydration could surely be improved, is not thereby well served?

Though they are rare, we believe there are such cases. The treatments entailed are not benign. Their effects are far short of ideal. Furthermore, many of the patients most likely to have inadequate food and fluid intake are also likely to suffer the most serious side effects of these therapies.

Patients who are allowed to die without artificial hydration and nutrition may well die more comfortably than patients who receive conventional amounts of intravenous hydration.[3] Terminal pulmonary edema, nausea, and mental confusion are more likely when patients have been treated to maintain fluid and nutrition until close to the time of death.

Thus, those patients whose "need" for artificial nutrition and hydration arises only near the time of death may be harmed by its provision. It is not at all clear that they receive any benefit in having a slightly prolonged life, and it does seem reasonable to allow a surrogate to decide that, for this patient at this time, slight prolongation of life is not warranted if it involves measures that will probably increase the patient's suffering as he or she dies.

Even patients who might live much longer might not be well served by artificial means to provide fluid and food. Such patients might include those with fairly severe dementia for whom the restraints required could be a constant source of fear, discomfort, and struggle. For such a patient, sedation to tolerate the feeding mechanisms might preclude any of the pleasant experiences that might otherwise have been available. Thus, a decision not to intervene, except perhaps briefly to ascertain that there are no treatable causes, might allow such a patient to live out a shorter life with fair freedom of movement and freedom from fear, while a decision to maintain artificial nutrition and hydration might consign the patient to end his or her life in unremitting anguish. If this were the case a surrogate decision maker would seem to be well justified in refusing the treatment.

INAPPROPRIATE
MORAL CONSTRAINTS

Four considerations are frequently proposed as moral constraints on foregoing medical feeding and hydration. We find none of these to dictate that artificial nutrition and hydration must always be provided.

The Obligation to Provide "Ordinary" Care. Debates about appropriate medical treatment are often couched in terms of "ordinary" and "extraordinary" means of treatment. Historically, this distinction emerged in the Roman Catholic tradition to differentiate optional treatment from treatment that was obligatory for medical professionals to offer and for patients to accept.[4] These terms also appear in many secular contexts, such as court decisions and medical codes. The recent debates about ordinary and extraordinary means of treatment have been interminable and often unfruitful, in part because of a lack of clarity about what the terms mean. Do they represent the premises of an argument or the conclusion, and what features of a situation are relevant to the categorization as "ordinary" or "extraordinary"?[5]

Several criteria have been implicit in debates about ordinary and extraordinary means of treatment; some of them may be relevant to determining whether and which treatments are obligatory and which are optional. Treatments have been distinguished according to their simplicity (simple/complex), their naturalness (natural/artificial), their customariness (usual/unusual), their invasiveness (noninvasive/invasive), their chance of success (reasonable chance/futile), their balance of benefits and burdens (proportionate/disproportionate), and their expense (inexpensive/costly). Each set of paired terms or phrases in the parentheses suggests a continuum: as the treatment moves from the first of the paired terms to the second, it is said to become less obligatory and more optional.

However, when these various criteria, widely used in discussions about medical treatment, are carefully examined, most of them are not morally relevant in distinguishing optional from obligatory medical treatments. For example, if a rare, complex, artificial, and invasive treatment offers a patient a reasonable chance of nearly painless cure, then one would have to offer a substantial justification not to provide that treatment to an incompetent patient.

What matters, then, in determining whether to provide a treatment to a competent patient is not a prior determination that this treatment is "ordinary" per se, but rather a determination that the treatment is likely to provide this patient benefits that are sufficient to make it worthwhile to endure the burdens that accompany the treatment. To this end, some of the considerations listed above are irrelevant: whether a treatment is likely to succeed is an obvious example. But such considerations taken in isolation are inconclusive. Rather, the surrogate decision maker is obliged to assess the desirability to this patient of each of the options presented, including nontreatment. For most people at most times, this assessment would lead to a clear obligation to provide food and fluids.

But sometimes, as we have indicated, providing food and fluids through medical interventions may fail to benefit and may even harm some patients. Then the treatment cannot be said to be obligatory, no matter how usual and simple its provisions may be. If "ordinary" and "extraordinary" are used to convey the conclusion about the obligation to treat, providing nutrition and fluids would have become, in these cases, "extraordinary."

Since this phrasing is misleading, it is probably better to use "proportionate" and "disproportionate," as the Vatican now suggests,[6] or "obligatory" and "optional."

Obviously, providing nutrition and hydration may sometimes be necessary to keep patients comfortable while they are dying even though it may temporarily prolong their dying. In such cases, food and fluids constitute warranted palliative care. But in other cases, such as a patient in a deep and irreversible coma, nutrition and hydration do not appear to be needed or helpful, except perhaps to comfort the state and family.[7] And sometimes the interventions needed for nutrition and hydration are so burdensome that they are harmful and best not utilized.

The Obligation to Continue Treatments Once Started. Once having started a mode of treatment, many caregivers find it very difficult to discontinue it. While this strongly felt difference between the ease of withholding a treatment and the difficulty of withdrawing it provides a psychological explanation of certain actions, it does not justify them. It sometimes even leads to a thoroughly irrational decision process. For example, in caring for a dying, comatose patient, many physicians apparently find it harder to stop a functioning peripheral IV than not to restart one that has infiltrated (that is, has broken through the blood vessel and is leaking fluid into surrounding tissue), especially if the only way to reestablish an IV would be to insert a central line into the heart or to do a cutdown (make an incision to gain access to the deep large blood vessels).[8]

What factors might make withdrawing medical treatment morally worse than withholding it? Withdrawing a treatment seems to be an action, which, when it is likely to end in death, initially seems more serious than an omission that ends in death. However, this view is fraught with errors. Withdrawing is not always an act: failing to put the next infusion into a tube could be correctly described as an omission, for example. Even when withdrawing is an act, it may well be morally correct and even morally obligatory. Discontinuing intravenous lines in a patient now permanently unconscious in accord with that patient's well-informed advance directive would certainly be such a case. Furthermore, the caregiver's obligation to serve the patient's interests through both acts and omissions rules out the exculpation that accompanies omissions in the usual course of social life. An omission that is not warranted by the patient's interests is culpable.

Sometimes initiating a treatment creates expectations in the minds of caregivers, patients, and family that the treatment will be continued indefinitely or until the patient is cured. Such expectations may provide a reason to continue the treatment as a way to keep a promise. However, as with all promises, caregivers could be very careful when initiating a treatment to explain the indications for its discontinuation, and they could modify preconceptions with continuing reevaluation and education during treatment. Though all patients are entitled to expect the continuation of care in the patient's best interests, they are not and should not be entitled to the continuation of a particular mode of care.

Accepting the distinction between withholding and withdrawing medical treatment as morally significant also has a very unfortunate implication: caregivers may become unduly reluctant to begin some treatments precisely because they fear that they will be locked into continuing treatments that are no longer of value to the patient. For example, the physician who

115

had been unwilling to stop the respirator while the infant, Andrew Stinson, died over several months is reportedly "less eager to attach babies to respirators now."[9] But if it were easier to ignore malnutrition and dehydration and to withhold treatments for these problems than to discontinue the same treatments when they have become especially burdensome and insufficiently beneficial for this patient, then the incentives would be perverse. Once a treatment has been tried, it is often much clearer whether it is of value to this patient, and the decision to stop it can be made more reliably.

The same considerations should apply to starting as to stopping a treatment, and whatever assessment warrants withholding should also warrant withdrawing.

The Obligation to Avoid Being the Unambiguous Cause of Death. Many physicians will agree with all that we have said and still refuse to allow a choice to forego food and fluid because such a course seems to be a "death sentence." In this view death seems to be more certain from malnutrition and dehydration than from foregoing other forms of medical therapy. This implies that it is acceptable to act in ways that are likely to cause death, as in not operating on a gangrenous leg, only if there remains a chance that the patient will survive. This is a comforting formulation for caregivers, to be sure, since they can thereby avoid feeling the full weight of the responsibility for the time and manner of a patient's death. However, it is not a persuasive moral argument.

First, in appropriate cases discontinuing certain medical treatments is generally accepted despite the fact that death is as certain as with nonfeeding. Dialysis in a patient without kidney function or transfusions in a patient with severe aplastic anemia are obvious examples. The dying that awaits such patients often is not greatly different from dying of dehydration and malnutrition.

Second, the certainty of a generally undesirable outcome such as death is always relevant to a decision, but it does not foreclose the possibility that this course is better than others available to this patient.[10] Ambiguity and uncertainty are so common in medical decision making that caregivers are tempted to use them in distancing themselves from direct responsibility. However, caregivers are in fact responsible for the time and manner of death for many patients. Their distaste for this fact should not constrain otherwise morally justified decisions.

The Obligation to Provide Symbolically Significant Treatment. One of the most common arguments for always providing nutrition and hydration is that it symbolizes, expresses, or conveys the essence of care and compassion. Some actions not only aim at goals, they also express values. Such expressive actions should not simply be viewed as means to ends; they should also be viewed in light of what they communicate. From this perspective food and water are not only goods that preserve life and provide comfort; they are also symbols of care and compassion. To withhold or withdraw them—to "starve" a patient—can never express or convey care.

Why is providing food and water a central symbol of care and compassion? Feeding is the first response of the community to the needs of newborns and remains a central mode of nurture and comfort. Eating is associated with social interchange and community, and providing food for someone else is a way to create and maintain bonds of sharing and expressing concern. Furthermore, even the relatively low levels of hunger and thirst that most people have experienced are decidedly uncomfortable, and the common image of severe malnutrition or dehydration is one of unremitting agony. Thus, people are rightly eager to provide food and water. Such provision is essential to minimally tolerable existence and a powerful symbol of our concern for each other.

However, *medical* nutrition and hydration, we have argued, may not always provide net benefits to patients. Medical procedures to provide nutrition and hydration are more similar to other medical procedures than to typical human ways of providing nutrition and hydration, for example, a sip of water. It should be possible to evaluate their benefits and burdens, as we evaluate any other medical procedure. Of course, if family, friends, and caregivers feel that such procedures affirm important values even when they do not benefit the patient, their feelings should not be ignored. We do not contend that there is an obligation to withhold or to withdraw such procedures (unless consideration of the patient's advance directives or current best interest unambiguously dictates that conclusion); we only contend that nutrition and hydration may be foregone in some cases.

The symbolic connection between care and nutrition or hydration adds useful caution to decision making. If decision makers worry over withholding or withdrawing medical nutrition and hydration, they may inquire more seriously into the circumstances that putatively justify their decisions. This is generally salutary for health care decision making. The critical inquiry may well yield the sad but justified conclusion that the patient will be served best by not using medical procedures to provide food and fluids. . . .

NOTES

We are grateful to Haavi Morreim and Steven DalleMura for their helpful comments on an earlier version of this paper. We are also grateful for the instruction provided Dr. Lynn by the staff and patients of The Washington Home and its Hospice.

1. See e.g., the President's Commission for the Study of Ethical Problems in Medicine and Biomedical and Behavioral Research, *Making Health Care Decisions* (Washington, D.C.: Government Printing Office, 1982).

2. President's Commission, *Deciding to Forego Life-Sustaining Treatment,* pp. 171-96.

3. Joyce V. Zerwekh, "The Dehydration Question," *Nursing83* (January 1983), 47-51, with comments by Judith R. Brown and Marion B. Dolan.

4. James J. McCartney, "The Development of the Doctrine of Ordinary and Extraordinary Means of Preserving Life in Catholic Moral Theology before the Karen Quinlan Case," *Linacre Quarterly* 47 (1980), 215ff.

5. President's Commission, *Deciding to Forego Life-Sustaining Treatment,* pp. 82-90. For an argument that fluids and electrolytes can be "extraordinary," see Carson Strong, "Can Fluids and Electrolytes be 'Extraordinary' Treatment?" *Journal of Medical Ethics* 7 (1981), 83-85.

6. The Sacred Congregation for the Doctrine of the Faith, *Declaration on Euthanasia,* Vatican City, May 5, 1980.

7. Paul Ramsey contends that "when a man is irreversibly in the process of dying, to feed him and to give him drink, to ease him and keep him comfortable—these are no longer given as means of preserving life. The use of a glucose drip should often be understood in this way. This keeps a patient who cannot swallow from feeling dehydrated and is often the only remaining 'means' by which we can express our present faithfulness to him during his dying." Ramsey, *The Patient as Person* (New Haven: Yale University Press, 1970), pp. 128-29. But Ramsey's suggestion would not apply to a patient in a deep irreversible coma, and he would be willing to disconnect the IV in the Quinlan case; see Ramsey, *Ethics at the Edges of Life: Medical and Legal Intersections* (New Haven: Yale University Press, 1978), p. 275. Bernard Towers describes an appropriate approach to comfort and dignity: "When a patient is conscious to even the smallest degree, and if he appears to be thirsty and to have a swallowing reflex, and if there is no contraindication to oral fluids, his comfort and dignity would surely demand that he be given nourishing liquids, or at least water. If he lapses into coma, good nursing practice has traditionally required sponging out the mouth and moistening the lips. Now, if he lapses into deep coma and is on a dying trajectory, would we then try to 'push' fluids by mouth or nasogastric tube? If we did, dignity would surely suffer. The 'comfort' of the patient would, of

course, be unaffected if the coma were deep enough and irreversible." Towers, "Irreversible Coma and Withdrawal of Life Support: Is It Murder If the IV Line Is Disconnected?" *Journal of Medical Ethics* 8 (1982), 205.

8. See Kenneth C. Micetich, Patricia H. Steinecker, and David C. Thomasma, "Are Intravenous Fluids Morally Required for a Dying Patient?" *Archives of Internal Medicine* 143 (May 1983), 975-78.

9. Robert and Peggy Stinson, *The Long Dying of Baby Andrew* (Boston: Little, Brown and Company, 1983), p. 355.

10. A recent article discussed a hypothetical case of maintaining a dying, comatose patient on a respirator while withdrawing IV fluids. The authors contend that this approach is not ironic because withdrawal of the respirator "creates the immediate consequence of death for which we must take responsibility. It represents an extreme form of abandonment." Nevertheless, they were willing to stop IV fluids, knowing that death would occur before long. As the article's survey reported, other physicians would have provided nutrition and fluids. See Micetich, Steinecker, and Thomasma, "Are Intravenous Fluids Morally Required for a Dying Patient?"

POSTSCRIPT

MUST FLUIDS AND NUTRITION ALWAYS BE GIVEN TO DYING PATIENTS?

On March 15, 1986, the American Medical Association's Council on Ethical and Judicial Affairs concluded that it is not unethical, under certain circumstances and with adequate safeguards, to discontinue artificial nutrition for hopelessly comatose patients. The AMA's position was cited one month later in the Florida *Corbett* case, in which the appeals court overruled a lower court ruling and said that the nasogastric tube maintaining the life of Mrs. Helen Corbett, a terminally ill 75-year-old woman, could have been removed with her husband's consent. The court stated: "We are unable to distinguish on a legal, scientific, or a moral basis between those artificial measures that sustain life—whether by means of 'forced' sustenance or 'forced' continuance of vital functions—of the vegetative, comatose patient who would soon expire without the use of those artificial means." A New Jersey court also held, in the case of Nancy Jobes, a 31-year-old woman in a persistent vegetative state, that feeding tubes could not be removed in the nursing home, if the staff disagreed, but could be removed at home.

However, the issue remains controversial. The United Handicapped Federation, a Minnesota disability rights coalition, has declared "full access to nutrition and hydration . . . to be a basic right of all persons . . . whether or not they are terminally ill." And the Florida Department of Health and Rehabilitative Services has ruled that nursing homes in that state may never discontinue tube feeding.

For an account of the *Brophy* case, see George J. Annas, "Do Feeding Tubes Have More Rights than Patients?" *Hastings Center Report,* February 1986. Annas's attack on the decision is followed by excerpts from the testimony of two moral experts at the trial—Patrick Derr in support of maintaining tube feeding, and John J. Paris opposed to it. See also the report of the President's Commission on the Study of Ethical Problems in Medicine and Biomedical and Behavioral Research, *Deciding to Forego Life-Sustaining Treatment* (Washington, D.C., 1983).

Daniel Callahan writes about the dangers of a routine policy of stopping food and nutrition in "Feeding the Dying Elderly," *Generations,* Winter 1985. Also see Dennis J. Horan and Edward R. Grant, "The Legal Aspects of Withdrawing Nourishment," *Journal of Legal Medicine* 5:4 (1984).

ISSUE 7

SHOULD PARENTS BE ALLOWED TO DECIDE TO WITHHOLD TREATMENT FROM NEWBORNS WITH BIRTH DEFECTS?

YES: Earl E. Shelp, from *Born to Die: Deciding the Fate of Critically Ill Newborns* (New York: The Free Press, 1986)

NO: C. Everett Koop, from "Ethical and Surgical Considerations in the Care of the Newborn with Congenital Abnormalities," in *Infanticide and the Handicapped Newborn,* edited by Dennis J. Horan and Melinda Delahoyde (Provo, Utah: Brigham Young University Press, 1982)

ISSUE SUMMARY

YES: Theologian Earl E. Shelp believes that parents should be the ultimate decision makers about medical treatment for severely diseased or defective newborns. They may morally choose to withhold treatment and even to bring about a merciful and aesthetic death.

NO: C. Everett Koop, a pediatric surgeon who is now Surgeon General of the United States, calls withholding treatment from newborns "infanticide" and faults the medical profession for acceding to the wishes of the families instead of protecting their patients.

The birth of a baby can be one of life's most joyous moments; but, if the baby is born with some severe defect, it can be one of its most tragic. Throughout history, the fate of abnormal babies has varied: Some societies have sanctioned killing them outright—the practice of infanticide; others have prohibited it officially, but without complete success; and some have given such infants special recognition, though often as "freaks of nature." For the most part, these birth-defective babies died, because there was little that anyone could do to correct the defects. Today, however, because of remarkable advances in medical technology and the development of a new medical specialty—neonatology, or the care of newborns—many infants who would almost certainly have died even a few decades ago can now be saved. But with this advance has come a terrible dilemma: Is it right to save a baby's life when its future is bleak or perhaps hopeless?

There are three types of cases in which the dilemma typically arises: First, some babies are born with a genetic defect—commonly known as Down's syndrome—which causes mental retardation. Some of these babies also have defects of the heart and esophagus, which must be corrected by surgery or they will die. The surgery does not affect their retardation, which may be mild or severe although this cannot be predicted at birth. Second, some babies are born with neural tube defects—that is, the spinal cord has not closed during fetal development. One form is *spina bifida,* in which there is an open lesion on the spinal column. Some cases are very severe and include mental retardation; others are quite mild. The lesion can be closed surgically; if it is not, the child is vulnerable to infections and likely to die at an early age. But the surgery does not remove the defect entirely. A third category of babies are those born prematurely; some congenital or inborn birth defect may be present, but often the babies' main problem is that their organs, particularly their lungs, are too immature to sustain life. Through aggressive measures, including mechanical respirators, even babies with a birth weight of one thousand grams (two pounds, three ounces) have a good chance of surviving, and those of 750 grams (under two pounds) can often be saved. But sometimes their condition, and the treatment itself, creates permanent problems such as neurological or learning disabilities. Some babies treated in this way cannot be weaned from the respirator and live on for months in neonatal intensive care units.

In many, perhaps most, of these cases there is no question about what to do: Parents and physicians want the babies treated to the maximum extent possible. In other cases there is also no moral problem, because there is nothing that can be done to save the baby's life. But in the difficult, in-between area—where treatment is possible but the outcome is uncertain or where the child will have a defect no matter what is done—there are sharp disagreements about what decision should be made and who should make it. All the questions about euthanasia that were raised about adults in the previous selections are present here as well, but with an added ethical dimension, since the babies are totally dependent on others to make decisions for them.

In the following selections, two clashing views emerge. Earl E. Shelp believes that parents, who will bear the burden of raising the child, should have the authority to decide whether to treat or not. The newborn, in his view, is not a "person" in a strict sense, that is, a moral agent with unqualified membership in the moral community and therefore holding certain rights. Parents can consider their own interests, as well as the infant's, in making their choice. C. Everett Koop finds this deferral to parents totally unacceptable, and describes cases in which parents have come to accept their children's handicaps. As an "ethical physician," he says, "I must come down on the side of life."

YES

Earl Shelp

DECIDING THE FATE OF CRITICALLY ILL NEWBORNS

. . . Parents of severely diseased or defective newborns may reasonably choose not to authorize life-prolonging interventions when one of several conditions obtain: (1) extended life is reasonably judged not to constitute a net benefit to the infant; (2) it is reasonably believed that the infant's condition is such that the capacities sufficient for a minimal independent existence or personhood in a strict sense cannot be attained; or (3) the costs to other persons, especially parents and family, are sufficient to defeat customary duties of beneficence toward a particular human infant.

Moral support for parental discretion in these matters is further strengthened by an understanding of human neonates as persons in a social sense, rather than as persons in a strict sense. Persons in a strict sense are moral agents, morally self-determining, unqualified members of the moral community, subjects of duties of beneficence, and bearers of rights to forebearance. Newborn human infants, normal or impaired, do not possess the properties or capacities sufficient for unqualified membership in the moral community, are not morally self-determining, or bearers of rights and duties, including those of forebearance and beneficence. Nevertheless, newborn infants can be understood as persons in a social sense because of their role in the moral order. The rights and duties they will bear when they become persons are held in trust for them and exercised in their behalf by parents, in normal circumstances, until a future time and for a future person yet to develop.

This view of parental responsibility and the moral status of newborn humans entails a commensurate understanding of parental authority. This is to say that parents are presumed to be authorities and to have authority to determine the care and nurture of their incompetent children. This authority would encompass judgments regarding the medical care of imperiled newborns that are reasonable under the circumstances and guided by relevant moral principles as interpreted by the particular moral community of which the parents are a part. These decisions warrant respect within a society that acknowledges its pluralism and protects the freedom of particular moral communities and agents to create, discover, and pursue their concrete view of the good. In these situations of reproductive tragedy, parents may conclude, on the basis of their competent understanding of the relevant medical facts, and in accord with their particular moral commitments, that death for an imperiled newborn would be a grace or otherwise morally justified. As the analysis of the alleged moral distinction between killing and letting die showed, a merciful and aesthetic death brought about by direct human intervention is as morally licit in these circumstances as standing by while the mortal process continues unhindered. The role of neonatologists and other members of the neonatal team is that of a sustaining presence, providing competent diagnoses and prognoses based on the best available medical evidence. Understood in this fashion, the neonatal medical team is free to cooperate with parental decisions to the degree that their cooperation does not violate their own moral commitments. Further, public policies that endeavor to override reasonable parental decisions in these matters are unjustified. They misperceive the proper role of the state with regard to parents and this class of infants, and the legal protections appropriate to the moral status of imperiled neonates.

These arguments support a general policy of tolerance of and respect for reasonable parental decisions regarding the treatment, nontreatment, or means of death for that class of severely diseased or defective newborns who satisfy at least one of the several conditions identified above. More specific policies are not morally justified according to the arguments provided here. Neither are they practical. The relevant circumstances of all possible cases are not predictable. Further, it would be difficult to keep them current with the ever-changing capacities of medicine to alter nature's course in these instances.

The defense of parental responsibility and authority with regard to treatment decisions for severely diseased or defective newborns provided here is not intended to disregard or disrespect the value of newborn human life. Neither have I intended to demean or ridicule moral senses and commitments different from those defended in this volume. Rather, the analyses of dilemmas in neonatology provided here are intended to place them in a moral perspective grounded in an understanding of relevant moral principles, informed by relevant research in custom, medicine, and law, and sensitive to the emotional dimensions of these tragic events.

These analyses and conclusions surely are controversial, but, in my judgment, they are defensible and superior to proposals to deprive parents of the responsibility and authority to make reasonable decisions regarding the medical care of their threatened infant. Specific counsel about what to do with very low birth weight, premature, Down syndrome, or spina bifida infants, for example, has not been provided. The burden of decisions in these cases rests properly on responsible parents who are free to make reasonable decisions consistent with their particular moral commitments. Neither has specific direction been given to medical personnel. As a sustaining presence they are enabled to sojourn with parents and newborn down a path often marked by ambivalence, uncertainty, and, perhaps paradoxically, loyalty to the good and the right as it is reasonably discerned by parents in complex and vexing circumstances. In short, the general policy advocated [here] is one that respects and defends the freedom of present moral agents, regardless of their specific role in situations of reproductive tragedy, to make reasonable decisions and to act in accord with the vision and norms of the particular moral community of which they are a part.

The moral issues and questions related to the medical treatment of imperiled newborn infants will not be settled for everyone by the positions taken [here]. Further, new dilemmas will emerge as the present limits of neonatal medicine to rescue anomalous newborns are broken. The moral question of whether we ought to do what we can do in every instance of reproductive tragedy will be asked again and again: at times for infants and conditions to which we have become accustomed, (e.g., Down syndrome with operable congenital defects); at other times, for treatments that are novel or new (e.g., cross-species transplantation of vital organs). No effort has been made to specify answers for either class of cases. Rather, as I have maintained throughout these pages, the wisdom of particular moral communities and agents are the places to turn for specific guidance. The approach

taken here is one in which freedom for moral agents is a value and a constraint upon what may be forced upon present persons without their consent. The moral visions and derived norms of particular communities that generate reasonable choices and conduct in response to complex and perplexing instances of human reproduction warrant respect in a moral pluralism where a single, compelling, concrete view of the good for a particular infant, family, community, and society is lacking. Where moral certainty is missing, where moral judgments are not universally agreed upon, where a moral pluralism is acknowledged and protected, tolerance and respect for considered differences should prevail while an analysis of vexing moral disagreements is sustained. This view holds not only for controversies in neonatology but for every area of moral decision making in which the pluralistic character of the moral community is made manifest by the disagreements that emerge. May we have the wisdom, patience, and courage to perceive the limitations of our particular moral visions and derived norms. And may we have the wisdom, patience, and courage to respect similar limitations that we perceive in the particular moral visions and derived norms of persons with whom we disagree.

NO
C. Everett Koop

ETHICAL AND SURGICAL CONSIDERATIONS IN THE CARE OF THE NEWBORN WITH CONGENITAL ABNORMALITIES

... Infanticide is the killing of a born infant by direct means or by withholding something necessary for its survival. This practice in the United States is extraordinarily important to those who are interested in the sanctity of human life because infanticide might never have come about had it not been for abortion on demand. When I read, in the months following the January 22, 1973 decision of the Supreme Court in *Roe v. Wade,* various references to Justice Blackmun's majority opinion in that case, my blood ran cold. You will remember that he considered the Hippocratic Oath which forbids abortion to be irrelevant. He spurned whatever morality he might have gleaned from the Judeo-Christian heritage of this country and turned instead to the pagan religions of Rome, of Greece, and of Persia. Although those countries practiced abortion, it was infanticide and euthanasia which were more important inhumanities in their cultures.

The second important thing to remember about infanticide is that it is euthanasia in an age group. There are many semantic differences in the English language on both sides of the Atlantic and infanticide is one of them. Infanticide in Great Britain usually means the killing of a born infant by the infant's mother. Infanticide in this country is the killing of a born infant by medical personnel in a hospital either by a direct act or much more commonly by the withholding of something necessary for the survival of that infant. Its hidden importance in reference to our concerns in the future is that I am certain the day will come when the euthanasia forces will say, "Why are you concerned about euthanasia? We have had euthanasia of infants for a long time and there has been no outcry."

The third important thing concerning infanticide is that it is being practiced by a segment of the medical profession from whom we have traditionally expected more—pediatricians and pediatric surgeons—and it is being ignored by a segment of our society from whom the victim has a right to expect more—namely, the law.

From the proceedings of the International Conference on Infanticide and Handicapped Newborns, sponsored by Americans United for Life, Legal Defense Fund, Chicago, 1980. Copyright ©1982, Americans United for Life. Reprinted by permission.

The medical profession has slipped its anchor and drifted away from the commitment which put the patient first in the recognition of the fact that he needed the help a physician could provide. This principle was rather universally understood in medicine not too long ago when morality was based on certain absolutes that the individual perceived as right or wrong. I am distressed that in an era of moral relativism, the life of a handicapped child can be forfeited to alleviate suffering in the family. If the practice of infanticide is a perversion of the former morality in medicine, that is bad enough. But if the situation is compounded by the fact that the law has turned its back as though infanticide did not exist, then we are indeed in trouble, for who knows the direction the extension of this philosophy will take next?

For almost thirty-five years now I have devoted the major part of my professional life to the management of children born with a congenital defect. I was, however, a surgeon of the skin and its contents in my early years. Therefore, my experience with congenital defects is broader than just the field that ordinarily is now called general pediatric surgery. Although in my more recent years my interests have been confined to those congenital anomalies incompatible with life but nevertheless amenable to surgical correction, there was a day when I was concerned with the management of cleft lips and palates, orthopedic defects, spina bifida and its complications, congenital heart disease, and major urologic defects.

I know what can be accomplished in the habilitation of a child born less than perfect. I know what can be done with that child's family. I know that these children become loved and loving, that they are creative, and that their entrance into a family is frequently looked back upon in subsequent years as an extraordinarily positive experience. Those who never have had the privilege of working with handicapped children who are being habilitated into our society after the correction of a congenital defect frequently tell me that such a child should be allowed to die or even encouraged to die because its life could obviously be nothing but unhappy and miserable. Yet it has been my constant experience that disability and unhappiness do not go hand in hand. The most unhappy children I have known have been completely normal. On the other hand, there is remarkable joy and happiness in the lives of most handicapped children; yet some have borne burdens that I would have indeed found very difficult to endure.

The first medical effort I know of in this country to educate the profession in the management of a defective newborn where death was one of the options in treatment is the film *Who Shall Survive?* produced by the Joseph P. Kennedy Foundation.[1] It depicts the manner in which a child with both Down's syndrome and duodenal atresia was given nothing by mouth until it expired from dehydration and starvation fifteen days later. Whatever was the intent of those who produced and financed this film, when it is seen during orientation week by new medical students across the country it is interpreted as an acceptable example of the management of a difficult problem in neonatology.

The first medical article along these lines to attract wide attention is entitled "Dilemmas of the Newborn Intensive Care Nursery," by Drs. Raymond S. Duff and A.G.M. Campbell of Yale University School of Medicine.[2] They acknowledge that over a two-year period about 14 percent of the deaths in their special care unit were those they permitted to happen because it was their considered judgment after discussion with the family that these children's lives were not worth living. It is impossible for the physician not to influence the family by innuendo alone; how much more if he counsels: "If this were my own child. . . ." The written word can never truly compete with the spoken word in matters such as this. I have to acknowledge that when I read the Duff and Campbell report, my emotions were a combination of fury and frustration. Yet, when I talk with Dr. Duff, I recognize that we have different concerns, and probably different understandings, of the ethics of the situation. My focus is on the life of the child; his is on the well-being of the family. My ethics might be said to be based on moral rules concerning absolutes of right and wrong, whereas I would suspect that his ethical principles are based more on a balance between the advantages to the patient and the disadvantages to the family.

My concerns about death as an option in the management of a handicapped newborn are centered not only on withholding treatment from the patient, but also on the implications of this form of management when extended to other children and to adults. This is because I believe in the "thin edge of the wedge" theory and in the dangers of the "slippery slope," whereas Dr. Duff does not see the slippery slope in the same light.

Drs. Duff and Campbell state in their article: "Survivors of these neonatal intensive care units may be healthy and their parents grateful, but in some instances continue to suffer from such conditions as chronic pulmonary disease, short bowel syndrome or various manifestations of brain damage. Others are severely handicapped by a myriad of congenital malformations that in previous times have resulted in death."[3] Because a newborn

child has the possibility of having dyspnea, oxygen dependence, incontinence, paralysis, a contracture, or a sexual handicap does not necessarily entitle the physician to decide that the child's life is not worth living. If we decide that this is a reason for terminating a child's life, how long will it be before the same thinking is extended to adults who already have these same signs and symptoms and might be considered candidates for some type of euthanasia program?

Drs. Duff and Campbell also state: "Often too, the parents' or siblings' rights to relief from the seemingly pointless, crushing burdens were important considerations."[4] It seems to me that this is solving a social problem by inattention to a newborn handicapped child resulting in his death. I do not think this is the proper use of medical expertise. As stated previously, society is the loser when the patient becomes the impersonal consumer and the profession is delivering a service.

When a double standard exists for the management of the newborn with a handicap, one can expect a double standard to follow for the care of the nonhandicapped newborns and for older patients as well. . . .

I have recently written the script for, acted in, and narrated several documentary films, collectively entitled *Whatever Happened to the Human Race?*, that I have undertaken with Francis A. Schaeffer, an American-born theologian-philosopher who lives in Switzerland.[5] The second of these films is on the subject of infanticide. I think one of the most compelling scenes in any of the films is one held in my living room where four of my patients born with defects incompatible with life and who were operated upon by me on the first day or two of life were assembled with four other patients who had developed lethal problems in early childhood. They were not coached in any way concerning what answer they were to give to my questions. They were told we were making some documentary movies and were writing a book on the general topic of *Whatever Happened to the Human Race?* We allowed time for them to talk with each other for about an hour in order to feel comfortable before being asked to participate in the film.

The patients at the time ranged in age from eleven to thirty-three years. One patient had been born with a number of major congenital anomalies down the midline of his body requiring, up to then, thirty-seven operative procedures for correction. Another was born without an esophagus, requiring transplantation of the colon to replace that absent organ. Still another was born with a tumor of the tongue necessitating almost total amputation of that structure in a series of operations. The fourth youngster with congenital defects was born with no rectum, no innervation of the bladder, and with major defects of the esophagus.

The other four children all had tumors. One was a benign tumor of the bones of the face, which had required a number of operations for correction and we still had not achieved perfection. The other three had cancers of the adrenal gland, of the parotid gland, and of the uterus, respectively. There can be no doubt about how such young people feel concerning the joy of living, despite the time-consuming and usually painful medical and surgical procedures they have endured to correct birth defects or situations discovered in early childhood. Here are samples of their comments:

> Because the start was a little abnormal, it doesn't mean you're going to finish that way. I'm a normal, functioning human being, capable of doing anything anybody else can.
>
> At times it got very hard, but life is certainly worth living. I married a wonderful guy and I'm just so happy.
>
> At the beginning it was a little difficult going back to school after surgery, but then things started looking up, with a little perseverance and support. I am an anesthetist and I'm happily married. Things are going great for me.
>
> I really think that all my operations and all the things I had wrong with me were worth it, because I really enjoy life and I don't really let the things that are wrong with me bother me.
>
> If anything, I think I've had an added quality to my life—an appreciation of life. I look forward to every single morning.
>
> Most of the problems are what my parents went through with the surgery. I've now been teaching high school for eight years and it's a great joy.
>
> They spend millions of dollars to send men to the moon. I think they can spend any amount necessary to save someone's life. A human life is so important because it's a gift—not something you can give, so you really don't have the right to take it either.
>
> I really don't consider myself handicapped. Life is just worth living. What else can I say?[6]

In another part of the film we talk to a young man who is now a graduate student. He was a thalidomide baby, born without a left leg and without arms below the elbows. When we asked this young man what he thought about those who say that people born with such serious birth defects should be eliminated, this, in part, was his reply.

> They don't really see that what they are talking about is murder. I know, when I was born, the first thing my dad said to my mom was that "this one needs our

love more." An individual with a handicap needs our love and needs us to help him grow into the being that God has made him to be. They are advocating that we destroy these children before they're even given a chance to live and to conquer their handicaps.

I'm very glad to be alive. I live a full, meaningful life. I have many friends and many things that I want to do in life. I think the secret of living with a handicap is realizing who you are—that you are a human being, somebody who is very special—looking at the things that you *can* do in spite of your handicap, and maybe even through your handicap.[7]

Anxious to know in my own patients what perceptions parents had years after their encounter with a surgical procedure to save a handicapped newborn's life, a study was done on thirty-one families in which I personally had operated on a child more than fifteen years before for the correction of esophageal atresia.[8] When fifty-three parents were asked what type of overall effect the situation had on the family, only two said the effect was strong and negative. Seven said the effect was mild and negative, ten said it was strong and positive, and fourteen claimed the effect was mild and positive. Eighteen parents thought there was *no* impact on the family. . . .

If any group of physicians knows what can be accomplished by surgery on the handicapped newborn—and the proper support of the patient and his family in subsequent years—it is pediatric surgeons. Drs. Anthony Shaw, Judson G. Randolph, and Barbara Manard surveyed members of the surgical section of the American Academy of Pediatrics in reference to the management of newborns with handicaps.[9] Of the 400 pediatric surgeons queried, 267 (67 percent) completed questionnaires. A separate group of 308 pediatricians completed 190 questionnaires (62 percent). The first question was, "Do you believe that the life of each and every newborn infant should be saved if it is within our ability to do so?" Eighty percent of those surgeons with my kind of background answered no.[10]

Here are some other readily remembered statistics. Seventy-six percent of the pediatric surgeons would acquiesce in the parents' decision to refuse consent for surgery in a newborn with intestinal obstruction if the infant also had Down's syndrome, or mongolism.[11] An almost unbelievable fact is that 8 percent of the surgeons (respondents) said they would acquiesce to the parents' wishes if the child had nothing other than simple intestinal atresia, the operation which is almost 100 percent successful and life after which is completely normal.[12]

To return to the infant with duodenal obstruction, which is fatal but easily correctable, and Down's syndrome, the following percentages are significant. Twenty-three percent of the pediatric surgeons group would move the parents in the direction of not signing a consent for surgery and an operative permit making it the physician's decision whether or not to let the baby die; nevertheless, if the family desired surgery the surgeon would perform it.[13] Over half of the same group said they would provide the parents with all known facts and make the decision completely the parents'. (Surely the bias of the doctor would show through.) Only 16 percent would try to persuade the parents to allow surgery but would not take them to court on refusal. Three percent would get a court order if the parents refused consent for operation.[14]

The schizophrenic nature of these replies is indicated by the fact that if they acquiesce to the parents' decision to withhold lifesaving surgery 63 percent would have stopped all supportive treatment, 30 percent would have given oral feedings which of course would be vomited immediately, but less than .05 percent would have terminated the infant's life by an injection of a drug such as morphine. . . .[15]

I practice medicine in the realm of trust between my patient's family and me. I do withhold treatment from patients under certain circumstances, but if I do, I have to know three things: an extraordinary amount about the disease process in question, an extraordinary amount about my patient, and an extraordinary amount about the relationship of my patient to the disease process in question. If I do not know all of these three, then I must, as an ethical physician, in any decision process come down on the side of life. . . .

REFERENCES

1 *Report of the Joseph P. Kennedy Foundation Int'l Symposium on Human Rights, Retardation and Research,* Oct. 16, 1971. For an extended version of the Johns Hopkins case study, *see* Gustafson, "Mongolism, Parental Desires and the Right to Life," 16 *Perspectives in Biology & Med.* 529 (1973).

2 Duff & Campbell, "Moral and Ethical Dilemmas In The Special-Care Nursery," 289 *New Eng. J. Med.* 890 (1973).

3 *Id.* at 890.

4 *Id.* at 891.

5 F. Schaeffer & C.E. Koop, *Whatever Happened to the Human Race?* (1979).

6 *Id.* at 64-65.

7 *Id.* at 65.

8 Koop et al., "The Social, Psychological and Economic Problems of the Patient's Family After Secondary Repair of Esophegeal Atresia," 17 *Kinderchirurgie* (Supp. July, 1975).

9 Shaw, Randolph, & Manard, "Ethical Issues in Pediatrics Surgery: A National Survey of Pediatricians and Pediatric Surgeons," 60 *Pediatrics* 588 (1977).

10 *Id.* at 589. Of 259 responses from pediatric surgeons, 17 percent said yes and 83 percent said no. "Because the respondents [were] not a random sample of either [pediatric surgeons or pediatricians] but represented self-selected subgroups of entire populations, the use of inferential statistics is inappropriate." *Id.*

11. *Id.* at 590. Fifty percent of the pediatricians' group responded that they would acquiesce in such a decision.

12 *Id.* at 590-91. The authors note, however, that these respondents' answers to other questions indicated that most had read the question too hastily. These physicians were not more likely than others to refuse to operate on a baby with Down's syndrome. *Id.* at 591.

13 *Id.* at 591-92.

14 *Id.* Several of those who responded checked more than one option. (The pediatric surgeons usually chose to move the parents in the direction of not signing, and also to provide the parents with information and make the decision completely theirs.)

15 *Id.* at 592-93. It is interesting to note the difference between the responses of the pediatric surgeons and the pediatricians. Generally, the pediatricians were more willing to attempt to save the infant's life.

POSTSCRIPT

SHOULD PARENTS BE ALLOWED TO DECIDE TO WITHHOLD TREATMENT FROM NEWBORNS WITH BIRTH DEFECTS?

In April 1982 a baby, known only as "Baby Doe," was born in Bloomington, Indiana, with Down's syndrome and other defects. The parents, on the physician's advice, decided not to authorize surgery for the child and to withhold nutrition as well. The case was reported to the local authorities by a concerned nurse and was brought to court, where a judge upheld the parents' decision. "Baby Doe" died after six days.

In March 1983 the Department of Health and Human Services (DHHS) issued a regulation establishing a "hotline," which people could call if they wanted to report a case of "child abuse or neglect." That rule was later declared invalid by a federal court. In October 1983, on Long Island, New York, Baby Jane Doe was born with spina bifida and other birth defects. Her parents refused surgery but agreed to other forms of treatment. DHHS sought to make the hospital where she was a patient release her records, under Section 504 of the Rehabilitation Act of 1973. The U.S. Supreme Court ruled against DHHS in June 1986 and said that the care of newborns is a matter for the states, not the federal government, to regulate. A Congressional compromise bill, enacted in 1984 and implemented by DHHS regulations in April 1985, requires state child protection agencies to set up policies to deal with potential cases of abuse.

See "Checkmating the Baby Doe Regulations," by George J. Annas (Hastings Center Report, August 1986). Helga Kuhse and Peter Singer, in *Should the Baby Live? The Problem of Handicapped Infants* (New York: Oxford, 1985) support parental decision-making authority and direct killing in some instances. For a view supporting treatment, see Paul Ramsey, *Ethics at the Edges of Life* (Yale, 1978), chapters 5-8. Also see Jeff Lyon, *Playing God in the Nursery* (New York: Norton, 1985) and Thomas Murray and Arthur Caplan, editors, *Which Babies Shall Live?* (Clifton, NJ: Humana, 1985).

ISSUE 8

CAN SUICIDE BE RATIONAL?

YES: Mary Rose Barrington, from "Apologia for Suicide," in M. Pabst Battin and David J. Mayo, editors, *Suicide: The Philosophical Issues* (New York: St. Martins Press, 1980)

NO: Herbert Hendin, M.D., from "The Right to Suicide," in *Suicide in America* (New York: W.W. Norton & Company, 1982)

ISSUE SUMMARY

YES: Mary Rose Barrington, a British solicitor (attorney), argues that humane and advanced societies must embrace the notion of "rational suicide" in a world that is increasingly crowded and populated by the aged, who would prefer a "planned death" to a long wait to be "arbitrarily extinguished."
NO: Psychiatrist Herbert Hendin emphasizes that suicide is a pathological response to life's problems and that instead of intellectual attempts to rationalize or glorify suicide, we need efforts to improve our lives together.

Suicide in literature and history has a romantic and even mythic quality: Consider Romeo, who could not live without his Juliet; the altruistic suicide in 1912 of Captain Oates, who walked out to his death in the Antarctic snow in an attempt to help Robert Scott and his other doomed companions; and the suicides of members of the French Resistance who chose death rather than reveal the names of their comrades under Nazi torture. Even the suicide in 1963 of Sylvia Plath, the young American poet who put her head in a gas oven (fully expecting, it now appears, to be rescued at the last minute), has been idealized. Many famous suicides—Marilyn Monroe, for example—have become legendary.

The realities of suicide, however, are more mundane. Although much of the discussion focuses on the terminally ill, very few dying people actually kill themselves. Suicide rates vary from country to country, but around the world suicide is among the first five causes of death for white males from ten to fifty-five years of age, and the second cause of death for white males from the ages of fifteen to nineteen (accidental death is first). In this country, the suicide rate among women and among young people is increasing, and it is highest of all among young black men. Those who are most likely to succeed in suicide attempts are older men who are divorced, widowed, or single; who abuse alcohol or drugs; or who are physically or mentally ill.

Suicide has been known since primitive times; however, the word did not appear until the seventeenth century. Until then it was known as "self-homicide" or "self-murder." The idea that taking one's own life can be a moral choice has a mixed history. It has been both approved and condemned, glorified and vilified. Early peoples generally had a horror of suicide, believing that the ghost of the suicide would return. The Athenians buried suicides outside the city and away from other graves, with the hand that did the self-murdering buried apart. Neither the Old Testament nor the New Testament directly prohibit suicide, and early Christianity was marked by a penchant for suicide and martyrdom. But by the sixth century, Christian theologians legislated against it, spurred on by St. Augustine's conviction that because each soul is immortal, each life is equally valuable. To reject life is to reject the gift of God, he said. St. Thomas Aquinas declared that not only was suicide a violation of a duty to God but it also violated the natural law and harmed the community. Kant argued on philosophical grounds that suicide degrades the worth of human life and is always immoral. By the eighteenth century, suicide had been made illegal in most European countries. Suicide continues to be considered a sin by the Catholic Church and a crime in many places.

But the opposing view also has deep roots. In Plato's *Phaedo* (the account of the trial and death of Socrates), Socrates declares that there are times when a person would be better off dead. Socrates chose to drink the hemlock fixed as the method of execution by the Athenian court; he, in some sense, committed suicide. In the first century A.D., the Roman philosopher Seneca wrote: "The wise man will live as long as he ought, not as long as he can." The nineteenth-century Scottish philosopher David Hume provided a more modern justification for suicide. He found that it involved no "transgression of our duty either to God, our neighbor, or ourselves." Perhaps the most persuasive contemporary philosopher who argues that suicide can be moral is Richard B. Brandt. He says: "The most that the moral critic of suicide could hold, then, is that there is *some* moral obligation not to do what one knows will cause one's death; but he surely cannot deny that circumstances exist in which there are obligations to do things which, in fact, will result in one's death."

The contemporary debate focuses not so much on whether people have a right to suicide but on whether it is rational—that is, the most sensible choice to make in a given situation. If it is not rational, then it should be prevented. Mary Rose Barrington believes that our current crisis of overpopulation and an aging society makes suicide a rational choice for the elderly. "To insist on the obligation of old people to live through a period of decline and helplessness," she says, "seems to me to be lacking in a feeling for the demands of human *self*-respect." Arguing against this position and also against the other claims that suicide is rational, Herbert Hendin presents clinical evidence that potential suicides are disturbed people who need help rather than approval.

YES   Mary Rose Barrington

APOLOGIA FOR SUICIDE

Of the many disagreeable features inherent in the human condition, none is more unpalatable than mortality. Many people declare that they find the concept of survival and immortal life both inconceivable and preposterous; but they will usually admit to a minimal pang at the thought of being snuffed out in due course and playing no further part in the aeons to come. That aeons have already passed before they were born is a matter that few people take to heart, and they tend on the whole to be rather glad not to have experienced the hardships of life before the era of the Public Health Acts and pain-killing drugs. To cease from being after having once existed seems altogether different and altogether terrible. This is an odd conclusion, bearing in mind that whereas before birth one must be reckoned to have had no effect on the course of events at all, the very act of birth and the shortest of lives may produce incalculable and possibly cataclysmic effects by indirect causation. Viewed in this light we might all be filled with satisfaction to think that our every move will send ripples of effects cascading down time. In fact, speculations of this kind do little if anything to satisfy the immortal longings, and even though being remembered kindly by others is generally felt to be something of a comfort, absolute death remains absolutely appalling. Many people who have no religious convictions save themselves from despair by filing away in their minds some small outside chance that they might, after all, survive, perhaps as some semi-anonymous cog in a universal system; many others resolutely refuse to give any thought to death at all.

If human convictions and behavior were a direct function of logical thinking, one would expect that the more firmly a person believed in the survival of his soul in an existence unhampered by the frequently ailing body, the more ready he would be to leave this world and pass on to the next. Nothing of the sort appears to be the case, at least for those whose religion is based on the Old Testament. Self-preservation is presented in such religions as a duty, though one that is limited by some inconsistent provisos. Thus a person may sacrifice his life to save others in war, or he may die a martyr's death in a just cause; but if he were to reason that there was not enough food in the family to go round, and therefore killed himself to save the others from starvation (a fate, like many others, considerably worse than death), this would be regarded as the sin, and erstwhile crime, of suicide. Whether performed for his own benefit or to benefit others, the act of suicide would be condemned as equivalent to breaking out from prison before the expiry of the term fixed, a term for which there can be no remission.

The old notions about suicide, with an influence still lingering on, are well summarized by Sir William Blackstone in his famous *Commentaries on the Laws of England* (1765-9): "The suicide is guilty of a double offence: one spiritual, in invading the prerogative of the Almighty and rushing into his immediate presence uncalled for; the other temporal, against the King, who hath an interest in the preservation of all his subjects."[1]

Religious opposition to suicide is of decreasing importance as people become ever more detached from dogmas and revelationary teachings about right and wrong. The important matter to be considered is that while the humanist, the agnostic or the adherent of liberal religion seldom condemns suicide as a moral obliquity, he appears on the whole to find it as depressing and horrifying as the religious believer for whom it is sinful. There are many reasons for this, some good, and some regrettable.

Indoctrination against suicide is regrettably to be found at all levels. In itself the tendentious expression "to commit suicide" is calculated to poison the unsuspecting mind with its false semantic overtones, for, apart from the dangerous practice of committing oneself to an opinion, most other things committed are, as suicide once was, criminal offences.[2] People are further influenced by the unhappy shadow cast over the image of suicide by the wide press coverage given to reports of suicide by students who are worried about their examinations, or girls who are upset over a love affair, or middle-aged people living alone in bedsitting-rooms who kill themselves out of depression—troubles that might all have been surmounted, given time. In pathetic cases such as these, it is not, as it seems to me, the act of suicide that is horrifying, but the extreme unhappiness that must be presumed to have induced it. Death from despair is the thing that ought to make us shudder, but the shudder is often extended to revulsion against the act of suicide that terminates the despair, an act that may be undertaken in very different circumstances.

The root cause of the widespread aversion to suicide is almost certainly death itself rather than dislike of the means by which death is brought about. The leaf turns a mindless face to the sun for one summer before falling for ever into the mud; death, however it comes to pass, rubs our clever faces in the same mud, where we too join the leaves. The inconceivability of this transformation in status is partly shot through with an indirect illumination, due to the death of others. Yet bereavement is not death. Here to mourn, we are still here, and the imagination boggles at the notion that things could ever be otherwise. Not only does the imagination boggle, as to some extent it must, but the mind unfortunately averts. The averted mind acknowledges, in a theoretical way, that death does indeed happen to people here and there and now and then, but to some extent the attitude to death resembles the attitude of the heavy smoker to lung cancer; he reckons that if he is lucky it will not happen to *him*, at least not yet, and perhaps not ever. This confused sort of faith in the immortality of the body must underlie many a triumphal call from the hospital ward or theatre, that the patient's life has been saved—and he will therefore die next week instead of this week, and in rather greater discomfort. People who insist that life must always be better than death often sound as if they are choosing eternal life in contrast to eternal death, when the fact is that they have no choice in the matter; it is death now, or death later. Once this fact is fully grasped it is possible for the question to arise as to whether death now would not be preferable.

Opponents of suicide will sometimes throw dust in the eyes of the uncommitted by asking at some point why one should ever choose to go on living if one once questions the value of life; for as we all know, adversity is usually round the corner, if not at our heels. Here, it seems to me, a special case must be made out for people suffering from the sort of adversity with which the proponents of euthanasia are concerned: namely, an apparently irremediable state of physical debility that makes life unbearable to the sufferer. Some adversities come and go; in the words of the Anglo-Saxon poet reviewing all the disasters known to Norse mythology, "That passed away, so may this." Some things that do not pass away include inoperable cancers in the region of the throat that choke their victims slowly to death. Not only do they not pass away, but like many extremely unpleasant conditions they cannot be alleviated by pain-killing drugs. Pain itself can be controlled,

provided the doctor in charge is prepared to put the relief of pain before the prolongation of life; but analgesics will not help a patient to live with total incontinence, reduced to the status of a helpless baby after a life of independent adulthood. And for the person who manages to avoid these grave afflictions there remains the spectre of senile decay, a physical and mental crumbling into a travesty of the normal person. Could anything be more reasonable than for a person faced with these living deaths to weigh up the pros and cons of living out his life until his heart finally fails, and going instead to meet death half-way?

It is true, of course, that, all things being equal, people do want to go on living. If we are enjoying life, there seems no obvious reason to stop doing so and be mourned by our families and forgotten by our friends. If we are not enjoying it, then it seems a miserable end to die in a trough of depression, and better to wait for things to become more favourable. Most people, moreover, have a moral obligation to continue living, owed to their parents while they are still alive, their children while they are dependent, and their spouses all the time. Trained professional workers may even feel that they have a duty to society to continue giving their services. Whatever the grounds, it is both natural and reasonable that without some special cause nobody ever wants to die yet. But must these truisms be taken to embody the whole truth about the attitude of thinking people to life and death? A psychiatrist has been quoted as saying: "I don't think you can consider anyone normal who tries to take his own life."[3] The abnormality of the suicide is taken for granted, and the possibility that he might have been doing something sensible (for him) is not presented to the mind for even momentary consideration. It might as well be argued that no one can be considered normal who does not want to procreate as many children as possible, and this was no doubt urged by the wise men of yesterday; today the tune is very different, and in this essay we are concerned with what they may be singing tomorrow.

There is an obvious connection between attitudes to birth and to death, since both are the fundamentals of life. The experience of this century has shown that what may have appeared to be ineradicably basic instincts can in fact be modified in an advanced society, and modified not merely by external pressures, but by corresponding feedback movement from within. Primitive people in general take pride in generating large families, apparently feeling in some deep-seated way that motherhood proves the femaleness of the female, and that fatherhood proves the maleness of the male, and that the position in either case is worth proving very amply. This simple pride is not unknown in advanced countries, although public applause for feats of childbearing is at last beginning to freeze on the fingertips, and a faint rumble of social disapproval may be heard by an ear kept close to the ground. The interesting thing is that it is not purely financial considerations that have forced people into limiting their progeny, and least of all is it the public weal; people have actually come to prefer it. Women want to lead lives otherwise than as mothers; men no longer feel themselves obliged to assert their virility by pointing to numerous living tokens around them; and most parents prefer to concentrate attention and affection upon a couple rather than a pack. The modification in this apparently basic drive to large-scale procreation is now embraced

not with reluctance, but with enthusiasm. My thesis is that humane and advanced societies are ripe for a similar and in many ways equivalent swing away from the ideal of longevity to the concept of a planned death.

It may be worth pausing here to consider whether the words "natural end," in the sense usually ascribed to the term, have much bearing on reality. Very little is "natural" about our present-day existence, and least natural of all is the prolonged period of dying that is suffered by so many incurable patients solicitously kept alive to be killed by their disease. The sufferings of animals (other than man) are heart-rending enough, but a dying process spread over weeks, months or years seems to be one form of suffering that animals are normally spared. When severe illness strikes them they tend to stop eating, sleep and die. The whole weight of Western society forces attention on the natural right to live, but throws a blanket of silence over the natural right to die. If I seem to be suggesting that in a civilized society suicide ought to be considered a quite proper way for a well-brought-up person to end his life (unless he has the good luck to die suddenly and without warning), that is indeed the tenor of my argument; if it is received with astonishment and incredulity, the reader is referred to the reception of recommendations made earlier in the century that birth control should be practised and encouraged. The idea is no more extraordinary, and would be equally calculated to diminish the sum total of suffering among humankind.

This will probably be taken as, or distorted into, a demand for the infliction of the death penalty on retirement. And yet the bell tolls for me no less than for others. Apart from the possibility that he may

137

actually have some sympathy for the aged, no one casting a fearful eye forward into the future is likely to advocate treatment of the old that he would not care to see applied to himself, lest he be hoist with his own petard. It cannot be said too many times that so long as people are blessed with reasonable health, reasonable independence and reasonable enjoyment of life, they have no more reason to contemplate suicide than people who are half their age, and frequently half as sprightly as many in their seventies and eighties today. Attention is here being drawn to people who unfortunately have good reason to question whether or not they want to exercise their right to live; the minor infirmities of age, and relative weakness, and a slight degree of dependence on younger people who regard the giving of a helping hand as a natural part of the life-cycle, do not give rise to any such question. The question arises when life becomes a burden rather than a pleasure.

Many middle-aged people are heard to express the fervent wish that they will not live to be pain-ridden cripples, deaf, dim-sighted or feeble-minded solitaries, such that they may become little else than a burden to themselves and to others. They say they *hope* they will die before any of these fates descend upon them, but they seldom affirm that they *intend* to die before that time; and when the time comes, it may barely cross their minds that they could, had they then the determination, take the matter into their own hands. The facile retort will often be that this merely goes to show that people do not really mean what they say and that like all normal, sensible folk, they really want to live on for as long as is physically possible. But this, I would suggest, is a false conclusion. They mean exactly what they say,

but the conditions and conditioning of society make it impossible for them to act in accordance with their wishes. To face the dark reality that the future holds nothing further in the way of joy or meaningful experience, and to face the fact without making some desperate and false reservation, to take the ultimate decision and act upon it knowing that it is a gesture that can never be repeated, such clearsightedness and resolution demand a high degree of moral strength that cannot but be undermined by the knowledge that this final act of self-discipline would be the subject of headshakings, moralizings and general tut-tutting.

How different it would be if a person could talk over the future with his family, friends and doctors, make arrangements, say farewells, take stock of his life, and know that his decision about when and how to end his life was a matter that could be the subject of constructive and sympathetic conference, and even that he could have his chosen ones around him at the last. As things are at present, he would always be met with well-meant cries of "No, no, you mustn't talk like that," and indeed anyone taking a different line might feel willy-nilly that his complicity must appear unnatural and lacking in affection. We feel that we *ought* to become irrational at the idea that someone we care for is contemplating ending his own life, and only the immediate spectacle of intense suffering can shock us out of a conditioned response to this situation. The melancholy result is that a decision that cries out for moral support has to be taken in cheerless isolation, and if taken at all is usually deferred until the victim is in an advanced state of misery.

But supposing the person contemplating suicide is not in fact undergoing or expecting to undergo severe suffering, but is merely an elderly relation, probably a mother, in fragile health, or partially disabled, and though not acutely ill is in need of constant care and attention. It would be unrealistic to deny the oppressive burden that is very often cast on the shoulders of a young to middle-aged person, probably a daughter, by the existence of an ailing parent, who may take her from her career when she is a young woman in her thirties or forties, and leave her, perhaps a quarter of a century later, an elderly, exhausted woman, demoralized over the years by frequently having had to choke back the wish that her mother would release her by dying. Even in a case such as this, human feeling does demand, I would think, that the younger person must still respond to intimations of suicide with a genuinely felt, "No, no."

But what of the older person's own attitude? Here we arrive at the kernel of the violent and almost panic-stricken reaction of many people to the idea of questioning whether it is better, in any given situation, to be or not to be. For if there is no alternative to continued living, then no choice arises, and hence there can be no possibility of an older person, who is a burden to a younger person, feeling a sense of obligation to release the captive attendant from willing or unwilling bondage, no questioning of the inevitability of the older person's living out her full term. But what if there were a real choice? What if a time came when, no longer able to look after oneself, the decision to live on for the maximum number of years were considered a mark of heedless egoism? What if it were to be thought that *dulce et decorum est pro familia mori*? This is a possibility that makes many people shrink from the subject, because they find the prospect too frightful to contemplate. Is it (to be charitable) because they always think themselves into the position of the younger person, so that "No, no" rises naturally to their lips, or is it (to be uncharitable) because they cannot imagine themselves making a free sacrifice of this sort?

This very controversial issue is, it may be remarked, outside the scope of voluntary euthanasia, which is concerned exclusively with cases where a patient is a burden to *himself*, and whether or not he is a burden to others plays no part whatever. The essence of voluntary euthanasia is the co-operation of the doctor in making crucial decisions; the "burden to others," on the contrary, must make all decisions and take all responsibility himself for any actions he might take. The issue cannot, however, be ignored, because the preoccupation of many opponents of voluntary euthanasia with its supposed implications, suggests that few people have any serious objection to the voluntary termination of a gravely afflicted life. This principal theme is usually brushed aside with surprising haste, and opponents pass swiftly on to the supposed evils that would flow from making twilight existence optional rather than obligatory. It is frequently said that hard-hearted people would be encouraged to make their elderly relatives feel that they had outlived their welcome and ought to remove themselves, even if they happened to be enjoying life. No one can say categorically that nothing of the sort would happen, but the sensibility of even hard-hearted people to the possible consequences of their own unkindness seems just as likely. A relation who had stood down from life in a spirit of magnanimity and family affection would, after an inevitable period of heart-searching and self-recrimination, leave behind a pleasant memory; a victim of callous treatment hanging like an accusing albatross around the neck of the living would suggest another and rather ugly story. Needless to say, whoever was responsible would not in any event be the sort of person to show consideration to an aged person in decline.

Whether or not some undesirable fringe results would stem from a free acceptance of suicide in our society, the problem of three or four contemporaneous generations peopling a world that hitherto has had to support only two or three is with us here and now, and will be neither generated nor exacerbated by a fresh attitude to life and death. The disabled, aged parent, loved or unloved, abnegating or demanding, is placed in one of the tragic dilemmas inherent in human existence, and one that becomes more acute as standards of living rise. One more in the mud-hut is not a problem in the same way as one more in a small, overcrowded urban dwelling; and the British temperament demands a privacy incompatible with the more sociable Mediterranean custom of packing a grandmother and an aunt or two in the attic. Mere existence presents a mild problem; disabled existence presents a chronic problem. The old person may have no talent for being a patient, and the young one may find it intolerable to be a nurse. A physical decline threatens to be accompanied by an inevitable decline in the quality of important human relationships—human relationships, it is worth repeating, not superhuman ones. Given superhuman love, patience, fortitude and all other sweet-natured qualities in a plenitude not normally present in ordinary people, there would be no problem. But the problem is there, and voluntary termination of life offers a possible solution that may be better than none at all. The young have been urged from time immemorial to have valiant hearts, to lay down their lives for their loved ones when their lives have hardly started; it may be that in time to come the disabled aged will be glad to live in a society that approves an honourable death met willingly, perhaps in the company of another "old soldier" of the same generation, and with justifiable pride. Death taken in one's own time, and with a sense of purpose, may in fact be far more bearable than the process of waiting to be arbitrarily extinguished.[4] A patient near the end of his life who arranged his death so as, for example, to permit an immediate transfer of a vital organ to a younger person, might well feel that he was converting his death into a creative act instead of waiting passively to be suppressed.

A lot of kindly people may feel that this is lacking in respect for the honourable estate of old age; but to insist on the obligation of old people to live through a period of decline and helplessness seems to me to be lacking in a feeling for the demands of human *self*-respect. They may reply that this shows a false notion of what constitutes self-respect, and that great spiritual qualities may be brought out by dependence and infirmity, and the response to such a state. It is tempting in a world dominated by suffering to find all misery purposeful, and indeed in some situations the "cross-to-bear" and the willing bearer may feel that they are contributing a poignant note to some cosmic symphony that is richer for their patience and self-sacrifice. Since we are talking of options and not of compulsions, people who felt like this would no doubt continue to play their chosen parts; but what a truly ruthless thing to impose those parts on people who feel that they are meaningless and discordant, and better written out....

NOTES

1   Sir William Blackstone, *Commentaries on the Laws of England,* 18th edition, ed. Arthur Ryland (London: Sweet, Pheney, Maxwell, Stevens & Sons, 1829), Vol. IV, p. 189.
2   Professor Flew points out the greater virtues of the French *"se suicider."* See Antony Flew, "The Principle of Euthanasia," in A.B. Downing, ed., *Euthanasia and the Right to Death* (London: Peter Owen, 1969), p. 46, n. 13. We should perhaps be grateful not to be burdened with an expression like the German *"Selbstmord,"* i.e., "self-murder."
3   Reported in *The Observer* (June 26, 1967).
4   It will be noted that reference is made here in all cases to the aged. In a longer exposition I would argue that very different considerations apply to the young disabled who have not yet enjoyed a full life span, and who should be given far greater public assistance to enable them to enjoy life as best they can.

NO   Herbert Hendin

THE RIGHT TO SUICIDE

Partly as a response to the failure of suicide prevention, partly in reaction to commitment abuses, and perhaps mainly in the spirit of accepting anything that does not physically harm anyone else, we see suicide increasingly advocated as a fundamental human right. Many such advocates deplore all attempts to prevent suicide as an interference with that right. It is a position succinctly expressed by Nietzsche when he wrote, "There is a certain right by which we may deprive a man of life, but none by which we may deprive him of death."[1] Taken from its social and psychological context, suicide is regarded by some purely as an issue of personal freedom.

The psychiatrist Thomas Szasz has been an articulate contemporary spokesman for this point of view.[2] Szasz believes we rationalize an oppressive policy toward deviations like suicide and drug abuse by calling them illnesses and use psychiatrists and psychologists as enforcers of that policy. While not advocating drug use, Szasz believes that "dangerous drugs, addicts and pushers are the scapegoats of our modern, secular, therapeutically imbued societies," and that "the ritual persecution of these pharmacological and human agents must be seen against the historical backdrop of the ritual persecution of other scapegoats, such as witches, Jews, and madmen."[3] Of suicide prevention, Szasz writes, "He who does not accept and respect those who want to reject life does not truly accept and respect life itself." Causing one's own death, Szasz goes on, "should be called 'suicide' only by those who disapprove of it; and should be called 'death control' by those who approve of it."[4]

The often transient and ambivalent quality of the impulse to commit suicide is not recognized by Szasz, who believes that successful suicides intend to die and that unsuccessful ones do not. Here the clinical evidence contradicts him. Ambivalence toward suicide is indicated by the fact that three-fourths of all suicides communicate their intentions, often with the hope that something will be done to make their suicide unnecessary. In a high proportion of cases, such

Reprinted from *Suicide in America* by Herbert Hendin, M.D., by permission of the author and W.W. Norton & Company, Inc. Copyright ©1982 by Herbert Hendin.

communications are varied, repeated, and expressed to more than one individual. Studies of those who have survived serious suicide attempts have revealed that a fantasy of being rescued is frequently present.

What has misled Szasz and the clinicians who make a rigid separation between those who survive suicide attempts and those who do not is the evidence that many so-called attempted suicides are not even ambivalent about suicide—they clearly want to live. This in no way contradicts the clinical evidence that a large number of those who kill themselves are ambivalent in the sense that they do something irrevocable in a state of uncertainty.

Many people have speculated that if you could talk to someone who was in midair after jumping from a tall tower, you might find out that he no longer was so sure he wanted to die. Over the past thirty years I have seen four people who survived six-story suicide jumps. Two wished to survive as soon as they had jumped, two said they did not, but one of the latter two who professed to be furious at having survived made no subsequent suicide attempts.

Moreover, in a majority of cases, we do not know at once how serious the individual is about suicide. It is estimated that only one out of ten suicide attempts results in death, a figure that tends to confirm the view that suicidal individuals are not unambivalently intent on dying. Similarly, studies of the subsequent mortality rates of survivors show that only about 1 percent of all survivors kill themselves within one year. If for no other reason than the persuasive evidence of ambivalence surrounding suicide, some intervention—even if it is very short-term and narrowly circumscribed—seems clearly warranted and desirable.

Most suicidal patients who come to hospitals do so as a consequence of in-

juries sustained in their suicide attempts. Are we to refuse treatment for such injuries out of respect for the patient's suicidal intent? Most of these patients recovering from their injuries in hospitals have not asked for help; some will accept it and others will reject it when it is offered. Should we not even offer it unless the patient explicitly requests it? Few who argue for the "right to suicide" are likely to make the same argument with regard to a suicidal child or adolescent.

Szasz claims that man's inhumanity, demonstrable in such practices as slavery in the United States and totalitarianism in the Soviet Union and in Nazi Germany, refutes the contention that we value everyone's life or the suicide's life more than he does. Presumably we should recognize that we are intrinsically evil and cease to try or pretend to try to be otherwise.

Szasz, who is passionately eloquent in defending the right to suicide and the right to use or sell drugs, seems to show little sympathy for the desperately wretched lives of drug abusers and of those who would kill themselves. His position would be more understandable if his legitimate concerns about social and medical coercion were accompanied by a corresponding concern for the plight of those whose lives are self-destructively out of control, many of whom want help. As it is, Szasz invites a policy of indifference to them. His argument that social help undermines individual autonomy has been used in the past to justify opposition to every form of social reform.

Szasz makes no claim, however, that society should help, support, or encourage the suicide in his efforts to kill himself. He believes that it would be sufficient if society recognized that it had no right to interfere. But those arguing for "the right to suicide" go further. Many supporters of euthanasia see suicide in a social context, believe that context makes evident the social utility of suicidal death, and want social support, encouragement, and even help in carrying out suicide.

Much of the argument for suicide focuses on the elderly. The increasing number of old people, the inadequate care provided by nursing homes, and the economic cost to both families and society of caring for the infirm elderly are used to support the view that suicide must be accepted, encouraged, and protected. Mary Rose Barrington, a solicitor of the Supreme Court of the Judicature of England and a past chairperson of the Voluntary Euthanasia Society, tells us that "the problem of three or four contemporary generations peopling a world that heretofore has had to support only two or three is with us here and now."[5] What a sad commentary on us and our culture it would be if our response to the social changes required by the increasing number of the elderly were to be euthanasia.

Many of those who once advocated euthanasia for elderly, infirm suffering patients have broadened their position to include the right to suicide for everyone. Reflecting this change, the British Voluntary Euthanasia Society is now called EXIT.

Barrington and Eliot Slater, an English psychiatrist and advocate of euthanasia, include chronic illness—regardless of what age—as a justification for suicide. Slater tells us, "If a chronically sick man dies, he ceases to be a burden on himself, on his family, on the health services and on the community. If we can do nothing to get a patient better, but do our best to retard the process of dying—extend it perhaps over months and years—we are adding to the totality of ill health and incapacity. To take an obvious example, transplant surgery, in providing a spare set for people who have run through the pair of kidneys, liver and heart, increases the number of people in the community who at one time are suffering from diseases of the kidneys, liver and heart. There is, of course, absolutely no limit to the burdens we can go on piling up, by trying to keep badly damaged individuals alive."[6] Such social Darwinism, if carried to a logical conclusion, would force us to cease our efforts to help and perhaps to encourage the suicide of all who are disabled, chronically ill, or handicapped.

Barrington tells us that, unlike people, animals when struck by severe illness have the good sense to stop eating and die. Actually, some human beings do so too; they are usually people whose spirit has been so crushed by life that they offer little resistance to illness. Some primitive cultures, such as that of Alor, demonstrated a cultural tendency toward such a response, but Alor was a society that crushed the adaptive capacity of most of its inhabitants. We need not believe that suffering is good for the character in order to understand that the capacity to deal with adversity, including illness, is one of the features of psychosocial stability. . . .

We need not argue the issue of whether it is rational for an individual with a painful terminal illness to refuse extraordinary life-saving measures or to arrange more actively to end his life. Most would agree it is, and that is precisely why supporters of the "right to suicide" or "death control" position are constantly presenting the case of a patient suffering from incurable, painful cancer as the case on which they based their argument. In reality, however, such understandable cases form only a small percentage of all suicides, or potential suicides. The majority of suicides confront us with the problem of understanding people whose situation does not seem, from an outsider's viewpoint, hopeless or often even critical. The knowledge that there are more suicides by people who wrongly believe themselves to be suffering from cancer than there are suicides by those who actually have cancer puts the problem in some perspective.

Such advocates of the "right to suicide" as Barrington and Slater think our opposition to suicide is based on our fear of accepting and dealing with death. They wish to raise our consciousness on the matter. Barrington, for example, writes, "People who insist that life must always be better than death often sound as if they are choosing eternal life in contrast to eternal death, when the fact is that they have no choice in the matter; it is death now, or death later. Once this fact is fully grasped it is possible for the question to arise as to whether death now would not be preferable." She also believes that consciousness is best raised early, and she suggests that children be encouraged to write compositions "envisaging why and in what circumstances they propose to end their lives."[7]

The "right to suicide" advocates propose for all of us a heightened consciousness about death, a consciousness that is in fact intrinsic to the adaptation of suicidal individuals. The person facing imminent death who is in intractable pain and arranges to end his life may be a suicide in the dictionary definition of the term, but not in the psychological sense. The suicide is more apt to be someone for whom death must be imminent when it is not, for whom death is a necessary part of his or her adaptation to life, and for whom the possibility of self-inflicted death may make life more bearable.

Potentially suicidal people make death the center of their existence. As the poet Anne Sexton, who went on to kill herself, put it, "talking death" is "life" for suicides.[8] They are often people who take continued comfort from the fact that if things get too bad they can or will end their lives. In dealing with the preoccupation with death, they are concerned with how and when death can be implemented; some find comfort in persuading others to join them in their preoccupation. A recent psychiatric report of a small "epidemic" of suicide and suicide attempts on a college campus was traced to one young man who had dealt with his own preoccupation with suicide by involving others in what amounted to a suicide club.[9] A constructive effort to deal with a similar preoccupation with death was made by a professional woman I saw who was absorbed with killing herself and had made one almost fatal attempt, while making a second career for herself as a volunteer worker in a suicide prevention center. In trying to persuade others to stay alive, she was trying to persuade herself.

Albert Camus states at the opening of *The Myth of Sisyphus,* "There is but one truly serious philosophical problem, and that is suicide. Judging whether life is or is not worth living amounts to answering the fundamental question of philosophy."[10] This statement, quoted approvingly in books and articles on suicide, echoes the "Is life worth living?" question posed in a famous essay on suicide by William James, who was evidently seriously suicidal for a significant period in his life.[11] The young [man] who spent his high school years making lists of reasons why he should keep living reflects in a less sophisticated manner the problem with which James and Camus were wrestling. Both James and Camus ultimately affirm the value of life, but whether or not to end one's life is not the central question for most people.

Individuals who spend years planning

their death are suicidal. Such persons may wait for the first sign of serious illness associated with age to kill themselves, but they have been suicidal for a long time. Yet in the current climate such people are sometimes regarded as an avant-garde who can guide us in matters of life and death.

A good example is provided in the well-publicized case of Jo Roman, a Manhattan artist and former social worker. After years of advocating choosing the time of one's own death, she called her friends in to say good-bye, arranged to have the group's conversation videotaped, then spent the evening with her husband and a close friend before taking a fatal overdose of pills. She was 62 and had been diagnosed as having a breast tumor that would have been treatable by mastectomy, but she did not wish to have that done. In a letter that she requested be sent to *The New York Times* following her suicide, she said that she was carrying out her suicide "more than a decade earlier than she had planned." She explained that before the cancer was diagnosed fourteen months earlier, she had planned to end her life around 1992, when she would have been 75. Her video-tapes on her advocacy of "self-termination" were subsequently shown in an educational television documentary. The *Times* reporter accepted the story very much at face value, depicting her as a pioneer.[12]

A somewhat comparable story had been written for the magazine section of the same newspaper the year before by a man who had decided to kill himself if he was told that a colostomy would be necessary to save him from a rectal cancer. He, too, was determined not to accept a mutilating procedure and felt he would rather die than do so. Both individuals believed their decisions were not simply private matters but examples that they hoped would help to change social attitudes.

Although mastectomies and colostomies are traumatic procedures for anyone to undergo, the majority of people who need them fortunately do choose to live, and their commitments to life and to other people are such that most of them make satisfactory adjustments. It would be sadly preposterous if the attitude that people who need such surgical procedures should choose death instead were to become prevalent.

A related illustration is provided by a vigorous, handsome doctor of 52 who killed himself after a minor heart attack. A bachelor, he prided himself on his appearance, his ability as a tennis player, and his sexual conquests. He spent his social life in a series of casual affairs with women, becoming acutely uncomfortable if a relationship lasted more than a month. He took his heart attack as an even greater attack on his self-image and lifestyle and defended himself by suicide.

People whose investment in their appearance and intactness is so great that they will die rather than accept the changes of age or disease are likely to be ones whose capacity for caring for others is impaired. Mrs. Roman, the *Times* story noted only parenthetically, had given her two children away at the time of an earlier divorce, when they were six and four, to a friend who had raised them. Her story had some similarities to that of a recent patient I had seen who had decided to die rather than undergo removal of a malignant but operable tumor. The woman had been suicidal before the diagnosis of the tumor, although the tumor strengthened her determination to kill herself. She, too, had given her young children to her parents to raise following an earlier divorce.

Even without a knowledge of suicide,

common sense would indicate that there is something morbid about people who, while still vigorous and healthy, spend their time worrying about controlling the circumstances of their death. Before glorifying these pioneers of "self-termination," we would do well to remember that these individuals who accept life only on their own terms have much in common psychodynamically with much less romanticized suicides.

Media attempts to glorify suicide would be less significant if they were not accompanied by a marked increase in intellectual attempts to find a rational basis for suicide. More and more philosophers are being drawn into discussions of the ethics of suicide, so that Camus's remark that suicide is the essential question for philosophy is truer now than when he made it. Most such writing attempts to defuse the absolute nature of suicide by a process of intellectual assimilation. The issues of living and dying are rationalized into a language and style that at times seem more appropriate to descriptive economics. The German psychiatrist-philosopher Alfred Hoche addressed the problem at the beginning of this century, but his approach is typical of current evaluations of the right to die in terms of the cost-effectiveness of life to one's self.

Hoche proposed the term *Bilanz Selbstmord* or "balance sheet suicide" to refer to cases in which individuals assumed to be mentally unimpaired dispassionately took stock of their life situation and, having found it unacceptable or untenable and foreseeing no significant change for the better, decided to end their lives.[13] Richard Brandt, past president of the American Philosophical Association, in a modern version of balance sheet suicide, tries to outline how we can evaluate which decision to make.[14] He sees a close analogy

between a rational decision for suicide and the decision of the directors of a firm to declare bankruptcy and go out of business. He is aware that depression may impair one's judgment about future probabilities, but he seems to feel that the aware individual can make allowance for this possible error in his calculations.

Neither Hoche's nor Brandt's arguments are convincing. The tendency to think that life can be measured on a balance scale is itself a characteristic of suicidal people. Their thought processes often seem tailored to narrow possibilities, for their rigidity often makes them unable to see alternative solutions, while depression alters their judgment about possibilities for the future. . . .

Theoretical formulations of the moral or philosophical merits of suicide, divorced from clinical knowledge of suicidal individuals, bear little relation to the issues at work in suicidal individuals and have little value for the development of social policy. Commonly overlooked by such formulations is the extraordinary coerciveness associated with suicidal behavior. From the attempt to coerce life by making grandiose conditions on reality that reality cannot fulfill to the "If you love me, you will be willing to die with me!" test put to a reluctant partner in a suicide pact, self-destruction and destructiveness to others go hand in hand. The suicide pact is often a form of tyranny, affirming one partner's desire to control the life of the other. The coercive grandiosity of the Reverend Jim Jones, in a bizarre and exaggerated way, suggests the social relations of many who are suicidal and who bind others to them "even unto death.". . .

Although our efforts to prevent individual suicides should not be of the sort that devalue life even more than suicide

147

does, when pathology is psychosocial—when the community has a stake in it—personal rights are not without limits. Some years ago I wrote that if suicidal people were to organize to recruit others to their point of view, as happens in Robert Louis Stevenson's story "The Suicide Club," society should be able to intervene.[15] The emergence of and growing acclaim for societies that exist to facilitate the suicide of their members in England and in the United States should be regarded with alarm. They are not merely distributing "how to do it" information. They are the avant-garde of a larger attempt to seek social approval and institutionalization for suicide. If they succeed, their success will be a reflection of how, as a culture, we are turning from efforts to improve our lives together toward the lesser goal of helping each other die.

NOTES

1   Nietzsche, *Human, All-Too-Human*, trans. H. Zimmern (Edinburgh: Foulis, 1909), p. 88.

2   Szasz, *The Myth of Mental Illness: Foundations of a Theory of Personal Conduct*, rev. ed. (New York: Harper & Row, 1974); idem, *Law, Liberty, and Psychiatry: An Inquiry into the Social Uses of Mental Health Practices* (New York: Collier Books, 1968); idem, *Ceremonial Chemistry: The Ritual Persecution of Drugs, Addicts, and Pushers* (Garden City, N.Y.: Anchor Books, 1974); idem, *The Second Sin* (Garden City, N.Y.: Anchor Books, 1974); idem, "The Ethics of Suicide," *Antioch Review* 31 (1971): 7-17.

3   Szasz, *Ceremonial Chemistry*, pp. xi, xii.

4   Szasz, *The Second Sin*, pp. 75, 76.

5   Barrington, "Apologia for Suicide," in *Suicide: The Philosophical Issues*, ed. M.P. Battin and D. Mayo (New York: St. Martin's, 1980), p. 98.

6   Slater, "Choosing the Time to Die," in ibid., pp. 202-3.

7   Barrington, "Apologia for Suicide," p. 101.

8   Quoted by J. Oates in "The Art of Suicide," in *Suicide: The Philosophical Issues*, ed. Battin and Mayo, p. 165.

9   W. Binns, D. Kerkinan, and S. Schroeder, "Destructive Group Dynamics: An Account of Some Peculiar Interrelated Incidents of Suicide and Suicidal Attempts in a University Dormitory," *Journal of the American College Health Association* 14 (1966): 350-56.

10   Camus, *The Myth of Sisyphus and Other Essays*, trans. J. O'Brien (New York: Vintage Books, 1959), p. 3.

11   James, *Is Life Worth Living?* (Philadelphia: Weston, 1896).

12   *New York Times*, 17 June 1979.

13   Hoche, "Vom Sterben," in *Aus der Werkstatt* (Munich: Jehmann, 1935), pp. 210-32.

14   Brandt, "The Morality and Rationality of Suicide," in *A Handbook for the Study of Suicide*, ed. S. Perlin (New York: Oxford University Press, 1975), pp. 61-76.

15   Stevenson, *The Suicide Club* (New York: Beres, 1941).

POSTSCRIPT

CAN SUICIDE BE RATIONAL?

In March 1983, the well-known writer Arthur Koestler and his wife Cynthia were found dead—double suicides—in their London apartment. In his seventies, Koestler had been ill for several years, but his wife was much younger and presumably in good health. Both had been active supporters of Exit— the British organization that endorses the idea of rational suicide and provides explicit information on how to achieve it. In this country an organization called Hemlock has the same aims. The Koestlers' suicides raised the further ethical question of the extent of marital devotion: Was her suicide rational or the result of depression?

Tom L. Beauchamp's article, "Suicide and the Value of Life" in *Matters of Life and Death,* edited by Tom Regan (Random House, 1980) is a comprehensive discussion of the philosophical aspects of suicide. The concept of suicide is clarified by R.F. Holland in "Suicide," reprinted in *Moral Problems,* second edition, edited by James Rachels (Harper & Row, 1975). Thomas S. Szasz in "The Ethics of Suicide" (*Antioch Review,* Spring 1971) argues against suicide intervention on the grounds that it interferes with individual liberty. A. Alvarez's *The Savage God: A Study of Suicide* is both a study of suicide in literature and history and an account of the author's own failed attempt. See also *A Handbook for the Study of Suicide,* edited by Seymour Perlin (Oxford, 1975), which contains Richard Brandt's views; and Philip E. Devine, *The Ethics of Homicide* (Cornell, 1978), a condemnation of suicide. In addition to editing (with David J. Mayo), *Suicide: The Philosophical Issues,* from which the selection by Mary Rose Barrington was taken, M. Pabst Battin has written *Ethical Issues in Suicide* (Prentice-Hall, 1982) and *Suicide and Ethics* with Ronald W. Maris (Human Sciences Press, 1983).

UN photo by Gaston Guarda.

PART III
TREATING THE
MENTALLY ILL

Because they are dependent upon the greater society in so many respects, we have a special responsibility to the mentally ill among us. This seems a simple ethical standard, but as in most questions of this nature, it is rarely simple in practice. There is a school of psychological thought that holds that mental illness does not exist, but is in fact an invention of society to be used to control those among us who refuse to adhere to accepted rules of behavior. If the experts cannot agree that mental illness exists, how can we determine when to hold individuals responsible for their actions, such as criminals who plead insanity as a defense, and when to absolve them of culpability on the grounds that they were not acting as free agents? Therapists are constantly called upon to balance the needs of their patients against the needs of society to be protected from their irrational behavior. In fact, therapists are often called upon to protect their clients from themselves by committing them to institutions. This section examines the ethical dimensions of these thorny issues.

Is it a Therapist's Duty to Protect
Potential Victims of Violence?

Should the Insanity Defense Be
Abolished?

Is Involuntary Commitment to Mental
Institutions Immoral?

ISSUE 9

DO THERAPISTS HAVE A DUTY TO PROTECT POTENTIAL VICTIMS OF VIOLENCE?

YES: Justice Mathew O. Tobriner, from Majority opinion in *Tarasoff* v. *Regents of the University of California* (California Supreme Court, July 1, 1976)

NO: Justice William P. Clark, from Dissenting opinion in *Tarasoff* v. *Regents of the University of California* (California Supreme Court, July 1, 1976)

ISSUE SUMMARY

YES: Mathew O. Tobriner, a justice in the Supreme Court of California, asserts that when a physician or a psychotherapist learns in the course of treatment that a mentally ill patient plans to commit a violent act against a third person, the public interest requires that the therapist warn that person, even if it violates the patient's right to privacy.

NO: William P. Clark, a justice in the same court, dissents from the majority view. He argues that unless patients can be assured of confidentiality, those who need treatment will not seek it and that in order to protect themselves against lawsuits and prosecution for a failure to warn, therapists will commit patients to mental hospitals, often unnecessarily.

"If I tell you a secret, will you promise not to tell anyone?" This simple question, familiar from childhood, captures two important features of human relationships: the need to confide one's fears and hopes to another person and the need to trust that person not to reveal the secret. If the person who receives the confidence agrees not to reveal it, he or she has made a promise. All ethical systems place a high value on promise-keeping.

When this exchange occurs in a professional relationship—between patient and physician or therapist, client and attorney, or priest and confessor—there is even more at stake. The professional, as part of achieving that status, has accepted an ethical code that states that confidentiality will be maintained. One of the earliest formulations of this concept is found in the Hippocratic Oath, which is still sworn to by all physicians: "What I may see or hear in the course of the treatment or even outside of the treatment in regard to the life of men, which on no account one must spread abroad, I will keep to myself. . . ."

But no value is absolute, and some exceptions to the rule of confidentiality are well established. For example, considerations of public health underlie laws that require physicians to report certain contagious diseases such as syphilis, measles, meningitis, and (most recently) acquired immune deficiency syndrome (AIDS). Similarly, a physician must report cases of gunshot wounds to the authorities, since a crime may have been committed. Physicians and social workers and others are required by law to report suspected cases of child abuse, so that a child who is being harmed physically or mentally can be protected.

These examples show that a threat to the health of the public or a crime against another person (as in the case of child abuse) can clearly override an individual's rights to confidentiality. But in recent years a new question has arisen: As Sissela Bok, a philosopher who has written extensively on secrets, puts it: "Does a professional owe confidentiality to clients who reveal plans or acts that endanger others directly?" The question, she says, arises equally for the lawyer whose client lets it be known that he plans a bank robbery, for the pediatrician who suspects that a mother drugs her children to keep them quiet, and for the psychiatrist whose patient reveals his violent jealousy of his wife. This last situation will be addressed in the following two selections. If, in the course of psychological therapy, a person makes threats against someone else, should the therapist be required to breach confidentiality and warn the potential victim? The problem is particularly common in the treatment of mental patients. It is imperative for therapeutic reasons that patients feel free to express their innermost thoughts and fantasies. However, if their threats are real, the victim can be seriously harmed or—as in the case of Tatiana Tarasoff, to be described below—even killed. A complicated factor is the difficulty (some say the impossibility) of predicting accurately whether a person will actually commit the violent act he or she announces.

The two selections that follow are from the same court ruling. In writing the majority opinion in the case of *Tarasoff* v. *Board of Regents of the University of California,* Justice Mathew O. Tobriner explains the court's opinion that the public interest in protecting against violent assault outweighs its interest in safeguarding the confidential character of psychotherapeutic communication. Justice William B. Clark dissented from his colleagues' views, arguing that imposing a duty on therapists to warn potential victims will impair the treatment of many who would never become violent and will actually result in more violence because those who need treatment will not seek it. The ones who will be protected, he says, are the therapists, who will commit patients to mental hospitals rather than risk a lawsuit or prosecution.

YES

Justice Mathew O. Tobriner

MAJORITY OPINION IN *TARASOFF v. REGENTS* *OF THE UNIVERSITY OF CALIFORNIA*

On October 27, 1969, Prosenjit Poddar killed Tatiana Tarasoff. Plaintiffs, Tatiana's parents, allege that two months earlier Poddar confided his intention to kill Tantiana to Dr. Lawrence Moore, a psychologist employed by the Cowell Memorial Hospital at the University of California at Berkeley. They allege that on Moore's request, the campus police briefly detained Poddar, but released him when he appeared rational. They further claim that Dr. Harvey Powelson, Moore's superior, then directed that no further action be taken to detain Poddar. No one warned plaintiffs of Tatiana's peril. . . .

We shall explain that defendant therapists cannot escape liability merely because Tatiana herself was not their patient. When a therapist determines, or pursuant to the standards of his profession should determine, that his patient presents a serious danger of violence to another, he incurs an obligation to use reasonable care to protect the intended victim against such danger. The discharge of this duty may require the therapist to take one or more of various steps, depending upon the nature of the case. Thus it may call for him to warn the intended victim or others likely to apprise the victim of the danger, to notify the police, or to take whatever other steps are reasonably necessary under the circumstances. . . .

PLAINTIFFS' COMPLAINTS

. . . Plaintiff's first cause of action, entitled "Failure to Detain a Dangerous Patient," alleges that on August 20, 1969, Poddar was a voluntary outpatient receiving therapy at Cowell Memorial Hospital. Poddar informed Moore, his therapist, that he was going to kill an unnamed girl, readily identifiable as Tatiana, when she returned home from spending the summer in Brazil. Moore, with the concurrence of Dr. Gold, who had initially examined Poddar, and Dr. Yandell, assistant to the director of the department of psychiatry,

From Majority Opinion, *Tarasoff v. Regents of the University of California,* California Supreme Court, July 1, 1976.

decided that Poddar should be committed for observation in a mental hospital. Moore orally notified Officers Atkinson and Teel of the campus police that he would request commitment. He then sent a letter to Police Chief William Beall requesting the assistance of the police department in securing Poddar's confinement.

Officers Atkinson, Brownrigg, and Halleran took Poddar into custody, but, satisfied that Poddar was rational, released him on his promise to stay away from Tatiana. Powelson, director of the department of psychiatry at Cowell Memorial Hospital, then asked the police to return Moore's letter, directed that all copies of the letter and notes that Moore had taken as therapist be destroyed, and "ordered no action to place Prosenjit Poddar in 72-hour treatment and evaluation facility."

Plaintiffs' second cause of action, entitled "Failure to Warn on a Dangerous Patient," incorporates the allegations of the first cause of action, but adds the assertion that defendants negligently permitted Poddar to be released from police custody without "notifying the parents of Tatiana Tarasoff that their daughter was in grave danger from Prosenjit Poddar." Poddar persuaded Tatiana's brother to share an apartment with him near Tatiana's residence; shortly after her return from Brazil, Poddar went to her residence and killed her.

Plantiffs' third cause of action, entitled "Abandonment of a Dangerous Patient," seeks $10,000 punitive damages against defendant Powelson. Incorporating the crucial allegations of the first cause of action, plaintiffs charge that Powelson "did the things herein alleged with intent to abandon a dangerous patient, and said acts were done maliciously and oppressively."

Plaintiffs' fourth cause of action, for "Breach of Primary Duty to Patient and the Public," states essentially the same allegations as the first cause of action, but seeks to characterize defendants' conduct as a breach of duty to safeguard their patient and the public. Since such conclusory labels add nothing to the factual allegations of the complaint, the first and fourth causes of action are legally indistinguishable. . . .

. . . We direct our attention . . . to the issue of whether plaintiffs' second cause of action can be amended to state a basis for recovery.

PLAINTIFFS CAN STATE A CAUSE OF ACTION AGAINST DEFENDANT THERAPISTS FOR NEGLIGENT FAILURE TO PROTECT TATIANA

The second cause of action can be amended to allege that Tatiana's death proximately resulted from defendant's negligent failure to warn Tatiana or others likely to apprise her of her danger. Plaintiffs contend that as amended, such allegations of negligence and proximate causation, with resulting damages, establish a cause of action. Defendants, however, contend that in the circumstances of the present case they owed no duty of care to Tatiana or her parents and that, in the absence of such duty, they were free to act in careless disregard of Tatiana's life and safety.

In analyzing this issue, we bear in mind that legal duties are not discoverable facts of nature, but merely conclusory expressions that, in cases of a particular type, liability should be imposed for damage done. "The assertion that liability must . . . be denied because defendant bears no 'duty' to plaintiff 'begs the essential question—whether the plaintiff's interests are entitled to legal protection against the defendant's conduct. . . . [Duty] is not sacrosanct in itself, but only an expression of the sum total of those considerations of policy which lead the law to say that the particular plaintiff is entitled to protection.' "

In the landmark case of *Rowland v. Christian* (1968), Justice Peters recognized that liability should be imposed "for an injury occasioned to another by his want of ordinary care or skill" as expressed in section 1714 of the Civil Code. Thus, Justice Peters, quoting from *Heaven v. Pender* (1883) stated: " 'Whenever one person is by circumstances placed in such a position with regard to another . . . that if he did not use ordinary care and skill in his own conduct . . . he would cause danger of injury to the person or property of the other, a duty arises to use ordinary care and skill to avoid such danger.' "

We depart from "this fundamental principle" only upon the "balancing of a number of considerations"; major ones "are the foreseeability of harm to the plaintiff, the degree of certainty that the plaintiff suffered injury, the closeness of the connection between the defendant's conduct and the injury suffered, the moral blame attached to the defendant's conduct, the policy of preventing future harm, the extent of the burden to the defendant and consequences to the community of imposing a duty to exercise care with resulting liability for breach, and the availability, cost and prevalence of insurance for the risk involved."

The most important of these considerations in establishing duty is foreseeability. As a general principle, a "defendant owes a duty of care to all persons who are foreseeably endangered by his conduct, with respect to all risks which make the conduct unreasonably dangerous." As we shall explain, however, when the avoidance of foreseeable harm requires a defendant to control the conduct of another person, or to warn of such conduct, the common law has traditionally imposed liability only if the defendant bears some special relationship to the dangerous person or to the potential victim. Since the relationship between a therapist and his patient satisfies this requirement, we need not here decide whether foreseeability alone is sufficient to create a duty to exercise reasonable care to protect a potential victim of another's conduct.

Although, as we have stated above, under the common law, as a general rule, one person owed no duty to control the conduct of another nor to warn those endangered by such conduct, the courts have carved out an exception to this rule in cases in which the defendant stands in some special relationship to either the person whose conduct needs to be controlled or in a relationship to the foreseeable victim of that conduct. Applying this exception to the present case, we note that a relationship of defendant therapists to either Tatiana or Poddar will suffice to establish a duty of care: as explained in section 315 of the Restatement Second of Torts, a duty of care may arise from either "(a) a special relation . . . between the actor and the third person which imposes a duty upon the actor to control the third person's conduct, or (b) a special relation . . . between the actor and the other which gives to the other a right of protection."

Although plaintiff's pleadings assert no special relation between Tatiana and defendant therapists, they establish as between Poddar and defendant therapists the special relation that arises between a patient and his doctor or psychotherapist. Such a relationship may support affirmative duties for the benefit of third persons. Thus, for example, a hospital must exercise reasonable care to control the behavior of a patient which may endanger other persons. A doctor must also warn a patient if the patient's condition or medication renders certain conduct, such as driving a car, dangerous to others.

Although the California decisions that recognize this duty have involved cases in which the defendant stood in a special relationship *both* to the victim and to the person whose conduct created the danger, we do not think that the duty should logically be constricted to such situations. Decisions of other jurisdictions hold that the single relationship of a doctor to his patient is sufficient to support the duty to exercise reasonable care to protect others against dangers emanating from the patient's illness. The courts hold that a doctor is liable to persons infected by his patient if he negligently fails to diagnose a contagious disease, or having diagnosed the illness, fails to warn members of the patient's family.

Since it involved a dangerous mental patient, the decision in *Merchants Nat. Bank & Trust Co. of Fargo v. United States* (1967) comes closer to the issue. The Veterans Administration arranged for the patient to work on a local farm, but did not inform the farmer of the man's background. The farmer consequently permitted the patient to come and go freely during nonworking hours; the patient borrowed a car, drove to his wife's residence and killed her. Notwithstanding the lack of any "special relationship" between the Veterans Administration and the wife, the court found the Veterans Administration liable for the wrongful death of the wife.

In their summary of the relevant rulings Fleming and Maximov conclude that the "case law should dispel any notion that to impose on the therapists a duty to take precautions for the safety of persons threatened by a patient, where due care so requires, is in any way opposed to contemporary ground rules on the duty rela-tionship. On the contrary, there now seems to be sufficient authority to support the conclusion that by entering into a doctor-patient relationship the therapist becomes sufficiently involved to assume some responsibility for the safety, not only of the patient himself, but also of any third person whom the doctor knows to be threatened by the patient." [Fleming & Maximov, *The Patient or His Victim: The Therapist's Dilemma* (1974) 62 Cal. L. Rev. 1025. 1030.]

Defendants contend, however, that imposition of a duty to exercise reasonable care to protect third persons is unworkable because therapists cannot accurately predict whether or not a patient will resort to violence. In support of this argument amicus ["friend of the court"] representing the American Psychiatric Association and other professional societies cites numerous articles which indicate that therapists, in the present state of the art, are unable reliably to predict violent acts; their forecasts, amicus claims, tend consistently to overpredict violence, and indeed are more often wrong than right. Since predictions of violence are often erroneous, amicus concludes, the courts should not render rulings that predicate the liability of therapists upon the validity of such predictions.

The role of the psychiatrist, who is indeed a practitioner of medicine, and that of the psychologist who performs an allied function, are like that of the physician who must conform to the standards of the profession and who must often make diagnoses and predictions based upon such evaluations. Thus the judgment of the therapist in diagnosing emotional disorders and in predicting whether a patient presents a serious danger of violence is comparable to the judgment which doctors and professionals must regularly render under accepted rules of responsiblity.

We recognize the difficulty that a therapist encounters in attempting to forecast whether a patient presents a serious danger of violence. Obviously we do not require that the therapist, in making that determination, render a perfect performance; the therapist need only exercise "that reasonable degree of skill, knowledge, and care ordinarily possessed and exercised by members of [that professional specialty] under similar circumstances." Within the broad range of reasonable practice and treatment in which professional opinion and judgment may differ, the therapist is free to exercise his or her own best judgment without liability; proof, aided by hindsight, that he or she judged wrongly is insufficient to establish negligence.

In the instant case, however, the pleadings do not raise any question as to failure of defendant therapists to predict that Poddar presented a serious danger of violence. On the contrary, the present complaints allege that defendant therapists did in fact predict that Poddar would kill, but were negligent in failing to warn.

Amicus contends, however, that even when a therapist does in fact predict that a patient poses a serious danger of violence to others, the therapist should be absolved of any responsibility for failing to act to protect the potential victim. In our view, however, once a therapist does in fact determine, or under applicable professional standards reasonably should have determined, that a patient poses a serious danger of violence to others, he bears a duty to exercise reasonable care to protect the foreseeable victim of that danger. While the discharge of this duty of due care will necessarily vary with the facts of each case, in each instance the adequacy of the therapist's conduct must be measured

against the traditional negligence standard of the rendition of reasonable care under the circumstances. As explained in Felming and Maximov, *The Patient or His Victim: The Therapist's Dilemma* (1974), "... the ultimate question of resolving the tension between the conflicting interests of patient and potential victim is one of social policy, not professional expertise. ... In sum, the therapist owes a legal duty not only to his patient, but also to his patient's would-be victim and is subject in both respects to scrutiny by judge and jury.". ...

The risk that unnecessary warnings may be given is a reasonable price to pay for the lives of possible victims that may be saved. We would hesitate to hold that the therapist who is aware that his patient expects to attempt to assassinate the President of the United States would not be obligated to warn the authorities because the therapist cannot predict with accuracy that his patient will commit the crime.

Defendants further argue that free and open communication is essential to psychotherapy; that "unless a patient ... is assured that ... information [revealed by him] can and will be held in utmost confidence, he will be reluctant to make the full disclosure upon which diagnosis and treatment ... depends." The giving of a warning, defendants contend, constitutes a breach of trust which entails the revelation of confidential communications.

We recognize the public interest in supporting effective treatment of mental illness and in protecting the rights of patients to privacy and the consequent public importance of safeguarding the confidential character of psychotherapeutic communication. Against this interest, however, we must weigh the public interest in safety from violent assault. The Legislature has undertaken the difficult task of balancing the countervailing concerns. In Evidence

Code section 1014, it established a broad rule of privilege to protect confidential communications between patient and psychotherapist. In Evidence Code section 1024, the Legislature created a specific and limited exception to the psychotherapist-patient privilege: "There is no privilege ... if the psychotherapist has reasonable cause to believe that the patient is in such mental or emotional condition as to be dangerous to himself or to the person or property of another and that disclosure of the communication is necessary to prevent the threatened danger."

We realize that the open and confidential character of psychotherapeutic dialogue encourages patients to express threats of violence, few of which are ever executed. Certainly a therapist should not be encouraged routinely to reveal such threats; such disclosures could seriously disrupt the patient's relationship with his therapist and with the persons threatened. To the contrary, the therapist's obligations to his patient require that he not disclose a confidence unless such disclosure is necessary to avert danger to others, and even then that he do so discreetly, and in a fashion that would preserve the privacy of his patient to the fullest extent compatible with the prevention of the threatened danger.

The revelation of a communication under the above circumstances is not a breach of trust or a violation of professional ethics; as stated in the Principles of Medical Ethics of the American Medical Association (1957), section 9; "A physician may not reveal the confidence entrusted to him in the course of medical attendance ... *unless he is required to do so by law or unless it becomes necessary in order to protect the welfare of the individual or of the community.*" (Emphasis added.) We conclude that the public policy favoring protection of the confidential character of patient-psychotherapist communications must yield to the extent to which disclosure is essential to avert danger to others. The protective privilege ends where the public peril begins.

Our current crowded and computerized society compels the interdependence of its members. In this risk-infested society we can hardly tolerate the further exposure to danger that would result from a concealed knowledge of the therapist that his patient was lethal. If the exercise of reasonable care to protect the threatened victim requires the therapist to warn the endangered party or those who can reasonably be expected to notify him, we see no sufficient societal interest that would protect and justify concealment. The containment of such risks lies in the public interest. For the foregoing reasons, we find that plaintiffs' complaints can be amended to state a cause of action against defendants Moore, Powelson, Gold, and Yandell and against the Regents as their employer, for breach of a duty to exercise reasonable care to protect Tatiana. . . .

NO

Justice William P. Clark

DISSENTING OPINION IN
TARASOFF v. REGENTS OF THE
UNIVERSITY OF CALIFORNIA

Until today's majority opinion, both legal and medical authorities have agreed that confidentiality is essential to effectively treat the mentally ill, and that imposing a duty on doctors to disclose patient threats to potential victims would greatly impair treatment. Further, recognizing that effective treatment and society's safety are necessarily intertwined, the Legislature has already decided effective and confidential treatment is preferred over imposition of a duty to warn.

The issue whether effective treatment for the mentally ill should be sacrificed to a system of warnings is, in my opinion, properly one for the Legislature, and we are bound by its judgment. Moreover, even in the absence of clear legislative direction, we must reach the same conclusion because imposing the majority's new duty is certain to result in a net increase in violence. . . .

COMMON LAW ANALYSIS

Entirely apart from the statutory provisions, the same result must be reached upon considering both general tort principles and the public policies favoring effective treatment, reduction of violence, and justified commitment.

Generally, a person owes no duty to control the conduct of another. Exceptions are recognized only in limited situations where (1) a special relationship exists between the defendant and injured party, or (2) a special relationship exists between defendant and the active wrongdoer, imposing a duty on defendant to control the wrongdoer's conduct. The majority does not contend the first exception is appropriate to this case.

Policy generally determines duty. Principal policy considerations include foreseeability of harm, certainty of the plaintiff's injury, proximity of the defendant's conduct to the plaintiff's injury, moral blame attributable to defendant's conduct, prevention of future harm, burden on the defendant, and consequences to the community.

Overwhelming policy considerations weigh against imposing a duty on psycho-

From Dissenting Opinion, *Tarasoff v. Regents of the University of California,* California Supreme Court, July 1, 1976.

therapists to warn a potential victim against harm. While offering virtually no benefit to society, such a duty will frustrate psychiatric treatment, invade fundamental patient rights and increase violence.

The importance of psychiatric treatment and its need for confidentiality have been recognized by this court. "It is clearly recognized that the very practice of psychiatry vitally depends upon the reputation in the community that the psychiatrist will not tell." [Slovenko, *Psychiatry and a Second Look at the Medical Privilege* (1960) 6 Wayne L.Rev.175, 188.]

Assurance of confidentiality is important for three reasons.

DETERRENCE FROM TREATMENT

First, without substantial assurance of confidentiality, those requiring treatment will be deterred from seeking assistance. It remains an unfortunate fact in our society that people seeking psychiatric guidance tend to become stigmatized. Apprehension of such stigma—apparently increased by the propensity of people considering treatment to see themselves in the worst possible light—creates a well-recognized reluctance to seek aid. This reluctance is alleviated by the psychiatrist's assurance of confidentiality.

FULL DISCLOSURE

Second, the guarantee of confidentiality is essential in eliciting the full disclosure necessary for effective treatment. The psychiatric patient approaches treatment with conscious and unconscious inhibitions against revealing his innermost thoughts. "Every person, however well-motivated, has to overcome resistances to therapeutic exploration. These resistances seek support from every possible source

and the possibility of disclosure would easily be employed in the service of resistance." (Goldstein & Katz, *Psychiatrist-Patient Privilege: The GAP Proposal and the Connecticut Statute*, 36 Conn. Bar J., 175, 179; see also, 118 Am.J.Psych. 734, 735.) Until a patient can trust his psychiatrist not to violate their confidential relationship, "the unconscious psychological control mechanism of repression will prevent the recall of past experiences." [Butler, *Psychotherapy and Griswold: Is Confidentiality a Privilege or a Right?* (1971) 3 Conn.L.Rev. 599, 604.]

SUCCESSFUL TREATMENT

Third, even if the patient fully discloses his thoughts, assurance that the confidential relationship will not be breached is necessary to maintain his trust in his psychiatrist—the very means by which treatment is effected. "[T]he essence of much psychotherapy is the contribution of trust in the external world and ultimately in the self, modelled upon the trusting relationship established during therapy" (Dawidoff, *The Malpractice of Psychiatrists*, 1966 Duke L.J. 696, 704.) Patients will be helped only if they can form a trusting relationship with the psychiatrist. All authorities appear to agree that if the trust relationship cannot be developed because of collusive communication between the psychiatrist and others, treatment will be frustrated.

Given the importance of confidentiality to the practice of psychiatry, it becomes clear the duty to warn imposed by the majority will cripple the use and effectiveness of psychiatry. Many people, potentially violent—yet susceptible to treatment—will be deterred from seeking it; those seeking it will be inhibited from making revelations necessary to effective treatment; and, forcing the psychiatrist to violate the patient's

161

trust will destroy the interpersonal relationship by which treatment is effected.

VIOLENCE AND CIVIL COMMITMENT

By imposing a duty to warn, the majority contributes to the danger to society of violence by the mentally ill and greatly increases the risk of civil commitment—the total deprivation of liberty—of those who should not be confined. The impairment of treatment and risk of improper commitment resulting from the new duty to warn will not be limited to a few patients but will extend to a large number of the mentally ill. Although under existing psychiatric procedures only a relatively few receiving treatment will ever present a risk of violence, the number making threats is huge, and it is the latter group—not just the former—whose treatment will be impaired and whose risk of commitment will be increased.

Both the legal and psychiatric communities recognize that the process of determining potential violence in a patient is far from exact, being fraught with complexity and uncertainty.

In fact precision has not even been attained in predicting who of those having already committed violent acts will again become violent, a task recognized to be of much simpler proportions.

This predictive uncertainty means that the number of disclosures will necessarily be large. As noted above, psychiatric patients are encouraged to discuss all thoughts of violence, and they often express such thoughts. However, unlike this court, the psychiatrist does not enjoy the benefit of overwhelming hindsight in seeing which few, if any, of his patients will ultimately become violent. Now, confronted by the majority's new duty, the psychiatrist must instantaneously calculate potential violence from each patient on each visit. The difficulties researchers have encountered in accurately predicting violence will be heightened for the practicing psychiatrist dealing for brief periods in his office with heretofore nonviolent patients. And, given the decision not to warn or commit must always be made at the psychiatrist's civil peril, one can expect most doubts will be resolved in favor of the psychiatrist protecting himself.

Neither alternative open to the psychiatrist seeking to protect himself is in the public interest. The warning itself is an impairment of the psychiatrist's ability to treat, depriving many patients of adequate treatment. It is to be expected that after disclosing their threats, a significant number of patients, who would not become violent if treated according to existing practices, will engage in violent conduct as a result of unsuccessful treatment. In short, the majority's duty to warn will not only impair treatment of many who would never become violent but worse, will result in a net increase in violence.

The second alternative open to the psychiatrist is to commit his patient rather than to warn. Even in the absence of threat of civil liability, the doubts of psychiatrists as to the seriousness of patient threats have led psychiatrists to overcommit to mental institutions. This overcommitment has been authoritatively documented in both legal and psychiatric studies. This practice is so prevalent that it has been estimated that "as many as twenty harmless persons are incarcerated for every one who will commit a violent act." [Steadman & Cocozza, *Stimulus/Response: We Can't Predict Who Is Dangerous* (Jan. 1975) 8 Psych. Today 32, 35.]

Given the incentive to commit created by the majority's duty, this already serious situation will be worsened. . . .

POSTSCRIPT

DO THERAPISTS HAVE A DUTY TO PROTECT POTENTIAL VICTIMS OF VIOLENCE?

The decision in *Tarasoff* was widely criticized by lawyers and mental health professionals. Nevertheless, the doctrine that therapists have a duty to protect potential victims has been endorsed by several other state and federal courts, for example, in New Jersey, Nebraska, Indiana, Kansas, Georgia, Michigan, Washington, and Kansas. In one New Jersey case, a court held a psychiatrist liable for failing to protect a former girlfriend who was killed by an adolescent patient—even though the patient had never expressed any intent to harm her and had talked only about his jealous feelings. However, some courts have limited the duty to protect to known, identifiable victims. A 1986 decision of the Vermont Supreme Court, on the other hand, in a case involving a barn burning, creates liability for property damage as well as for personal injury.

Prosenjit Poddar, the man who killed Tatiana Tarasoff, was convicted of second-degree murder but the conviction was overturned on appeal because the jury had been incorrectly instructed. Since more than five years had elapsed since the crime, the state decided not to retry Poddar but to release him if he would promise to return to India, which he did.

In 1978, two years after the *Tarasoff* decision, a study of a thousand California therapists, reported in the *Stanford Law Review,* suggested that the decision had led them to give more credence to threats expressed by patients. A quarter of the respondents indicated that patients were less willing to talk about violent thoughts after they had been warned that such material might not be held confidential. Many therapists felt anxious about knowing the limits of the duty to protect, and some refused to take on patients where violence might be discussed. However, another survey in 1984 showed less concern but also inaccurate understanding of professional responsibility.

For the aftermath of the decision, see Vanessa Merton, "Confidentiality and the 'Dangerous' Patient: Implications of *Tarasoff* for Psychiatrists and Lawyers," *Emory Law Journal* (Vol. 31, 1982); Paul S. Appelbaum, "Tarasoff and the Clinician: Problems in Fulfilling the Duty to Protect," *American Journal of Psychiatry* (April 1985); and Alan A. Stone, "Vermont Adopts Tarasoff: A Real Barn-Burner," *American Journal of Psychiatry* (March 1986). *Bad Karma: A True Story of Obsession and Murder,* by Deborah Blum (Atheneum, 1986) is a popular version of the *Tarasoff* case.

On confidentiality in general, see *Secrets* by Sissela Bok (Pantheon, 1982). LeRoy Walters discusses the philosophical justifications for the principle of medical confidentiality in "Ethical Aspects of Medical Confidentiality," in Tom L. Beauchamp and LeRoy Walters, *Contemporary Issues in Bioethics,* second edition (Wadsworth, 1982). See also Robert M. Veatch, *Case Studies in Medical Ethics* (Harvard, 1977), chapter 5; and Louis Everstine, et al., "Threats to Confidentiality," *American Psychologist* (September 1980).

ISSUE 10

SHOULD THE INSANITY DEFENSE BE ABOLISHED?

YES: Stephen Cohen, "It's a Mad, Mad Verdict," *The New Republic* (July 12, 1982)

NO: Richard J. Bonnie, "The Moral Basis of the Insanity Defense," *American Bar Association Journal* 69 (January 1983)

ISSUE SUMMARY

YES: Professor of law Stephen Cohen argues that the insanity defense as it now exists should be abolished because the psychiatric detection of mental illness is so unreliable and because it is so difficult to tell whether mental illness has impaired the defendant's capacity for free will.
NO: Professor of law Richard J. Bonnie counters with the view that the insanity defense should not be abandoned because it is fundamentally wrong to condemn and punish a person whose rational control over his or her behavior was impaired by mental illness.

On June 21, 1982, a jury found John W. Hinckley, Jr., "Not guilty by reason of insanity" for the crimes of shooting and wounding President Ronald Reagan, Press Secretary James Brady, a Secret Service guard, and a District of Columbia policeman. The prosecution, according to the verdict, had certainly proved that Hinckley had fired the gun (that was never questioned) but had failed to prove beyond a reasonable doubt that he was sane when he did it. Hinckley was not set free but was ordered confined to St. Elizabeth's Hospital, a mental institution.

The verdict stunned the American public. Almost immediately bills were introduced in Congress and in the states to abolish or amend the insanity plea or to introduce a new verdict of "Guilty but mentally ill." Something, it appeared, was terribly wrong when a person who clearly had committed a certain act and who did not appear to be "crazy"—indeed, who had carefully planned the event—escaped the full punishment of the law.

The Hinckley verdict, dramatic as it was, is only the most recent in a series of cases that have raised serious questions about the insanity defense. Even before the shooting of the president, legal scholars and psychiatrists had been considering whether the defense was being misused, whether it was of moral or practical value, and how it might be amended.

The idea that the insane should not be punished for acts that would be criminal if committed by normal people dates to the twelfth century. Medieval scholars developed the notion that only persons who are morally blameworthy—that is, who intentionally commit a crime and understand the significance of what they do—should be punished. The modern formulation of this idea is known as "McNaughtan's Rule," because it resulted from a case in 1843 in England when Daniel McNaughten shot and killed the secretary to Robert Peel, then prime minister. McNaughten's defense was that he was suffering from delusions that Peel's political party was persecuting him. In clarifying the grounds on which McNaughtan was acquitted, the House of Lords said: ". . . it must be clearly proved that, at the time of the committing of the act, the party accused was labouring under such a defect of reason, from disease of mind, as not to know the nature and quality of the act he was doing; or if he did know it, that he did not know he was doing what was wrong."

McNaughtan's Rule has largely been followed in both English and American law since then. An alternative way of formulating the defense—one that stressed the ability to control one's actions in addition to understanding them, as in McNaughtan—is the American Law Institute's code, adopted in 1962, which reads: "A person is not responsible for criminal conduct if at the time of such conduct as a result of mental disease or defect he lacks substantial capacity either to appreciate the criminality (wrongfulness) of his conduct or to conform his conduct to the requirements of the law."

Underlying the concept that a certain group of people—those who cannot understand or appreciate the wrongfulness of their acts—should be spared punishment is the belief that mental illness is real, that it can be diagnosed and treated, and that it can affect the capacity for free will. In this view, law is closely intertwined with medicine, and the testimony of psychiatrists and other mental health professionals carries much weight. This reliance of the justice system on the expertise of medicine has been considered humane and compassionate by some, and misguided and unwarranted by others.

The two selections that follow present opposing views of the insanity defense. Stephen Cohen says that the Hinckley jury reached the only verdict it could and that the law must be changed to restore public confidence in the principle of moral responsibility. Richard J. Bonnie disagrees, claiming that the insanity defense is essential to the moral integrity of the criminal law. He does, however, agree that the burden of proof in using the defense should be shifted to the defendant.

YES

Stephen Cohen

IT'S A MAD, MAD VERDICT

If the law truly means what it says, then John W. Hinckley Jr. had to be found not guilty of the attempted murder of the President of the United States. Not because he didn't do it—and not even because the defense proved that mental illness caused his acts—but because the jury could not help entertaining a reasonable doubt about Hinckley's sanity at the time of the shooting. As a matter of logic, that reasonable doubt left no lawful choice but to acquit the man who shot President Reagan and three other people in full view of hundreds of millions of television watchers.

Yet as the jury began to deliberate, few observers expected that kind of strict legal logic to prevail. Hinckley would certainly be convicted, the experts thought, if only because the idea that someone can shoot the President and not be punished for it is so abhorrent to both common sense and civil order. And if the initial reactions of ordinary people are any indication, the verdict has deeply outraged the sense of justice of most Americans.

Moreover, the verdict in this case seems to damage the stated purpose of the insanity defense, which is to affirm that most individuals are responsible for their actions, and, at the same time, to identify the very few who are utterly—and, in a moral sense, blamelessly—unable to control their conduct. In short, what the Hinckley case shows is that the insanity defense needs to be radically changed—in its definition of insanity, its allocation of the burden of proof, or both—or even abolished.

Hinckley's lawyers portrayed him as living out a delusion based on the movie *Taxi Driver,* obsessed with frustrated love for Jodie Foster, and suffering from a severe mental illness that caused his acts. The government, conceding that Hinckley was somewhat disturbed, argued that he nonetheless plotted and carried out the shooting as an easy means to achieve instant fame, and that he could have chosen not to attack the President. With expert opinion so deeply divided, why was acquittal a logical necessity? The answer is in the law on burden of proof—that is, who must prove what to the jury.

That law varies from jurisdiction to jurisdiction; in the federal court where Hinckley was tried, it happens to be unusually favorable to the defense. At the start, Hinckley, like all criminal defendants, was presumed by the law to be sane and therefore responsible for his conduct. But as soon as the defense introduced some evidence of insanity, the burden shifted to the prosecution. The defense was not obliged to prove that Hinckley was insane; the prosecution, on the other hand, *was* obliged to prove that he was sane, and to do so beyond a reasonable doubt. So even if the government's psychiatrists convinced the jury that Hinckley was probably sane, the picture drawn by the defense was enough to create a nagging doubt—and that, it turned out, was all it took.

The choice of experts for the defense team was deliberately unorthodox. For most insanity trials, lawyers hire forensic psychiatrists, professional witnesses who make a career of testifying in court and who engage in little outside medical practice. According to Dr. Willard Gaylin, a noted authority on psychiatry and law, "If you drew up a list of the fifty, one hundred, or ten thousand most prominent psychiatrists in the country, the doctors that lawyers use would not be on the list." These same psychiatrists turn up again and again in criminal cases. Like pro football players, they specialize in offense or defense, and their beliefs on critical issues seem to be determined more by the side they represent than by a fair examination of the issues.

The defense—in a stroke of brilliance or perhaps just an act of desperation— picked, as two of its three expert psychiatrists, eminent researchers in schizophrenia, Dr. Michael Bear and Dr. William Carpenter, neither of whom had prior courtroom experience. During the trial, the "untried" experts seemed awkward on the witness stand, especially in comparison with the polished performances of the experts on the opposing side; and the government argued that experts without criminal trial experience could not accurately evaluate criminal patients. The jury evidently disagreed.

The doubts raised by the defense psychiatrists were reinforced by other evidence. While awaiting trial, Hinckley twice tried to commit suicide. In May 1981 he swallowed a large number of Tylenol tablets. Six months later he jammed his cell door with a cracker box and hanged himself from the window bars. By the time guards climbed to his window from the outside and cut down his noose, he was turning blue. The judge was clearly worried that there might be a violent outburst or even another suicide attempt at the trial. Two federal marshals were stationed directly behind Hinckley at all times, with orders to keep lead pencils and paper clips out of his reach.

Sophisticated medical technology introduced physical evidence suggesting that Hinckley was abnormal. A CAT scan (a computer-enhanced, three-dimensional X-ray) showed organic abnormalities in Hinckley's brain, and a defense expert testified that folds, or solci, showed signs of atrophy. The prosecution challenged this testimony with its own expert who saw no evidence of atrophy in the brain pictures. If the atrophy does exist, it by no means proves that Hinckley was mentally ill, even though atrophy occurs ten times more often in schizophrenics than in apparently normal adults (30 percent versus 3 percent). But the effect of this evidence was to plant additional seeds of doubt.

The jury's doubts may also have been

167

strengthened by the grave errors committed by psychiatrists who treated Hinckley during the year before the shooting. Dr. Michael Hopper, who saw Hinckley about a dozen times, prescribed biofeedback and meditation exercises. He convinced Hinckley's father to banish Hinckley from home—despite the anguished protests of Hinckley's brother and sister, who felt that he could not cope in the outside world and wanted him committed to a mental hospital. Both Hopper and another psychiatrist, whom Hinckley saw while a student in Texas, treated him with valium for his complaints. Yet many doctors say that valium is "contraindicated" for schizophrenics, because it may cause violent behavior. According to the defense, to prescribe the drug for Hinckley was a medical disaster, or in the words of one of his lawyers, it was "like throwing gasoline on a lighted fire." Only hours before shooting Reagan, Hinckley says, he took twenty milligrams of valium, two to four times the usual dosage.

Survey the evidence of the defense on the issue of Hinckley's sanity: the suicide attempts, the CAT scan, the blunders of Dr. Hopper and other psychiatrists Hinckley was seeing, the experts' evaluations, and the emotional descriptions of Hinckley's troubles by his immediate family. Then consider the prosecution's case: the expert psychiatrists and the testimony of police and a physician who said Hinckley was calm and rational immediately after his arrest. And finally, recall the prosecution's very heavy burden of proof: to show decisively that Hinckley was sane.

Yet the announcement of the verdict had an extraordinary impact. Seasoned courtroom observers present during the entire trial were shocked. Why were they so certain that the jury would reject the insanity defense and convict Hinckley?

The first and greatest obstacle to acquittal was the undisputed fact that Hinckley had fired a bullet into the body of the President of the United States. During the past two decades, there have been eight attempts to murder Presidents, Presidential candidates, and other national leaders. Four victims died (John and Robert Kennedy, Martin Luther King, and Allard Lowenstein), one was crippled for life (George Wallace), one was seriously wounded (Ronald Reagan), and one emerged unscathed from two separate attempts (Jerry Ford). How, it was asked, could the jury possibly find Hinckley not guilty, knowing the message that it would send to potential assassins?

The second obstacle was the well-established reluctance of juries to acquit by reason of insanity except in the most extreme and obvious cases of mental disturbance. In federal court, where Hinckley was tried, the test for insanity is met if the defendant engages in criminal conduct either because he "lacks substantial capacity to appreciate the wrongfulness of his conduct or to conform his conduct to the requirements of law." But experienced trial lawyers know that this or any other legal formula has little impact on jurors, who tend to follow their own intuitive judgments regardless of what they are told by the judge. One criminal attorney calls it the "fireplug rule." He explains, "Jurors think you're sane unless you're a fireplug or swinging from the trees"—that is, unless you're stark staring mad or stark raving mad—and Hinckley is neither." Empirical studies bear out this impression. Juries in mock trials tend to reach the same results whether the definition of insanity they are given is broad or narrow, and they acquit only the most extremely and obviously mentally ill.

Prosecutor Roger Adelman certainly tried to appeal to the fireplug rule. Cross-examining defense expert William Carpenter, who claimed that Hinckley had suffered from schizophrenia for a number of years, Adelman demanded: "Didn't the defendant attend a Texas college and receive an A-minus on a book report? Didn't he manage to make plane reservations? Didn't he find his way in and out of New York City? And wasn't this during the same time you say he was suffering from schizophrenia?"

The third obstacle was the reluctance of juries to acquit if it leads to early release of the defendant. An informal poll I conducted of spectators queued up to enter the trial illustrates the point. Everyone in line agreed on two points: first, that Hinckley was absolutely loony, and second, that he should be convicted so that he'd be off the streets. What was the jury told about the consequences of a successful insanity defense? The judge answered for them in terms of abstract legal principles. Hinckley would be automatically committed to a mental hospital for fifty days, and he would then be entitled to a hearing to determine his eligibility for release. After that, he could seek a review in six months. This made it sound as if Hinckley could very well get out in a few years or even months.

In fact, Hinckley's future prospects are far less promising. Despite the acquittal, it seems certain that he will be confined for decades, if not for the rest of his life. He could be released only if a judge, after hearing from psychiatrists, finds that he is no longer dangerous. But what psychiatrist, even for hire, would risk such a prediction? And, if such a psychiatrist could be found, what judge would accept the prediction and order Hinckley's release? The jury, however, almost certainly could not learn these practical aspects from the theoretical cast of the instructions. The law does not require further explanation, and Judge Barrington Parker did not offer it on his own.

When these three obstacles are considered, it seems inconceivable that all twelve jurors could have found Hinckley not guilty. If ever there were a case in which the jury could be expected to suppress its "reasonable doubt," this was it. The overwhelming sentiment against the verdict indicates that the insanity defense is in need of substantial modification or, better, outright abolition.

One possibility is to lighten the government's burden of proof. Had Hinckley not been tried in a federal court—in a local District of Columbia court, for example—he could have faced an entirely different rule. The District of Columbia requires the defendant to carry the burden and to show "by a preponderance of the evidence" that he was insane. The case ended up in a federal rather than a local court, by the way, because of the recently enacted federal anti-assassination law. One of the ironies of this case is that a law designed expressly to protect Presidents made it easier to acquit someone who actually shot one.

But this does not mean that the federal burden of proof was necessarily the cause of the jury's failure to convict Hinckley. It does make it possible to say that acquittal was logically required. But in light of the jury's unanimous insanity verdict, it is doubtful that all twelve members would have convicted Hinckley even under a tougher burden of proof. At most, the result might have been a hung jury rather than a verdict of not guilty by reason of insanity.

A second possibility is to return to the narrow definition of insanity that existed in the nineteenth century, which called for acquittal only if the defendant could not tell right from wrong and this was the cause of the criminal act. In recent weeks there have been serious proposals to adopt the narrowest definition. But these efforts to reshape the boundaries of the legal definition of insanity are problematic, since jurors will continue to apply their own judgments of what is mentally aberrant.

Does, then, the insanity defense achieve its stated purposes? One argument is that it serves an important symbolic function: by excluding from blame those who commit crimes due to mental disease, we affirm that most will be held morally responsible. But instead of affirming moral responsibility, in the Hinckley case acquittal negates it. Particularly because the victim was the President, much of the public believes that Hinckley has duped the system and evaded responsibility for his acts.

And suppose that despite the very long odds against Hinckley's release, his attorneys contest his civil commitment at some point in the near future. Then the public will see positions flip-flop. The defense argued that Hinckley was sick; now it must contend that he is well. The government argues that he was well; now it must say that he is sick. As a matter of strict logic, neither side is being inconsistent, since the insanity defense is concerned with the moment when the crime was commited, and the focus of civil commitment is on future conduct. But this distinction is lost on the public, and the unseemly switch in positions will not do much for the principle of moral responsibility.

A second argument for the insanity defense is that it's wrong to punish someone who does not have the capacity for free choice. A six-year-old child, for example, who finds a loaded gun and pulls the trigger is not held criminally responsible for murder. By analogy, it is said, crimes caused by mental illness should not be punished. But the analogy is flawed. Although no one can pinpoint the precise moment when a child is sufficiently mature to be held responsible, the law uses age to draw a rough and ready, but distinct, line. But how do you tell whether an adult has free will?

Psychiatrists have tried to apply the concept of mental illness in determining who does and does not have free will. This approach mistakenly suggests that the process of detecting psychological disturbances closely resembles diagnosis of physical disease. Tuberculosis, for example, can be diagnosed according to reasonably objective criteria — the reaction to a skin test or the pattern on a chest X-ray—and has an established physical cause, the tuberculin bacillus. But the diagnostic criteria for schizophrenia are highly subjective. One person's delusions may be another's religion. As Lily Tomlin says, "If you speak to God, it's prayer; if God speaks to you, it's schizophrenia." The inherent vagueness in the concept of mental illness was illustrated in the furious debate between psychiatrists for the defense and the prosecution in the Hinckley case. And even if psychiatric detection of mental illness were reliable, there is a further issue: has the mental issue seriously impaired the defendant's free will? This is a question for a moral philosopher, not a medical psychiatrist.

For these reasons the insanity defense as it now exists should be abolished. It would, of course, be inhumane to find someone like Hinckley guilty and send him to prison without doing more. However heinous his acts and however much he deserves to be convicted, Hinckley is still terribly sick and needs psychiatric help for the period of his confinement. In this context, the analogy to physical illness is much more persuasive. Would we deny a convict treatment for TB, simply because he has been found guilty of a crime? Ideally, then, insanity should be relevant, not for the jury on the issue of guilt or innocence, but for the judge on sentencing. It should be reflected in the conditions under which the defendant is confined after conviction, and not in the jury's verdict on criminal responsibility.

The modern insanity standard evolved from an earlier political assassination case. In the 1840s, Daniel M'Naghten killed the private secretary of Sir Robert Peel, the British Prime Minister, in a bungled attempt on Peel's life. Although M'Naghten's acquittal by reason of insanity outraged the public at the time and seriously affronted Queen Victoria, the House of Lords upheld the verdict on appeal. If Hinckley's trial causes the insanity defense to be abolished, we will have come full circle. Political assassinations will have established and then abolished the insanity defense.

NO

Richard J. Bonnie

THE MORAL BASIS OF THE INSANITY DEFENSE

Two fundamentally distinct questions are intertwined in discussions of the insanity defense. One concerns the moral issue of responsibility, a question looking backward to the offender's mental condition at the time of the offense. The other is essentially dispositional and looks forward in time: what should be done with mentally disordered offenders, including those who are acquitted by reason of insanity, to minimize the risk of future recidivism?

This article addresses the issue of responsibility. Sweeping proposals to abolish the insanity defense should be rejected in favor of proposals to narrow it and shift the burden of proof to the defendant. The moral core of the defense must be retained, in my opinion, because some defendants afflicted by severe mental disorder who are out of touch with reality and are unable to appreciate the wrongfulness of their acts cannot justly be blamed and do not therefore deserve to be punished. The insanity defense, in short, is essential to the moral integrity of the criminal law.

But there are several observations to be made about the dispositional issues now receiving legislative attention.

First, the present dissatisfaction with the insanity defense is largely rooted in public concern about the premature release of dangerous persons acquitted by reason of insanity. Increased danger to the public, however, is not a necessary consequence of the insanity defense. The public can be better protected than is now the case in many states by a properly designed dispositional statute that assures that violent offenders acquitted by reason of insanity are committed for long-term treatment, including a period of postdischarge supervision or "hospital parole."

Second, a separate verdict of "guilty but mentally ill," which has been enacted in several states, is an ill-conceived way of identifying prisoners who are amenable to psychiatric treatment. It surely makes no sense for commitment procedures to be triggered by a jury verdict based on evidence

From "The Moral Basis of the Insanity Defense," *American Bar Association Journal,* 69, February 1983. Reprinted by permission of the *American Bar Association Journal.*

concerning the defendant's past rather than present mental condition and need for treatment. Decisions concerning the proper placement of incarcerated offenders should be made by correctional and mental health authorities, not by juries or trial judges. Of course, the "guilty but mentally ill verdict" may not reflect dispositional objectives so much as it does a desire to afford juries a "compromise" verdict in cases involving insanity pleas. If so, it should be rejected as nothing more than moral sleight of hand.

Third, it is often said that the participation of mental health professionals in criminal proceedings should be confined to the sentencing stage. Clinical expertise is likely to be most useful on dispositional rather than on responsibility questions, and, indeed, most clinical participation in the criminal process now occurs at the sentencing stage. Expert witnesses, however, cannot be excluded from the guilt stage so long as the defendant's mental condition is regarded as morally relevant to his criminal liability.

This brings the inquiry back to the issue of criminal responsibility.

The historical evolution of the insanity defense has been influenced by the ebb and flow of informed opinion concerning scientific understanding of mental illness and its relation to criminal behavior. But it is well to remember that, at bottom, the debate about the insanity defense and the idea of criminal responsibility raises fundamentally moral questions, not scientific ones. As Lord Hale observed three centuries ago, in *History of Pleas of the Crown,* the ethical foundations of the criminal law are rooted in beliefs about human rationality, deterrability, and free will. But these are articles of moral faith rather than scientific fact.

Some critics of the insanity defense believe that mentally ill persons are not substantially less able to control their behavior than normal persons and that, in any case, a decent respect for the dignity of those persons requires that they be held accountable for their wrong-doing on the same terms as everyone else. On the other hand, proponents of the defense, among whom I count myself, believe that it is fundamentally wrong to condemn and punish a person whose rational control over his or her behavior was impaired by the incapacitating effects of severe mental illness.

Few would dispute this as a moral claim. The question is how best to describe the moral criterion of irresponsibility and to minimize the number of cases in which the defense is successfully invoked by persons who should properly be punished.

CRIMINAL RESPONSIBILITY: THE OPTIONS

Putting aside details concerning the drafting of various tests, there are, in principle, three approaches to the insanity defense.

The Model Penal Code

One option is to leave the law as it now stands in a majority of the states and, by judicial ruling, in all of the federal courts. Apart from technical variations, this means the test proposed by the American Law Institute in its Model Penal Code. Under this approach, a person whose perceptual capacities were sufficiently intact that he had the criminal "intent" or mens rea required in the definition of the offense nonetheless can be found "not guilty by reason of insanity" if, by virtue of mental disease or defect, he lacked substantial capacity either to understand or appreciate the legal or moral significance of his actions, or to conform his conduct to the requirements of law. In other words, a person may be excused if his thinking was severely disordered—the so-called cognitive prong of the defense—or if his ability to control his behavior was severely impaired—the so-called volitional prong of the defense.

Revival of M'Naghten

The second option is to retain the insanity defense as an independent exculpatory doctrine—independent, that is, of mens rea—but to restrict its scope by eliminating the volitional prong. This approach would revive the M'Naghten test as the sole basis for exculpation on ground of insanity. This is the approach I favor, although I would modify the language used by the House of Lords in 1843 in favor of modern terminology that is simpler and has more clinical meaning. M'Naghten is now distinctly the minority position in this country. Fewer than one third of the states use this approach, although it is still the law in England.

Abolition: The Mens Rea Approach

The third option is the "mens rea" approach, which has been adopted in two states and has been endorsed by the Reagan administration. Its essential substantive effect is to abolish any criterion of exculpation, based on mental disease, that is independent of the mens rea elements of particular crimes. Instead, mentally ill (or retarded) defendants would be treated like everyone else.

CASE AGAINST THE MENS REA APPROACH

If the insanity defense were abolished, the law would not take adequate account of the incapacitating effects of severe mental illness. Some mentally ill defendants who were psychotic and grossly out of touch with reality may be said to have "intended" to do what they did but nonetheless may have been so severely disturbed that they were unable to understand or appreciate the significance of their actions. These cases do not arise frequently, but when they do a criminal conviction, which signifies the societal judgment that the defendant deserves to be punished, would offend the basic moral intuitions of the community. Judges and juries would be forced either to return a verdict of conviction, which they would regard as morally obtuse, or to acquit the defendant in defiance of the law. They should be spared that moral embarrassment.

The moral difficulty with the mens rea approach is illustrated by a case involving Joy Baker, a 31-year-old woman who shot and killed her aunt. According to her account—which no one has ever doubted—she became increasingly agitated and fearful during the days before the shooting; she was worried that her dogs, her children (ages eight and 11), and her neighbors were becoming possessed by the devil and that she was going to be "annihilated." On the morning of the shooting, after a sleepless night, she ran frantically around the house clutching a gun to her breast. Worried about what the children might do to her if they became demonically "possessed" and about what she might do to them to defend herself, she made them read and reread the 23d Psalm. Suddenly her aunt arrived unexpectedly. Unable to open the locked front door, and ignoring Mrs. Baker's frantic pleas to go away, the aunt came to the back door. When she reached through the broken screening to unlock the door, Mrs. Baker shot her.

The aunt then fell backward into the mud behind the porch, bleeding profusely.

"Why, Joy?" she asked. "Because you're the devil, and you came to hurt me," Joy answered. Her aunt said, "Honey, no, I came to help you." At this point, Mrs. Baker said, she became very confused and "I took the gun and shot her again just to relieve the pain she was having because she said she was hurt."

All the psychiatrists who examined Mrs. Baker concluded that she was acutely psychotic at the time she killed her aunt. The police who arrested her and others in the small rural community agreed that she must have been crazy because there was no rational explanation for her conduct. She was acquitted. Yet, had there been no insanity defense, she could have been acquitted only in defiance of the law. Although she was clearly out of touch with reality and unable to understand the wrongfulness of her conduct, she had the "criminal intent" or mens rea required for some form of criminal homicide. If we look only at her conscious motivation for the second shot and do not take into account her highly regressed and disorganized emotional condition, she was technically guilty of murder (euthanasia being no justification, of course). Moreover, even if the first shot had been fatal, she probably would have been guilty of manslaughter because her delusional belief that she was in imminent danger of demonic annihilation was, by definition, unreasonable.

These technical points, of course, may make little practical difference in the courtroom. If the expert testimony in Joy Baker's case were admitted to disprove mens rea, juries might ignore the law and decide, very bluntly, whether the defendant was "too crazy" to be convicted. The cause of rational criminal law reform, however, is not well served by designing rules of law in the expectation that they will be ignored or

nullified when they appear unjust in individual cases.

THE CASE FOR NARROWING THE DEFENSE

While I do not favor abolition of the "cognitive" prong of the insanity defense, I agree with critics who believe the risks of fabrication and "moral mistakes" in administering the defense are greatest when the experts and the jury are asked to speculate whether the defendant had the capacity to "control" himself or whether he could have "resisted" the criminal impulse. I favor narrowing the defense by eliminating its so-called volitional prong or control test.

Few people would dispute the moral predicate for the control test—that a person who "cannot help" doing what he did is not blameworthy. Unfortunately, however, there is no scientific basis for measuring a person's capacity for self-control or for calibrating the impairment of that capacity. There is, in short, no objective basis for distinguishing between offenders who were undeterrable and those who were merely undeterred, between the impulse that was irresistable and the impulse not resisted, or between substantial impairment of capacity and some lesser impairment. Whatever the precise terms of the volitional test, the question is unanswerable, or it can be answered only by "moral guesses." To ask it at all invites fabricated claims, undermines equal administration of the penal law, and compromises its deterrent effect.

Sheldon Glueck of the Harvard Law School observed in *Mental Disorder and the Criminal Law* (1925) that the 19th century effort to establish irresistible impulse as a defense met judicial resistance because "much less than we know today

175

was known of mental disease." He predicted "that with the advent of a more scientific administration of the law—especially with the placing of expert testimony upon a neutral, unbiased basis and in the hands of well-qualified experts—much of the opposition to judicial recognition of the effect of disorders of the . . . impulses should disappear." He added that "expert, unbiased study of the individual case will aid judge and jury to distinguish cases of pathological irresistible impulse from those in which the impulse was merely unresisted."

The opposition to the control test did not disappear in Professor Glueck's generation. In 1955, when the Model Penal Code was being drafted, *M'Naghten* still constituted the exclusive test of insanity in two thirds of the states. Advances in clinical understanding of mental illness in the 1940s and 1950s, however, inspired a new era of optimism about the potential contributions of psychiatry to a progressive and humane penal law. This renewed optimism was reflected in the model code's responsibility test that included "substantial" volitional impairment as an independent ground of exculpation.

The Model Penal Code has had an extraordinary impact on criminal law. For this we should be thankful, but I believe the code approach to criminal responsibility should be rejected. Psychiatric concepts of mental abnormality remain fluid and imprecise, and most academic commentary within the last ten years continues to question the scientific basis for assessment of volitional incapacity.

The volitional inquiry probably would be manageable if the insanity defense were permitted only in cases involving psychotic disorders. When the control test is combined with a loose or broad interpretation of the term "mental disease," however, the inevitable result is unstructured clinical speculation regarding the "causes" of criminal behavior in any case in which a defendant can be said to have a personality disorder, an impulse disorder, or any other diagnosable abnormality.

For example, it is clear enough in theory that the insanity defense is not supposed to be a ground for acquittal of persons with weak behavior controls who misbehave because of anger, jealousy, fear, or some other strong emotion. These emotions may account for a large proportion of all homicides and other assaultive crimes. Many crimes are committed by persons who are not acting "normally" and who are emotionally disturbed at the time. It is not uncommon to say that they are temporarily "out of their minds." But this is not what the law means or should mean by "insanity." Because the control test, as now construed in most states, entitles defendants to insanity instructions on the basis of these claims, I am convinced that the test involves an unacceptable risk of abuse and mistake.

It might be argued, of course, that the risk of mistake should be tolerated if the volitional prong of the defense is morally necessary. The question may be put this way: Are there clinically identifiable cases involving defendants whose behavior controls were so pathologically impaired that they ought to be acquitted although their ability to appreciate the wrongfulness of their actions was unimpaired? I do not think so. The most clinically compelling cases of volitional impairment involve the so-called impulse disorders—pyromania, kleptomania, and the like. These disorders involve severely abnormal compulsions that ought to be taken into account in sentencing, but the exculpation of pyromaniacs would be out of touch with commonly shared moral intuitions.

A PROPOSED TEST

The sole test of legal insanity should be whether the defendant, as a result of severe mental disease, was unable "to appreciate the wrongfulness of his conduct." My statute would read:

"Defense of [Insanity] [Nonresponsibility Due to Mental Disease].

"A. A person charged with a criminal offense shall be found [not guilty by reason of insanity] [not guilty only by reason of insanity] [not responsible due to mental disease] [guilty of a criminal act but not responsible due to mental disease] if he proves, by the greater weight of the evidence, that, as a result of mental disease or mental retardation, he was unable to appreciate the wrongfulness of his conduct at the time of the offense.

"B. As used in this section, the terms mental disease or mental retardation include only those severely abnormal mental conditions that grossly and demonstrably impair a person's perception or understanding of reality and that are not attributable primarily to the voluntary ingestion of alcohol or other psychoactive substances."

This language, drawn from the Model Penal Code, uses clinically meaningful terms to ask the same question posed by the House of Lords in *M'Naghten* 150 years ago. It is a necessary and sufficient test of criminal responsibility. During the past ten years we have evaluated hundreds of cases at our clinic. Only a handful have involved what I would regard as morally compelling claims of irresponsibility, and all of these would be comprehended by the proposed formulation. This test is fully compatible with the ethical premises of the penal law. Results reached by judges and juries in particular cases ordinarily would be congruent with the community's moral sense.

Some clinicians have argued that the volitional prong of the defense is morally necessary to take adequate account of psychotic deterioration, especially in cases involving affective disorders like manic-depressive illness. My view is that a test of insanity that focuses exclusively on the defendant's ability to "appreciate the wrongfulness of his conduct" is broad enough to encompass all cases of severe psychotic deterioration. This is because the term "appreciate" is designed to encompass "affective" dimensions of major mental illness.

BURDEN OF PERSUASION

Much has been said about the proper allocation of the burden of proof since the Hinckley trial. This issue does not arise under the mens rea option, because the prosecution clearly must bear the burden of proving all elements of the crime beyond a reasonable doubt. If the insanity defense is retained as an independent basis of exculpation, the argument may be put that the defendant should bear the burden of persuading the fact-finder of the truth or sufficiency of his claim.

Some commentators have argued that the prosecution should bear the burden of persuading the fact-finder, beyond a reasonable doubt, of all facts regarded as necessary to establish an ethically adequate predicate for criminal liability. When so-called defenses are concerned, the question is whether a just penal law could fail to give exculpatory effect to the claim. Consider entrapment and self-defense, for example. If the law need not recognize the defense at all—as is true for claims of entrapment, I submit—it is entirely proper to recognize it only if the defendant bears the risk of nonpersuasion. If exculpation is morally required if certain facts exist—as is true for claims of self-defense, I would argue—then, as a general rule, the prosecution should bear the risk and be required to negate the existence of those facts beyond a reasonable doubt.

The issue in the present context is whether the insanity defense presents any special considerations that warrant a departure from the general rule disfavoring burden shifting on ethically essential predicates for liability. This is a close question, but on balance, I think the answer is yes. In defenses of justification (self-defense) and situational excuses (duress), the defendant's claim must be linked to external realities and can be tested against ordinary experience, thereby reducing the likelihood of successful fabrication or jury confusion. A defendant's claim that he had a mental disorder that disabled him from function-ing as a normal person, however, is not linked to the external world and by definition cannot be tested against ordinary experience. The concept of knowing, understanding, or appreciating the legal or moral significance of one's actions also is more fluid and less precise than many aspects of the elements of the penal law.

PUBLIC CONCERNS SATISFIED

The insanity defense, as I have defined it, should be narrowed, not abandoned, and the burden of persuasion may properly be shifted to the defendant. Like the mens rea proposal, this approach adequately responds to public concern about possible misuse of the insanity defense. Unlike the mens rea proposal, it is compatible with the basic doctrines and principles of Anglo-American penal law.

POSTSCRIPT

SHOULD THE INSANITY DEFENSE
BE ABOLISHED?

Since the Hinckley verdict three states—Idaho, Montana, and Utah—have abolished the insanity defense. Several other states—including Alaska, Georgia, Illinois, Indiana, Kentucky, Michigan, Delaware, and New Mexico—have established verdicts of "Guilty but mentally ill." Others are considering similar revisions of their criminal law, and several different proposals have been introduced at the federal level.

Several major professional organizations—the American Bar Association (ABA), the American Psychiatric Association (APA), the National Mental Health Association (NMHA), and the American Medical Association (AMA) have issued reports on the subject. Both the ABA and the APA oppose abolition of the insanity defense and the establishment of "Guilty but mentally ill" statutes, which they consider the same as abolition, but they support revisions that would limit the use of the defense to grossly psychotic individuals. In effect, their proposals would return the standard to the McNaughton Rule, which focused on the defendant's ability to understand the consequences of his action rather than his ability to control them. The NMHA, on the other hand, stressed that the public fear of the defense was based on "myths" rather than realities. Nevertheless, it acknowledged the public's concern and suggested an alternate defense called "Not responsible by reason of insanity." The AMA supports the abolition of the special defense of insanity and its replacement by a statute providing for acquittal when the defendant, as a result of mental disease or defect, lacks the state of mind required for a criminal intent.

For the texts of the ABA and APA proposals, see *Mental Disability Law Reporter* (March-April 1983); the NMHA's report was published under the title *Myths and Realities* in March 1983 by the association in Arlington, Virginia. The AMA's report was published in the *Journal of the American Medical Association* (June 8, 1984). Two books that favor revision of the insanity defense are Norval Morris, *Madness and the Criminal Law* (Chicago, 1982) and William Winslade and Judith Ross, *The Insanity Plea* (Scribner's, 1983). The relationship between law and psychiatry in a dramatic murder case is explored in Willard Gaylin, *Who Killed Bonnie Garland?* (Simon & Schuster, 1982). Also see *By Reason of Insanity*, edited by Lawrence Zelic Freedman (Scholarly Resources, 1983) and *The Insanity Defense and the Trial of John W. Hinckley, Jr.*, by Lincoln Caplan (Godine, 1984).

ISSUE 11

IS INVOLUNTARY COMMITMENT TO MENTAL INSTITUTIONS IMMORAL?

YES: Thomas S. Szasz, from "Involuntary Mental Hospitalization: A Crime Against Humanity," in *Ideology and Insanity* (New York: Doubleday, 1970)

NO: Paul Chodoff, from "The Case for Involuntary Hospitalization of the Mentally Ill," *American Journal of Psychiatry* 133:5 (May 1976)

ISSUE SUMMARY

YES: Psychiatrist Thomas S. Szasz maintains that the detention of persons in mental institutions against their will is a crime against humanity. People are committed not because they are "mentally ill" or "dangerous" but because society wants to control their behavior.

NO: Psychiatrist Paul Chodoff believes that the rights of the mentally ill to be treated are being set aside in the rush to give them their freedom. He favors a return to the use of medical criteria by psychiatrists, albeit with legal safeguards.

In every society, some people behave in odd and nonconforming ways, though what is considered abnormal may vary considerably. Throughout history explanations of why some people are "crazy" or "mad" have varied: The moon was the cause (hence "lunatic"), thought some early peoples; the devil or spirits did it, thought others. Some of these deviant people were kept in chains and displayed publicly for the amusement of the crowds; others were loaded onto "ships of fools" and set free to wander. Still others were tolerated within their community or even respected because they were thought to have special powers. As early as 1400 in England a special institution designed to house the outcasts—Bethlehem Royal Hospital, or "Bedlam"—was established. One can only imagine what it was like, since "bedlam" now means a place of great confusion and disorder.

In our own times, the most prevalent view is that people whose behavior is strange and often self-destructive are "sick" and need treatment. They are, it is said, "mentally ill." The medical model of deviant behavior developed in the nineteenth century as part of the growth of scientific knowledge, the belief in rationality, and a sense of social responsibility about the helpless. Laws permitting people to be hospitalized in mental institutions against their will are based on the assumption, inherent in the medical model, that the state has a right—even an obligation—to provide treatment for those whose condition has impaired their capacity for rational thought.

Against the conventional view is the philosophy of an influential group of "anti-psychiatrists." Two of the most prominent—R.D. Laing of Scotland and Thomas S. Szasz of the United States—were themselves trained as psychiatrists. But they reject the notion that there is such a thing as "mental illness"; it is, they say, only a label that society has placed on those whose behavior it rejects, for social, ethical, political, aesthetic, or other reasons.

In the U.S., the pendulum has swung back and forth between periods in which involuntary commitment has been relatively easy to accomplish and periods in which its use has been restricted. As psychiatrist Paul S. Appelbaum has put it, "When concern with rapid treatment has been paramount (as in the Progressive Era at the turn of the century), procedures have been streamlined to permit greater physician and family discretion. On the other hand, when concern with civil liberties has been on the ascendance, as in the 1970s, procedures have come more closely to resemble the criminal model." In this model patients have rights of due process, including the right to an attorney and limited duration of stay.

An important limitation on the state's right to commit people to mental institutions was set forth in the 1975 Supreme Court decision of *Donaldson* v. *O'Connor.* That case involved Kenneth Donaldson, a forty-five-year-old man whose parents had committed him to a Florida mental hospital fifteen years earlier because they believed that he had a "persecution complex." The court ruled that the state cannot constitutionally confine a "nondangerous individual who is capable of surviving safely in freedom by himself or with the help of willing and responsible family members or friends."

The following selections represent two opposing views in this longstanding debate. Thomas S. Szasz cites medical, moral, historical, and literary evidence to show that commitment does not serve the purpose of helping or treating people whose behavior deviates from or threatens prevailing social norms or moral standards. Nor does it protect the rest of society from harm. Paul Chodoff insists that mental illness is not a myth and that those who suffer from it need care and treatment. With appropriate legal safeguards, involuntary commitment can be an effective and moral practice.

YES

Thomas S. Szasz

INVOLUNTARY
MENTAL HOSPITALIZATION:
A CRIME AGAINST HUMANITY

I

For some time now I have maintained that commitment—that is, the detention of persons in mental institutions against their will—is a form of imprisonment;[1] that such deprivation of liberty is contrary to the moral principles embodied in the Declaration of Independence and the Constitution of the United States;[2] and that it is a crass violation of contemporary concepts of fundamental rights.[3] The practice of "sane" men incarcerating their "insane" fellow men in "mental hospitals" can be compared to that of white men enslaving black men. In short, I consider commitment a crime against humanity.

Existing social institutions and practices, especially if honored by prolonged usage, are generally experienced and accepted as good and valuable. For thousands of years slavery was considered a "natural" social arrangement for the securing of human labor; it was sanctioned by public opinion, religious dogma, church, and state;[4] it was abolished a mere one hundred years ago in the United States; and it is still a prevalent social practice in some parts of the world, notably in Africa.[5] Since its origin, approximately three centuries ago, commitment of the insane has enjoyed equally widespread support; physicians, lawyers, and the laity have asserted, as if with a single voice, the therapeutic desirability and social necessity of institutional psychiatry. My claim that commitment is a crime against humanity may thus be countered—as indeed it has been—by maintaining, first, that the practice is beneficial for the mentally ill, and second, that it is necessary for the protection of the mentally healthy members of society.

Illustrative of the first argument is Slovenko's assertion that "Reliance solely on voluntary hospital admission procedures ignores the fact that some persons may desire care and custody but cannot communicate their desire directly."[6] Imprisonment in mental hospitals is here portrayed—by a professor of law!—as a service provided to persons by the state because they "desire" it but do not know how to ask for it. Felix defends involuntary mental hospitalization by asserting simply, "We *do* [his italics] deal with illnesses of the mind."[7]

Illustrative of the second argument is Guttmacher's characterization of my book *Law, Liberty, and Psychiatry* as ". . . a pernicious book . . . certain to produce intolerable and unwarranted anxiety in the families of psychiatric patients."[8] This is an admission of the fact that the families of "psychiatric patients" frequently resort to the use of force in order to control their "loved ones," and that when attention is directed to this practice it creates embarrassment and guilt. On the other hand, Felix simply defines the psychiatrist's duty as the protection of society: "Tomorrow's psychiatrist will be, as is his counterpart today, one of the gatekeepers of his community."[9]

These conventional explanations of the nature and uses of commitment are, however, but culturally accepted justifications for certain quasi-medical forms of social control, exercised especially against individuals and groups whose behavior does not violate criminal laws but threatens established social values.

II

What is the evidence that commitment does not serve the purpose of helping or treating people whose behavior deviates from or threatens prevailing social norms or moral standards; and who, because they inconvenience their families, neighbors, or superiors, may be incriminated as "mentally ill"?

1. *The medical evidence.* Mental illness is a metaphor. If by "disease" we mean a disorder of the physiochemical machinery of the human body, then we can assert that what we call functional mental diseases are not diseases at all.[10] Persons said to be suffering from such disorders are socially deviant or inept, or in conflict with individuals, groups, or institutions. Since they do not suffer from disease, it is impossible to "treat" them for any sickness.

Although the term "mentally ill" is usually applied to persons who do not suffer from bodily disease, it is sometimes applied also to persons who do (for example, to individuals intoxicated with alcohol or other drugs, or to elderly people suffering from degenerative disease of the brain). However, when patients with demonstrable diseases of the brain are involuntarily hospitalized, the primary purpose is to exercise social control over their behavior;[11] treatment of the disease is, at best, a secondary consideration. Frequently, therapy is non-existent, and custodial care is dubbed "treatment."

In short, the commitment of persons suffering from "functional psychoses" serves moral and social, rather than medical and therapeutic, purposes. Hence, even if, as a result of future research, certain conditions now believed to be "functional" mental illnesses were to be shown to be "organic," my argument against involuntary mental hospitalization would remain unaffected.

2. *The moral evidence.* In free societies, the relationship between physician and patient is predicated on the legal presumption that the individual "owns" his body and his personality.[12] The physician can examine and treat a patient only with his consent; the latter is free to reject treatment (for example, an operation for cancer).[13] After death, "ownership" of the person's body is transferred to his heirs; the physician must obtain permission from the patient's relatives for a postmortem examination. John Stuart Mill explicity affirmed that ". . . each person is the proper guar-

dian of his own health, whether bodily, or mental and spiritual."[14] Commitment is incompatible with this moral principle.

3. *The historical evidence.* Commitment practices flourished long before there were any mental or psychiatric "treatments" of "mental diseases." Indeed, madness or mental illness was not always a necessary condition for commitment. For example, in the seventeenth century, "children of artisans and other poor inhabitants of Paris up to the age of 25, . . . girls who were debauched or in evident danger of being debauched, . . ." and other "misérables" of the community, such as epileptics, people with venereal diseases, and poor people with chronic diseases of all sorts, were all considered fit subjects for confinement in the Hôpital Général.[15] And, in 1860, when Mrs. Packard was incarcerated for disagreeing with her minister-husband,[16] the commitment laws of the State of Illinois explicitly proclaimed that ". . . married women . . . may be entered or detained in the hospital at the request of the husband of the woman or the guardian. . . ., without the evidence of insanity required in other cases."[17] It is surely no coincidence that this piece of legislation was enacted and enforced at about the same time that Mill published his essay *The Subjection of Women.*[18]

4. *The literary evidence.* Involuntary mental hospitalization plays a significant part in numerous short stories and novels from many countries. In none that I have encountered is commitment portrayed as helpful to the hospitalized person; instead, it is always depicted as an arrangement serving interests antagonistic of those of the so-called patient.[19]

III

The claim that commitment of the "mentally ill" is necessary for the protection of the "mentally healthy" is more difficult to refute, not because it is valid, but because the danger that "mental patients" supposedly pose is of such an extremely vague nature.

1. *The medical evidence.* The same reasoning applies as earlier: If "mental illness" is not a disease, there is no medical justification for protection from disease. Hence, the analogy between mental illness and contagious disease falls to the ground: The justification for isolating or otherwise constraining patients with tuberculosis or typhoid fever cannot be extended to patients with "mental illness."

Moreover, because the accepted contemporary psychiatric view of mental illness fails to distinguish between illness as a biological condition and as a social role,[20] it is not only false, but also dangerously misleading, especially if used to justify social action. In this view, regardless of its "causes"—anatomical, genetic, chemical, psychological, or social—mental illness has "objective existence." A person either has or has not a mental illness; he is either mentally sick or mentally healthy. Even if a person is cast in the role of mental patient against his will, his "mental illness" exists "objectively"; and even if, as in the cases of the Very Important Person, he is never treated as a mental patient, his "mental illness" still exists "objectively"— apart from the activities of the psychiatrist.[21]

The upshot is that the term "mental illness" is perfectly suited for mystification: It disregards the crucial question of whether the individual assumes the role of mental patient voluntarily, and hence wishes to engage in some sort of interaction with the psychiatrist; or whether he is cast in that role against his will, and hence is opposed to such a relationship.

This obscurity is then usually employed strategically, either by the subject himself to advance *his* interests, or by the subject's adversaries to advance *their* interests.

In contrast to this view, I maintain, first, that the involuntarily hospitalized mental patient is, by definition, the occupant of an ascribed role; and, second, that the "mental disease" of such a person—unless the use of this term is restricted to demonstrable lesions or malfunctions of the brain—is always the product of interaction between psychiatrist and patient.

2. *The moral evidence.* The crucial ingredient in involuntary mental hospitalization is coercion. Since coercion is the exercise of power, it is always a moral and political act. Accordingly, regardless of its medical justification, commitment is primarily a moral and political phenomenon— just as, regardless of its anthropological and economic justifications, slavery was primarily a moral and political phenomenon.

Although psychiatric methods of coercion are indisputably useful for those who enjoy them, they are clearly not indispensable for dealing with the problems that so-called mental patients pose for those about them. If an individual threatens others by virtue of his beliefs or actions, he could be dealt with by methods other than "medical"; if his conduct is ethically offensive, moral sanctions against him might be appropriate; if forbidden by law, legal sanctions might be appropriate. In my opinion, both informal, moral sanctions, such as social ostracism or divorce, and formal, judicial sanctions, such as fine and imprisonment, are more dignified and less injurious to the human spirit than the quasi-medical psychiatric sanction of involuntary mental hospitalization.[22]

3. *The historical evidence.* To be sure, confinement of so-called mentally ill persons does protect the community from certain problems. If it didn't, the arrangement would not have come into being and would not have persisted. However, the question we ought to ask is not *whether* commitment protects the community from "dangerous mental patients," but rather from precisely *what danger* it protects and by *what means?* In what way were prostitutes or vagrants dangerous in seventeenth-century Paris? Or married women in nineteenth-century Illinois?

It is significant, moreover, that there is hardly a prominent person who, during the past fifty years or so, has not been diagnosed by a psychiatrist as suffering from some type of "mental illness." Barry Goldwater was called a "paranoid schizophrenic";[23] Whittaker Chambers, a "psychopathic personality";[24] Woodrow Wilson, a "neurotic" frequently "very close to psychosis";[25] and Jesus, "a born degenerate" with a "fixed delusional system," and a "paranoid" with a "clinical picture [so typical] that it is hardly conceivable that people can even question the accuracy of the diagnosis."[26] The list is endless.

Sometimes, psychiatrists declare the same person sane *and* insane, depending on the political dictates of their superiors and the social demand of the moment. Before his trial and execution, Adolph Eichmann was examined by several psychiatrists, all of whom declared him to be normal; after he was put to death, "medical evidence" of his insanity was released and widely circulated.

According to Hannah Arendt, "Half a dozen psychiatrists had certified him [Eichmann] as 'normal.'" One psychiatrist asserted, " . . . his whole psychological outlook, his attitude toward his wife and children, mother and father, sisters and friends, was 'not only normal but most desirable.'. . ." And the minister who regularly visited him in prison declared that

Eichmann was "a man with very positive ideas."[27] After Eichmann was executed, Gideon Hausner, the Attorney General of Israel, who had prosecuted him, disclosed in an article in *The Saturday Evening Post* that psychiatrists diagnosed Eichmann as " 'a man obsessed with a dangerous and insatiable urge to kill,' 'a perverted, sadistic personality.' "[28]

Whether or not men like those mentioned above are considered "dangerous" depends on the observer's religious beliefs, political convictions, and social situation. Furthermore, the "dangerousness" of such persons—whatever we may think of them—is not analogous to that of a person with tuberculosis or typhoid fever; nor would rendering such a person "non-dangerous" be comparable to rendering a patient with a contagious disease non-infectious.

In short, I hold—and I submit that the historical evidence bears me out—that people are committed to mental hospitals neither because they are "dangerous," nor because they are "mentally ill," but rather because they are society's scapegoats, whose persecution is justified by psychiatric propaganda and rhetoric.[29]

4. *The literary evidence.* No one contests that involuntary mental hospitalization of the so-called dangerously insane "protects" the community. Disagreement centers on the nature of the threat facing society, and on the methods of legitimacy of the protection it employs. In this connection, we may recall that slavery, too, "protected" the community: it freed the slaveowners from manual labor. Commitment likewise shields the non-hospitalized members of society: first, from having to accommodate themselves to the annoying or idiosyncratic demands of certain members of the community who have not violated any criminal statutes; and, second,

from having to prosecute, try, convict, and punish members of the community who have broken the law but who either might not be convicted in court, or, if they would be, might not be restrained as effectively or as long in prison as in a mental hospital. The literary evidence cited earlier fully supports this interpretation of the function of involuntary mental hospitalization.

IV

I have suggested that commitment constitutes a social arrangement whereby one part of society secures certain advantages for itself at the expense of another part. To do so, the oppressors must possess an ideology to justify their aims and actions; and they must be able to enlist the police power of the state to impose their will on the oppressed members. What makes such an arrangement a "crime against humanity"? It may be argued that the use of state power is legitimate when law-abiding citizens punish lawbreakers. What is the difference between this use of state power and its use in commitment?

In the first place, the difference between committing the "insane" and imprisoning the "criminal" is the same as that between the rule of man and the rule of law:[30] whereas the "insane" are subjected to the coercive controls of the state because persons more powerful than they have labeled them as "psychotic," "criminals" are subjected to such controls because they have violated legal rules applicable equally to all.

The second difference between these two proceedings lies in their professed aims. The principal purpose of imprisoning criminals is to protect the liberties of the law-abiding members of society.[31] Since the individual subject to commitment is not considered a threat to liberty in the same way as the accused criminal is (if he were, he would be prosecuted), his removal from society cannot be justified on the same grounds. Justification for commitment must thus rest on its therapeutic promise and potential: it will help restore the "patient" to "mental health." But if this can be accomplished only at the cost of robbing the individual of liberty, "involuntary mental hospitalization" becomes only a verbal camouflage for what is, in effect, punishment. This "therapeutic" punishment differs, however, from traditional judicial punishment, in that the accused criminal enjoys a rich panoply of constitutional protections against false accusation and oppressive prosecution, whereas the accused mental patient is deprived of these protections.[32] . . .

NOTES

1. Szasz, T.S.: "Commitment of the mentally ill: Treatment or social restraint?" *J. Nerv. & Ment. Dis.* 125:293-307 (Apr.-June) 1957.

2. Szasz, T.S.: *Law, Liberty, and Psychiatry: An Inquiry into the Social Uses of Mental Health Practices* (New York: Macmillan, 1963), pp. 149-90.

3. *Ibid.*, pp. 223-55.

4. Davis, D.B.: *The Problem of Slavery in Western Culture* (Ithaca, N.Y.: Cornell University Press, 1966).

5. See Cohen, R.: "Slavery in Africa." *Trans-Action* 4:44-56 (Jan.-Feb.), 1967; Tobin, R.L.: "Slavery still plagues the earth." *Saturday Review*, May 6, 1967, pp. 24-25.

6. Slovenko, R.: "The psychiatric patient, liberty, and the law." *Amer. J. Psychiatry*, 121:534-39 (Dec.), 1964, p. 536.

7. Felix, R.H.: "The image of the psychiatrist: Past, present, and future." *Amer. J. Psychiatry*, 121:318-22 (Oct.), 1964, p. 320.

8. Guttmacher, M.S.: "Critique of views of Thomas Szasz on legal psychiatry." *AMA Arch. Gen. Psychiatry*, 10:238-45 (March), 1964, p. 244.

9. Felix, op. cit., p. 231.

10. See Szasz, T.S.: "The myth of mental illness." This volume [original source] pp. 12-24; *The Myth of Mental Illness: Foundations of a Theory of Personal Conduct* (New York: Hoeber-Harper, 1961); "Mental illness is a myth." *The New York Times Magazine*, June 12, 1966, pp. 30 and 90-92.

11. See, for example, Noyes, A.P.: *Modern Clinical Psychiatry*, 4th ed. (Philadelphia: Saunders, 1956), p. 278.

12. Szasz, T.S.: "The ethics of birth control; or, who owns your body?" *The Humanist*, 20:332-36 (Nov.-Dec.) 1960.

13. Hirsch, B.D.: "Informed consent to treatment," in Averbach, A. and Belli, M.M., eds., *Tort and Medical Yearbook* (Indianapolis: Bobbs-Merrill, 1961), Vol. I, pp. 631-38.

14. Mill, J.S.: *On Liberty* [1859] (Chicago: Regnery, 1955), p. 18.

15. Rosen, G.: "Social attitudes to irrationality and madness in 17th and 18th century Europe." *J. Hist. Med. & Allied Sciences*, 18:220-40 (1963), p. 223.

16. Packard, E.W.P.: *Modern Persecution, or Insane Asylums Unveiled*, 2 Vols. (Hartford: Case, Lockwood, and Brainard, 1873).

17. Illinois Statute Book, Sessions Laws 15, Section 10, 1851. Quoted in Packard, E.P.W.: *The Prisoner's Hidden Life* (Chicago: published by the author, 1868), p. 37.

18. Mill, J.S.: *The Subjection of Women* [1869] (London: Dent, 1965).

19. See, for example, Chekhov, A.P.: *Ward No. 6,* [1892], in *Seven Short Novels by Chekhov* (New York: Bantam Books, 1963), pp. 106-57; De Assis, M.: *The Psychiatrist* [1881-82], in De Assis, M., *The Psychiatrist and Other Stories* (Berkeley and Los Angeles: University of California Press, 1963), pp. 1-45; London, J.: *The Iron Heel* [1907] (New York: Sagamore Press, 1957); Porter, K.A.: *Noon Wine* [1937], in Porter, K.A., *Pale Horse, Pale Rider: Three Short Novels* (New York: Signet, 1965), pp. 62-112; Kesey, K.: *One Flew Over the Cuckoo's Nest* (New York: Viking, 1962); Tarsis, V.: *Ward 7: An Autobiographical Novel* (London and Glasgow: Collins and Harvill, 1965).

20. See Szasz, T.S.: "Alcoholism: A socio-ethical perspective." *Western Medicine*, 7:15-21 (Dec.) 1966.

21. See, for example, Rogow, A.A.: *James Forrestal: A Study of Personality, Politics, and Policy* (New York: Macmillan, 1964); for a detailed criticism of this view, see Szasz, T.S.: "Psychiatric classification as a strategy of personal constraint." This volume [original source] pp. 190-217.

22. Szasz, T.S.: *Psychiatric Justice* (New York: Macmillan, 1965).

23. "The Unconscious of a Conservative: A Special Issue on the Mind of Barry Goldwater." *Fact*, Sept.-Oct. 1964.

24. Zeligs, M.A.: *Friendship and Fratricide: An Analysis of Whittaker Chambers and Alger Hiss* (New York: Viking, 1967).

25. Freud, S., and Bullitt, W.C.: *Thomas Woodrow Wilson: A Psychological Study* (Boston: Houghton Mifflin, 1967).

26. Quoted in Schweitzer, A.: *The Psychiatric Study of Jesus* [1913] transl. by Charles R. Joy (Boston: Beacon Press, 1956), pp. 37, 40-41.

11. IS INVOLUNTARY COMMITMENT IMMORAL?

27. Arendt, H.: *Eichmann in Jerusalem: A Report on the Banality of Evil* (New York: Viking, 1963), p. 22.

28. *Ibid.*, pp. 22-23.

29. For a full articulation and documentation of this thesis, see Szasz, T.S.: *The Manufacture of Madness: A Comparative Study of the Inquisition and the Mental Health Movement* (New York: Harper & Row, 1970).

30. Hayek, F.A.: *The Constitution of Liberty* (Chicago: University of Chicago Press, 1960), especially pp. 162-92.

31. Mabbott, J.D.: "Punishment" [1939], in Olafson, F.A., ed., *Justice and Social Policy: A Collection of Essays* (Englewood Cliffs, N.J.: Prentice-Hall, 1961), pp. 39-54.

32. For documentation, see Szasz, T.S.: *Law, Liberty, and Psychiatry: An Inquiry into the Social Uses of Mental Health Practices* (New York: Macmillan, 1963); *Psychiatric Justice* (New York: Macmillan, 1965).

NO

Paul Chodoff

THE CASE FOR INVOLUNTARY HOSPITALIZATION OF THE MENTALLY ILL

I will begin this paper with a series of vignettes designed to illustrate graphically the question that is my focus: under what conditions, if any, does society have the right to apply coercion to an individual to hospitalize him against his will, by reason of mental illness?

Case 1. A woman in her mid 50s, with no previous overt behavioral difficulties, comes to believe that she is worthless and insignificant. She is completely preoccupied with her guilt and is increasingly unavailable for the ordinary demands of life. She eats very little because of her conviction that the food should go to others whose need is greater than hers, and her physical condition progressively deteriorates. Although she will talk to others about herself, she insists that she is not sick, only bad. She refuses medication, and when hospitalization is suggested she also refuses that on the grounds that she would be taking up space that otherwise could be occupied by those who merit treatment more than she.

Case 2. For the past 6 years the behavior of a 42-year-old woman has been disturbed for periods of 3 months or longer. After recovery from her most recent episode she has been at home, functioning at a borderline level. A month ago she again started to withdraw from her environment. She pays increasingly less attention to her bodily needs, talks very little, and does not respond to questions or attention from those about her. She lapses into a mute state and lies in her bed in a totally passive fashion. She does not respond to other people, does not eat, and does not void. When her arm is raised from the bed it remains for several minutes in the position in which it is left. Her medical history and a physical examination reveal no evidence of primary physical illness.

Case 3. A man with a history of alcoholism has been on a binge for several weeks. He remains at home doing little else than drinking. He eats very little. He becomes tremulous and misinterprets spots on the wall as animals about to attack him, and he complains of "creeping" sensations in his body, which he attributes to infestation by insects. He does not seek help voluntarily, insists there is nothing wrong with him, and despite his wife's entreaties he continues to drink.

Case 4. Passersby and station personnel observe that a young woman has been spending several days at Union Station in Washington, D.C. Her behavior appears strange to others. She is finally befriended by a newspaper reporter who becomes

From, "The Case for Involuntary Hospitalization of the Mentally Ill," *American Journal of Psychiatry* 133:5, May 1976. Copyright © 1976, the American Psychiatric Association. Reprinted by permission.

aware that her perception of her situation is profoundly unrealistic and that she is, in fact, delusional. He persuades her to accompany him to St. Elizabeth's Hospital, where she is examined by a psychiatrist who recommends admission. She refuses hospitalization and the psychiatrist allows her to leave. She returns to Union Station. A few days later she is found dead, murdered, on one of the surrounding streets.

Case 5. A government attorney in his late 30s begins to display pressured speech and hyperactivity. He is too busy to sleep and eats very little. He talks rapidly, becomes irritable when interrupted, and makes phone calls all over the country in furtherance of his political ambitions, which are to begin a campaign for the Presidency of the United States. He makes many purchases, some very expensive, thus running through a great deal of money. He is rude and tactless to his friends, who are offended by his behavior, and his job is in jeopardy. In spite of his wife's pleas he insists that he does not have the time to seek or accept treatment, and he refuses hospitalization. This is not the first such disturbance for this individual; in fact, very similar episodes have been occurring at roughly 2-year intervals since he was 18 years old.

Case 6. Passersby in a campus area observe two young women standing together, staring at each other, for over an hour. Their behavior attracts attention, and eventually the police take the pair to a nearby precinct station for questioning. They refuse to answer questions and sit mutely, staring into space. The police request some type of psychiatric examination but are informed by the city attorney's office that state law (Michigan) allows persons to be held for observation only if they appear obviously dangerous to themselves or others. In this case, since the women do not seem homicidal or suicidal, they do not qualify for observation and are released.

Less than 30 hours later the two women are found on the floor of their campus apartment, screaming and writhing in pain with their clothes ablaze from a self-made pyre. One woman recovers; the other dies.

There is no conclusive evidence that drugs were involved (1).

Most, if not all, people would agree that the behavior described in these vignettes deviates significantly from even elastic definitions of normality. However, it is clear that there would not be a similar consensus on how to react to this kind of behavior and that there is a considerable and increasing ferment about what attitude the organized elements of our society should take toward such individuals. Everyone has a stake in this important issue, but the debate about it takes place principally among psychiatrists, lawyers, the courts, and law enforcement agencies.

Points of view about the question of involuntary hospitalization fall into the following three principal groups: the "abolitionists," medical model psychiatrists, and civil liberties lawyers.

THE ABOLITIONISTS

Those holding this position would assert that in none of the cases I have described should involuntary hospitalization be a viable option because, quite simply, it should never be resorted to under any circumstances. As Szasz (2) has put it, "we should value liberty more highly than mental health no matter how defined" and "no one should be deprived of his freedom for the sake of his mental health." Ennis (3) has said that the goal "is nothing less than the abolition of involuntary hospitalization."

Prominent among the abolitionists are the "anti-psychiatrists," who, somewhat surprisingly, count in their ranks a number of well-known psychiatrists. For them mental illness simply does not exist in the field of psychiatry (4). They reject entirely the medical model of mental illness and insist that acceptance of it relies on a fiction accepted jointly by the state and by psychiatrists as a device for exerting social control over annoying or unconventional people. The anti-psychiatrists hold that these people ought to be afforded the dignity of being held responsible for their behavior and required to accept its consequences. In addition, some members of this group believe that the phenomena of "mental illness" often represent essentially a tortured protest against the insanities of an irrational society (5). They maintain that society should not be encouraged in its oppressive course by affixing a prejorative label to its victims.

Among the abolitionists are some civil liberties lawyers who both assert their passionate support of the magisterial importance of individual liberty and react with repugnance and impatience to what they see as the abuses of psychiatric practice in this field—the commitment of some individuals for flimsy and possibly self-serving reasons and their inhuman warehousing in penal institutions wrongly called "hospitals."

The abolitionists do not oppose psychiatric treatment when it is conducted with the agreement of those being treated. I have no doubt that they would try to gain the consent of the individuals described earlier to undergo treatment, including hospitalization. The psychiatrists in this group would be very likely to confine their treatment methods to psychotherapeutic efforts to influence the aberrant behavior. They would be unlikely to use drugs and would certainly eschew such somatic therapies as ECT. If efforts to enlist voluntary compliance with treatment failed, the abolitionists would not employ any means of coercion. Instead, they would step aside and allow social, legal, and community sanctions to take their course. If a human being should be jailed

or a human life lost as a result of this attitude, they would accept it as a necessary evil to be tolerated in order to avoid the greater evil of unjustified loss of liberty for others (6).

THE MEDICAL MODEL PSYCHIATRISTS

I use this admittedly awkward and not entirely accurate label to designate the position of a substantial number of psychiatrists. They believe that mental illness is a meaningful concept and that under certain conditions its existence justifies the state's exercise, under the doctrine of parens patriae, of its right and obligation to arrange for the hospitalization of the sick individual even though coercion is involved and he is deprived of his liberty. I believe that these psychiatrists would recommend involuntary hospitalization for all six of the patients described earlier.

The Medical Model

There was a time, before they were considered to be ill, when individuals who displayed the kind of behavior I described earlier were put in "ships of fools" to wander the seas or were left to the mercies, sometimes tender but often savage, of uncomprehending communities that regarded them as either possessed or bad. During the Enlightenment and the early nineteenth century, however, these individuals gradually came to be regarded as sick people to be included under the humane and caring umbrella of the Judeo-Christian attitude toward illness. This attitude, which may have reached its height during the era of moral treatment in the early nineteenth century, has had unexpected and ambiguous consequences. It became overextended and partially perverted, and these excesses led to the reac-

191

tion that is so strong a current in today's attitude toward mental illness.

However, reaction itself can go too far, and I believe that this is already happening. Witness the disastrous consequences of the precipitate dehospitalization that is occurring all over the country. To remove the protective mantle of illness from these disturbed people is to expose them, their families, and their communities to consequences that are certainly maladaptive and possibly irreparable. Are we really acting in accordance with their best interests when we allow them to "die with their rights on" (1) or when we condemn them to a "preservation of liberty which is actually so destructive as to constitute another form of imprisonment" (7)? Will they not suffer "if [a] liberty they cannot enjoy is made superior to a health that must sometimes be forced on them" (8)?

Many of those who reject the medical model out of hand as inapplicable to so-called "mental illness" have tended to oversimplify its meaning and have, in fact, equated it almost entirely with organic disease. It is necessary to recognize that it is a complex concept and that there is a lack of agreement about its meaning. Sophisticated definitions of the medical model do not require only the demonstration of unequivocal organic pathology. A broader formulation, put forward by sociologists and deriving largely from Talcott Parsons' description of the sick role (9), extends the domain of illness to encompass certain forms of social deviance as well as biological disorders. According to this definition, the medical model is characterized not only by organicity but also by being negatively valued by society, by "nonvoluntariness," thus exempting its exemplars from blame, and by the understanding that physicians are the technically competent experts to deal with its effects (10).

Except for the question of organic disease, the patients I described earlier conform well to this broader conception of the medical model. They are all suffering both emotionally and physically, they are incapable by an effort of will of stopping or changing their destructive behavior, and those around them consider them to be in an undesirable sick state and to require medical attention.

Categorizing the behavior of these patients as involuntary may be criticized as evidence of an intolerably paternalistic and antitherapeutic attitude that fosters the very failure to take responsibility for their lives and behavior that the therapist should uncover rather than encourage. However, it must also be acknowledged that these severly ill people are not capable at a conscious level of deciding what is best for themselves and that in order to help them examine their behavior and motivation, it is necessary that they be alive and available for treatment. Their verbal message that they will not accept treatment may at the same time be conveying other more covert messages—that they are desperate and want help even though they cannot ask for it (11).

Although organic pathology may not be the only determinant of the medical model, it is of course an important one and it should not be avoided in any discussion of mental illness. There would be no question that the previously described patient with delirium tremens is suffering from a toxic form of brain disease. There are a significant number of other patients who require involuntary hospitalization because of organic brain syndrome due to various causes. Among those who are not overtly organically ill, most of the candidates for involuntary hospitalization suffer from schizophrenia or one of the major affective disorders. A growing and increasingly impressive body of evidence points to the presence of an important genetic-biological factor in these conditions; thus, many of them qualify on these grounds as illnesses.

Despite the revisionist efforts of the anti-psychiatrists, mental illness *does* exist. It does not by any means include all of the people being treated by psychiatrists (or by nonpsychiatrist physicians), but it does encompass those few desperately sick people for whom involuntary commitment must be considered. In the words of a recent article, "The problem is that mental illness is not a myth. It is not some palpable falsehood propagated among the populace by power-mad psychiatrists, but a cruel and bitter reality that has been with the human race since antiquity" (12, p. 1483).

Criteria for Involuntary Hospitalization

Procedures for involuntary hospitalization should be instituted for individuals who require care and treatment because of diagnosable mental illness that produces symptoms, including marked impairment in judgment, that disrupt their intrapsychic and interpersonal functioning. All three of these criteria must be met before involuntary hospitalization can be instituted.

1. *Mental illness.* This concept has already been discussed, but it should be repeated that only a belief in the existence of illness justifies involuntary commitment. It is a fundamental assumption that makes aberrant behavior a medical matter and its care the concern of physicians.

2. *Disruption of functioning.* This involves combinations of serious and often obvious disturbances that are both intrapsychic (for example, the suffering of severe depression) and interpersonal (for example, withdrawal from others because of depression). It does not include minor peccadilloes or eccentricities. Furthermore, the behavior in question must represent symptoms of the mental illness from which the patient is suffering. Among these symptoms are actions that are imminently or potentially dangerous in a physical sense to self or others, as well as other manifestations of mental illness such as those in the cases I have described. This is not to ignore dangerousness as a criterion for commitment but rather to put it in its proper place as one of a number of symptoms of the illness. A further manifestation of the illness, and indeed, the one that makes involuntary rather than voluntary hospitalization necessary, is impairment of the patient's judgment to such a degree that he is unable to consider his condition and make decisions about it in his own interests.

3. *Need for care and treatment.* The goal of physicians is to treat and cure their patients; however, sometimes they can only ameliorate the suffering of their patients and sometimes all they can offer is care. It is not possible to predict whether someone will respond to treatment; nevertheless, the need for treatment and the availability of facilities to carry it out constitute essential preconditions that must be met to justify requiring anyone to give up his freedom. If mental hospital patients have a right to treatment, then psychiatrists have a right to ask for treatability as a front-door as well as a back-door criterion for commitment (7). All of the six individuals I described earlier could have been treated with a reasonable expectation of returning to a more normal state of functioning.

I believe that the objections to this formulation can be summarized as follows.

1. The whole structure founders for those who maintain that mental illness is a fiction.

2. These criteria are also untenable to

those who hold liberty to be such a supreme value that the presence of mental illness per se does not constitute justification for depriving an individual of his freedom; only when such illness is manifested by clearly dangerous behavior may commitment be considered. For reasons to be discussed later, I agree with those psychiatrists (13, 14) who do not believe that dangerousness should be elevated to primacy above other manifestations of mental illness as a sine qua non for involuntary hospitalization.

3. The medical model criteria are "soft" and subjective and depend on the fallible judgment of psychiatrists. This is a valid objection. There is no reliable blood test for schizophrenia and no method for injecting grey cells into psychiatrists. A relatively small number of cases will always fall within a grey area that will be difficult to judge. In those extreme cases in which the question of commitment arises, competent and ethical psychiatrists should be able to use these criteria without doing violence to individual liberties and with the expectation of good results. Furthermore, the possible "fuzziness" of some aspects of the medical model approach is certainly no greater than that of the supposedly "objective" criteria for dangerousness, and there is little reason to believe that lawyers and judges are any less fallible than psychiatrists.

4. Commitment procedures in the hands of psychiatrists are subject to intolerable abuses. Here, as Peszke said, "It is imperative that we differentiate between the principle of the process of civil commitment and the practice itself" (13, p. 825). Abuses can contaminate both the medical and the dangerousness approaches, and I believe that the abuses stemming from the abolitionist view of no commitment at all are even greater. Measures to abate abuses of the medical approach include judicial review and the abandonment of indeterminate commitment. In the course of commitment proceedings and thereafter, patients should have access to competent and compassionate legal counsel. However, this latter safeguard may itself be subject to abuse if the legal counsel acts solely in the adversary tradition and undertakes to carry out the patient's wishes even when they may be destructive.

Comment

The criteria and procedures outlined will apply most appropriately to initial episodes and recurrent attacks of mental illness. To put it simply, it is necessary to find a way to satisfy legal and humanitarian considerations and yet allow psychiatrists access to initially or acutely ill patients in order to do the best they can for them. However, there are some involuntary patients who have received adequate and active treatment but have not responded satisfactorily. An irreducible minimum of such cases, principally among those with brain disorders and process schizophrenia, will not improve sufficiently to be able to adapt to even a tolerant society.

The decision of what to do at this point is not an easy one, and it should certainly not be in the hands of psychiatrists alone. With some justification they can state that they have been given the thankless job of caring, often with inadequate facilities, for badly damaged people and that they are now being subjected to criticism for keeping these patients locked up. No one really knows what to do with these patients. It may be that when treatment has failed they exchange their sick role for what has been called the impaired role (15), which implies a permanent negative evaluation of them coupled with a somewhat less benign societal attitude. At this point, perhaps a case

NO   Paul Chodoff

can be made for giving greater importance to the criteria for dangerousness and releasing such patients if they do not pose a threat to others. However, I do not believe that the release into the community of these severely malfunctioning individuals will serve their interests even though it may satisfy formal notions of right and wrong.

It should be emphasized that the number of individuals for whom involuntary commitment must be considered is small (although, under the influence of current pressures, it may be smaller than it should be). Even severe mental illness can often be handled by securing the cooperation of the patient, and certainly one of the favorable effects of the current ferment has been to encourage such efforts. However, the distinction between voluntary and involuntary hospitalization is sometimes more formal than meaningful. How "voluntary" are the actions of an individual who is being buffeted by the threats, entreaties, and tears of his family?

I believe, however, that we are at a point (at least in some jurisdictions) where, having rebounded from an era in which involuntary commitment was too easy and employed too often, we are now entering one in which it is becoming very difficult to commit anyone, even in urgent cases. Faced with the moral obloquy that has come to pervade the atmosphere in which the decision to involuntarily hospitalize is considered, some psychiatrists, especially younger ones, have become, as Stone (16) put it, "soft as grapes," when faced with the prospect of committing anyone under any circumstances. . . .

DISCUSSION

It is obvious that it is good to be at liberty and that it is good to be free from the consequences of disabling and dehumanizing illness. Sometimes these two values are incompatible, and in the heat of the passions that are often aroused by opposing views of right and wrong, the partisans of each view may tend to minimize the importance of the other. Both sides can present their horror stories—the psychiatrists, their dead victims of the failure of the involuntary hospitalization process, and the lawyers, their Donaldsons. There is a real danger that instead of acknowledging the difficulty of the problem, the two camps will become polarized, with a consequent rush toward extreme and untenable solutions rather than working toward reasonable ones.

The path taken by those whom I have labeled the abolitionists is an example of the barren results that ensue when an absolute solution is imposed on a complex problem. There are human beings who will suffer greatly if the abolitionists succeed in elevating an abstract principle into an unbreakable law with no exceptions. I find myself oppressed and repelled by their position, which seems to stem from an ideological rigidity which ignores that element of the contingent immanent in the structure of human existence. It is devoid of compassion.

The positions of those who espouse the medical model and the dangerousness approaches to commitment are, one hopes, not completely irreconcilable. To some extent these differences are a result of the vantage points from which lawyers and psychiatrists view mental illness and commitment. The lawyers see and are concerned with the failures and abuses of the process. Furthermore, as a result of their training, they tend to apply principles to classes of people rather than to take each instance as unique. The psychiatrists, on the other hand, are required to deal practically with the singular needs of individuals. They approach the problem from a clinical rather than a deductive stance. As physicians, they want to be in a position to take care of and to help suffering people whom they regard as sick patients. They sometimes become impatient with the rules that prevent them from doing this.

I believe we are now witnessing a pendular swing in which the rights of the mentally ill to be treated and protected are being set aside in the rush to give them their freedom at whatever cost. But is freedom defined only by the absence of external constraints? Internal physiological or psychological processes can contribute to a throttling of the spirit that is as painful as any applied from the outside. The "wild" manic individual without his lithium, the panicky hallucinator without his injection of fluphenazine hydrochloride and the understanding support of a concerned staff, the sodden alcoholic—are they free? Sometimes, as Woody Guthrie said, "Freedom means no place to go."

Today the civil liberties lawyers are in the ascendancy and the psychiatrists on the defensive to a degree that is harmful to individual needs and the public welfare. Redress and a more balanced position will not come from further extension of the dangerousness doctrine. I favor a return to the use of medical criteria by psychiatrists— psychiatrists, however, who have been chastened by the buffeting they have received and are quite willing to go along with even strict legal safeguards as long as they are constructive and not tyrannical.

REFERENCES

1. Treffert DA: The practical limits of patients' rights. Psychiatric Annals 5(4):91-96,, 1971
2. Szasz, T: Law, Liberty and Psychiatry. New York, Macmillan Co, 1963
3. Ennis B: Prisoners of Psychiatry. New York, Harcourt, Brace, Jovanovich, 1972
4. Szasz T: The Myth of Mental Illness. New York, Harper & Row, 1961
5. Laing R: The Politics of Experience. New York, Ballantine Books, 1967
6. Ennis B: Ennis on 'Donaldson.' Psychiatric News, Dec 3, 1975, pp 4, 19, 37
7. Peele R, Chodoff P, Taub N: Involuntary hospitalization and treatability. Observations from the DC experience. Catholic University Law Review 23:744-753, 1974
8. Michels R: The Right to Refuse Psychotropic Drugs, Hastings Center Report. Hastings-on-Hudson, NY, Hastings Institute of Health and Human Values, 1973
9. Parsons T: The Social System. New York, Free Press, 1951
10. Veatch RM: The medical model: its nature and problems. Hastings Center Studies 1(3):59-76, 1973
11. Katz J: The right to treatment—an enchanting legal fiction? University of Chicago Law Review 36:755-783, 1969
12. Moore MS: Some myths about "mental illness." Arch Gen Psychiatry 32:1483-1497, 1975
13. Peszke MA: Is dangerousness an issue for physicians in emergency commitment? Am J Psychiatry 132:825-828, 1975
14. Stone AA: Comment on Peszke MA: Is dangerousness an issue for physicians in emergency commitment? Ibid, 829-831
15. Siegler M, Osmond H: Models of Madness, Models of Medicine. New York, Macmillan Co, 1974
16. Stone A: Lecture for course on The Law, Litigation, and Mental Health Services. Adelphi, Md, Mental Health Study Center, September 1974

POSTSCRIPT

IS INVOLUNTARY COMMITMENT
TO MENTAL INSTITUTIONS IMMORAL?

As a result of the ideological power of the "anti-psychiatrists," the dreadful condition of many large state mental institutions in which patients had been "warehoused" for years, the development of antipsychotic medications to control overtly disruptive behavior, and the reduction of mental health budgets, a mass exodus of patients from institutions began in the 1970s. The promise of "deinstitutionalization," as this process is called, has not been fulfilled, and the streets of all major American cities are filled with homeless former mental patients who are both potential victims and potential victimizers. The debate over involuntary hospitalization that began two decades ago must now go on in a somewhat different context, for there are not as many institutions to which people can be confined, there is less optimism about patients' eventual restoration to normality, and there is, perhaps most important, less public money to support treatment.

As incidents in which released mental patients have committed violent crimes have become publicized, and as the growing problem of mental illness among homeless people has become more visible, the pendulum is swinging back toward involuntary commitment. In 1985 the American Psychiatric Association proposed a model law, which would reduce the emphasis on potential dangerousness as a criterion and would focus instead on "significant deterioration," a version of the "need for treatment standard."

Thomas Szasz's views are amplified in several books, among them *The Myth of Mental Illness,* revised edition (Harper & Row, 1974). A supporting view is found in Nicholas Kittrie, *The Right to Be Different: Deviance and Enforced Therapy* (Johns Hopkins, 1971). The justifications for involuntary hospitalization are found in Charles M. Culver and Bernard Gert, "The Morality of Involuntary Hospitalization," in *The Law-Medicine Relation: A Philosophical Critique,* edited by H.T. Engelhardt, Jr., and Stuart Spicker (Reidel, 1981). See George J. Annas, "*O'Connor* v. *Donaldson:* Insanity Inside Out," *Hastings Center Report* (August, 1976), and Michael A. Peszke, *Involuntary Treatment of the Mentally Ill: The Problem of Autonomy* (Thomas, 1975); also Richard Van Duizend, Bradley D. McGraw, and Ingo Keilitz, "An Overview of State Involuntary Civil Commitment Statutes," *Mental and Physical Disability Law Reporter* (May-June 1984). Also see Rebecca Dresser, "Involuntary Confinement: Legal and Psychiatric Perspectives," *Journal of Medicine and Philosophy* (August 1984).

WHO photo by E. Schwab.

PART IV
HUMAN AND ANIMAL EXPERIMENTATION

The goal of scientific research is knowledge that will benefit society. But to achieve that goal some individuals, human and animal, may have to be subjected to some risks. Is it ethical, for example, to cause embarrassment and anguish to an experimental subject by deceiving him in the hope of adding considerably to our store of knowledge concerning human behavior? Many researchers contend that to tell the truth is to make the experiment itself invalid and impossible to perform. It is held that the contribution to the greater good of human beings in general justifies the necessary suffering of individual subjects, both human and animal. This section contends with issues that could shape the future of experimental research.

Can Deception in Research be Justified?

Was it Ethical to Implant a Baboon Heart in Baby Fae?

Should Fetal Research Involving More than Minimal Risk be Banned?

Should Animal Experimentation Be Stopped?

ISSUE 12

CAN DECEPTION IN RESEARCH BE JUSTIFIED?

YES: Stanley Milgram, from "Subject Reaction: The Neglected Factor in the Ethics of Experimentation," *Hastings Center Report* 7:5 (October 1977)

NO: Thomas H. Murray, from "Learning to Deceive," *Hastings Center Report* 10:2 (April 1980)

ISSUE SUMMARY

YES: Psychologist Stanley Milgram believes that the central moral justification for allowing deceptive experiments is that the vast majority of subjects who take part in them find them acceptable after the rationale is explained.
NO: Social psychologist Thomas H. Murray argues that deception research is not only bad for subjects, but also harmful to researchers and to the goals of science itself.

Imagine the following situation: Two people come to a psychology laboratory to participate in a study about memory and learning—specifically, the researcher explains, about the effects of punishment on learning. One subject is a "teacher," and the other a "learner." The "learner" is strapped into a chair, and an electrode attached to his wrist. He is told to memorize a list of word pairs; whenever he makes an error he will be given electric shocks of increasing intensity. The "teacher" is then seated before an impressive shock generator, which has switches ranging from 15 volts to 450 volts. The researcher explains that when the "learner" gives a correct answer to a word pair, the "teacher" should move on to the next item. But when the answer is incorrect, the "teacher" must give him an electric shock—and at a higher voltage each time. As the experiment proceeds, the "learner" makes more and more mistakes and responds to the electric shocks with increasing protests, cries of pain, and finally screams of agony.

This experiment was real. It took place at Yale University in the early 1970s in Stanley Milgram's psychology laboratory. But the "learner" was an actor. He received no shocks and only pretended to be in pain. The "teacher" was the true subject of the experiment, which was not about learning at all but about obedience and authority. How far, Milgram wanted to know, would people go in following orders to inflict pain on someone who protests? A few people, he found, defied the researcher's orders. Most, despite obvious stress and discomfort, cooperated to a significant degree.

Much psychological and other social science research, particularly in the field of social psychology, is based on the use of deception to achieve its goals. Milgram's obedience experiments are particularly dramatic, but by no means rare. The moral dilemma posed by such research is: Is it justifiable to deceive subjects, thereby violating a basic ethical principle of truth-telling, in order to conduct a scientific experiment? Those who defend deception, such as Philip Zimbardo of Stanford University and Charles Smith of City University of New York, claim that deception produces beneficial knowledge that could not be obtained any other way. They point out that deception may be the only way to ensure that the subjects' responses are valid; that the only harms involved are temporary feelings of embarrassment or anger; and that after subjects are "debriefed" or told the true purpose of the experiment they do not object to it.

On the other side are those, such as Donald Warwick and Herbert Kelman of Harvard University and Diana Baumrind of the University of California at Berkeley, who believe that in principle it is unethical to deceive others, even for a scientific goal. Deception, they say, *wrongs* subjects (that is, it deprives them of the right to decide freely whether to participate in an experiment or not) even when it does not harm them physically or even psychologically. Research can be designed without deception to achieve the same answers, they argue. Furthermore, they believe that many subjects are reluctant to describe their true feelings about the research and in any case ought to be protected from what Baumrind calls "inflicted insights" (knowledge about oneself that one would rather not know—such as one's capacity to inflict pain on others). These opponents contend that deception research destroys trust in the researcher and in science itself, and makes it difficult to find truly "naive" or unsuspecting subjects.

The two selections that follow present the views of two social scientists with personal experience in deception research. Stanley Milgram describes the aftermath of his experiments and concludes that the main justification for his method was the subjects' own ultimate acceptance of it. Thomas Murray, on the other hand, describes why he stopped doing deception research: Not only did it harm the subjects, he says, but it also harmed him, and the larger enterprise of science itself.

YES
Stanley Milgram

SUBJECT REACTION: THE NEGLECTED FACTOR IN THE ETHICS OF EXPERIMENTATION

Social psychology is concerned with the way in which individual behavior, thoughts, and action are affected by the presence of other people. Although experimentation is not the only way of garnering knowledge in the discipline, it is a major tool of inquiry. As experiments in social psychology typically involve human subjects, they necessarily raise ethical issues, some of which I will discuss here.

INFORMED CONSENT

Many regard informed consent as the cornerstone of ethical practice in experimentation with human subjects. Yet social psychology has until now been unable to assimilate this principle into its routine experimental procedures. Typically, subjects are brought into an experiment without being informed of its true purpose. Indeed, sometimes subjects are misinformed. Is such a procedure ever justifiable?

Herbert Kelman[1] has distinguished two quite different explanations for not informing the potential subject of the nature of the experiment in which he is to take part. One might term the first the motivational explanation; that is, if one told the subject what the experiment was to be like, he might refuse to participate in it. Misinforming people to gain their participation appears a serious violation of the individual's rights, and cannot routinely constitute an ethical basis for subject recruitment.

The second, more typical, reason for not informing a subject is that many experiments in social psychology cannot be carried out if the subject knows about the experiment beforehand.

Consider in this connection Solomon Asch's classic study[2] of group pressure and conformity. The subject is told that he is to take part in a study on the perception of lines. He is asked to make a judgment as to which of three lines is equivalent in length to a standard line, but he does so in the presence of other individuals who, unknown to him, are working for the experimenter and give wrong answers. The experimenter's purpose is to see whether the subject will go along with the erroneous group information or resist the group and give the correct answer.

Clearly the subject is misinformed in several respects. He is told that he is to take part in an experiment on perception rather than group pressure. He is not informed that the others present are working for the experimenter, but is led to believe that they have the same relationship to the experimenter as he. It is apparent that if a subject were informed of the true purpose before participating in the study, he could not experience the psychological conflict that is at the crux of Asch's study. The subject is not denied the information because the experimenter fears he would not participate in the study, but for strictly epistemological reasons, that is, for somewhat the same reason the author of a murder mystery does not reveal to the reader who the culprit is: to do so would undermine the psychological effects of the reading experience.

A majority of the experiments carried out in social psychology use some degree of misinformation. Such practices have been denounced as "deception" by critics, and the term "deception experiment" has come to be used routinely, particularly in the context of discussions concerning the ethics of such procedures. But in such a context, the term "deception" somewhat biases the issue. It is preferable to use morally neutral terms such as "masking," "staging," or "technical illusions" in describing such techniques, because it is not possible to make an objective ethical judgment on a practice unless it is described in terms that are not themselves condemnatory.

Is the use of technical illusions ever justified in experiments? The simplest response, and the one that is most socially and ethically comfortable, is to assert unequivocally that they are not. We all know that honesty and a fully informed relationship with the subject is highly desirable and should be implemented whenever possible. The problem is that many people also believe strongly in the value of inquiry into social psychology, of its potential to enlighten us about human social behavior, and ultimately to benefit us in important ways. Admittedly, this is a faith, but one which impels us to carefully examine whether the illusions and misinformation required by experiments have any claim to legitimacy. We know that illusions are accepted in other domains without affronting our moral sensibilities. To use a simple-minded example, on radio programs, sound-effects of prancing horses are typically created by a sound-effects man who uses split coconut shells; rainfall is created by sand falling on metal sheets, and so forth. A certain number of listeners know about this, some do not; but we do not accuse such programs of deceiving their listeners. Rather we accept the fact that these are technical illusions used in support of a dramatic effort.

Most experiments in social psychology, at least the good ones, also have a dramatic component. Indeed, in the best experiments the subjects are brought into a dramaturgical situation in which the script is only partially written: it is the subject's actions that complete the script, providing the information sought by the investigator. Is the use of technical illusions to be permitted in radio programs, but not scientific inquiry?

There are many instances in everyday life in which misinformation is tolerated or regarded as legitimate. We do not cringe at the idea of giving children misinformation about Santa Claus, because we feel it is a benign illusion, and common sense tells us it is not harmful. Furthermore, the practice is legitimized by tradition. We may give someone misinformation that takes him to a surprise party. The absolutists may say that this is an immoral act, that in doing so one has lied to another person. But it is more important to focus on the person who is the recipient of this information. Does he find it a demeaning experience, or a delightful treat?

One thing is clear: masking and technical illusions ought never to be used unless they are indispensable to the conduct of an inquiry. Honesty and openness are the only desirable basis of transaction with people generally. This still leaves open the question of whether such devices are permissible when they cannot be avoided in a scientific inquiry.

There is another side to this issue. In the exercise of virtually every profession there may be some exemption from general moral practice which permits the profession to function. For example, although a citizen who has witnessed a murder has a moral obligation to come forth with this information, lawyers have a right—indeed an obligation—of "privileged communication." A lawyer may know that his client has committed a murder, and is obligated not to tell the authorities. In other words, a generally accepted moral obligation is suspended and transformed in the case of legal practice, because in the long run we consider this exemption beneficial to society.

Similarly, it is generally impermissible to examine the genitals of strange women. But it is a technical requirement for the practice of obstetrics and gynecology. Once again, for technical reasons, we suspend a general moral rule in the exercise of a profession, because we believe the profession is beneficial to society.

The question arises: is there any comparable exemption due the social scientist because of technical requirements in the kind of work he does, which in the long run, we believe will benefit society? It is true that most often the individual participant in an experiment is not the beneficiary. Rather it is society as a whole that benefits, or at least, that is the supposition of scientific inquiry.

Still another side to the staging by social psychologists is frequently overlooked. The illusions employed by most experiments are usually short-term. They are sustained only insofar as they are required for the purpose of the experiment. Typically, the subject is informed of the experiment's true character immediately after he has participated in it. If for thirty minutes the experimenter holds back on the truth, at the conclusion he reaffirms his confidence in the subject by extending his trust to him by a full revelation of the purpose and procedures of the experiment. It is odd how rarely critics of social psychology experiments mention this characteristic feature of the experimental hour.

From a formal ethical standpoint, the question of misinformation in social psychology experiments is important, because dissimulation subverts the possibility of informed consent. Indeed, the emphasis on "deception" has virtually preempted discussion of ethics among social psychologists. Some feel it is a misplaced emphasis. Support is given to this view by a recent study by Elinor Mannucci.[3] She questioned 192 laymen concerning their reaction to ethical aspects of psychology experiments, and found that they regarded deception as a relatively minor issue.

They were far more concerned with the quality of the experience they would undergo as subjects. For example, despite the "deceptive" elements in the Asch experiment the great majority of respondents in Mannucci's study were enthusiastic about it, and expressed admiration for its elegance and significance. Of course, the layman's view need not be the final word, but it cannot be disregarded, and my general argument is that far more attention needs to be given to the experiences and views of those who actually serve as subjects in experiments.

NEGATIVE EFFECTS

Is an experiment that produces some sort of negative, aversive, or stressful effect in the subject ever justified? In this matter, two parameters seem critical: first, the intensity of the negative experience, and second, its duration. Clearly, the discussion that follows refers to effects that do not permanently damage a subject, and which most typically do not exceed in intensity experiences which the subject might encounter in ordinary life.

One thing is clear. If we assert categorically that negative emotions can never ethically be created in the laboratory, then it follows that highly significant domains of human experience are excluded from experimental study. For example, we would never be able to study stress by experimental means; nor could we implicate human subjects in experiments involving conflict. In other words, only experiments that aroused neutral or positive emotions would be considered ethical topics for experimental investigation. Clearly, such a stricture would lead to a very lopsided psychology, one that carica-

tured rather than accurately reflected human experience.

Moreover, historically, among the most deeply informative experiments in social psychology are those that examine how subjects resolve conflicts, for example: Asch's study of group pressure studies the conflict between truth and conformity; Bibb Latané and John Darley's bystander studies[4] create a conflict as to whether the subject should implicate himself in other peoples' troubles or not get involved; my studies of obedience[5] create a conflict between conscience and authority. If the experience of conflict is categorically to be excluded from social psychology, then we are automatically denying the possibility of studying such core human issues by experimental means. I believe that this would be an irreparable loss to any science of human behavior.

My own studies of obedience were criticized because they created conflict and stress in some of the subjects. Let me make a few comments about this. First, in this experiment I was interested in seeing to what degree a person would comply with an experimental authority who gave orders to act with increasing harshness against a third person. I wanted to see when the subject would refuse to go on with the experiment. The results of the experiment showed first that it is more difficult for many people to defy the experimenter's authority than was generally supposed. The second finding is that the experiment often places a person in considerable conflict. In the course of the experiment subjects sometimes fidget, sweat, and break out in nervous fits of laughter. I have dealt with some of the ethical issues of this experiment at length elsewhere,[6] but let me make a few additional remarks here.

205

SUBJECT REACTION: A NEGLECTED FACTOR

To my mind, the central moral jusitification for allowing my experiment is that it was judged acceptable by those who took part in it. Criticism of the experiment that does not take account of the tolerant reaction of the participants has always seemed to me hollow. I collected a considerable amount of data on this issue, which shows that the great majority of subjects accept this experiment, and call for further experiments of this sort. The table below shows the overall reaction of participants to this study, as indicated in responses to a questionnaire. On the whole, these data have been ignored by critics or even turned against the experimenter, as when critics claim that "this is simply cognitive dissonance. The more subjects hated the experiment, the more likely they are to say they enjoyed it." It becomes a "damned-if-they-like-it and damned-if-they-don't" situation. Critics of the experiment fail to come to grips with what the subject himself says. Yet, I believe that the subject's viewpoint is of extreme importance, perhaps even paramount. Below I shall present some approaches to ethical problems that derive from this view.

Some critics assert that an experiment such as mine may inflict a negative insight on the subject. He or she may have diminished self-esteem because he has learned he is more submissive to authority than he might have believed. First, I readily agree that the investigator's responsibility is to make the laboratory session as constructive an experience as possible, and to explain the experiment to the subject in a way that allows his performance to be integrated in an insightful way. But I am not at all certain that we should hide truths from subjects, even negative truths. Moreover, this would set experimentation completely apart from other life experiences. Life itself often teaches us things that are less than pleasant, as when we fail an examination or do not succeed in a job interview. And in my judgment, participation in the obedience experiment had less effect on a participant's self-esteem than the negative

---

EXCERPT FROM QUESTIONNAIRE USED IN A FOLLOW-UP STUDY OF THE OBEDIENCE RESEARCH

Now that I have read the report, and all things considered...	*Defiant*	*Obedient*	*All*
1. I am very glad to have been in the experiment	40.0%	47.8%	43.5%
2. I am glad to have been in the experiment	43.8%	35.7%	40.2%
3. I am neither sorry nor glad to have been in the experiment	15.3%	14.8%	15.1%
4. I am sorry to have been in the experiment	0.8%	0.7%	0.8%
5. I am very sorry to have been in the experiment	0.0%	1.0%	0.5%

emotions engendered by a routine school examination. This does not mean that the stress of taking an examination is good, any more than the negative effects of the obedience experiments are good. It does mean that these issues have to be placed in perspective.

I believe that it is extremely important to make a distinction between biomedical interventions and those that are of a purely psychological character, particularly the type of experiment I have been discussing. Intervention at the biological level *prima facie* places a subject "at risk." The ingestion of a minute dose of a chemical or the infliction of a tiny surgical incision has the potential to traumatize a subject. In contrast, in all of the social psychology experiments that have been carried out, there is no demonstrated case of resulting trauma. And there is no evidence whatsoever that when an individual makes a choice in a laboratory situation—even the difficult choices posed by the conformity or obedience experiments—any trauma, injury, or diminution of well-being results. I onced asked a government official, who favored highly restrictive measures on psychology experiments, how many cases of actual trauma or injury he had in his files that would call for such measures. He indicated that not a single such case was known to him. If this is true, then much of the discussion about the need to impose government restrictions on the conduct of psychology experiments is unrealistic.

Of course, one difficulty in dealing with negative effects is the impossibility of proving their nonexistence. This is particularly true of behavioral or psychological effects. It seems that no matter what procedures one follows—interviewing, questionnaires, or the like—there is always the possibility of unforeseen negative effects, even if these procedures do not uncover them. Therefore, in an absolute sense, one can never establish the absence of negative effects. While this is logically correct, we cannot use this as a basis for asserting that such effects necessarily follow from psychological experimentation. All we can do is rely on our best judgment and assessment procedures in trying to establish the facts, and to formulate our policies accordingly.

IS ROLE PLAYING A SOLUTION?

Given these problems and the particular requirements of experiments in social psychology, is there any way to resolve these issues so that the subject will be protected, while allowing experimentation to continue? A number of psychologists have suggested that role playing may be substituted for any experiment that requires misinformation. Instead of bringing the subject into a situation whose true purpose and nature were kept from him, the subject would be fully informed that he was about to enter a staged situation, but he would be told to act *as if it* were real. For example, in the obedience experiment subjects would be told: "pretend you are the subject performing an experiment and you are giving shocks to another person." The subject would enter the situation knowing the "victim" was not receiving shocks, and he would go through his paces.

I do not doubt that role playing has a certain utility. Indeed, every good experimenter employs such role playing when he is first setting up his laboratory situation. He and his assistants often go through a dry run to see how the procedure flows. Thus, such simulation is not new, but now it is being asked to serve as the end point, rather than the starting point of an experimental investigation. However, there is a major scientific problem. Even after one has had a subject role play his way through an experimental procedure, we still must wonder whether the observed behavior is the same as that which a genuine subject would produce. So we must still perform the crucial experiment to determine whether role-played behavior corresponds to nonrole-played behavior.

Nor is role playing free of ethical problems. A most striking simulation in social psychology was carried out by Philip Zimbardo at Stanford University.[7] Volunteers were asked to take part in a mock prison situation. They were to simulate either the role of prisoner or guard with the roles chosen by lot. They were picked up at their homes by local police cars, and delivered to Zimbardo's mock prison. Even in the role-playing version of prison, the situation became rather ugly and unpleasant, and mock guards acted cruelly toward the mock prisoners. The investigator called off the simulation after six days, instead of the two weeks for which it had been planned. Morever, the simulation came under very heavy ethical criticism. The ethical problems that simulation was designed to solve did not all disappear. The more closely role-playing behavior corresponds to real behavior, the more it generates real emotions, including aversive states, hostile behavior, and so on. The less real emotions are present, the less adequate the simulations. From the standpoint of the aversive emotions aroused in a successful simulation, ethical problems still exist.

Kelman aptly summarized the state of simulation research when he stated that simulation is not so useless a tool of investigation as its critics first asserted, nor as free of ethical problems as its proponents believed.[8]

PRESUMPTIVE CONSENT

Recall that the major technical problem for social psychology research is that if subjects have prior knowledge of the purposes and details of an experiment they are often, by this fact, disqualified from participating in it. Informed consent thus remains an ideal that cannot always be attained. As an alternative, some psychologists have attempted to develop the doctrine of *presumptive consent*. The procedure is to solicit the view of a large number of people on the acceptability of an experimental procedure. These respondents would not themselves serve in the experiment, having been "spoiled" in the very process of being told the details and purposes of the experiment. But we could use their expressed views about participation as evidence of how people in general would react to participation. Assuming the experiment is deemed acceptable, new subjects would be recruited for actual participation. Of course, this is, ethically, a far weaker doctrine than that which relies on informed consent of the participant. Even if a hundred people indicate that they would be willing to take part in an experiment, the person actually chosen for participation might find it objectionable. Still, the doctrine of the "presumed consent of a reasonable person" seems to me better than no consent at all. That is, when for epistemological purposes the nature of a study cannot be revealed beforehand, one would try to determine in advance whether a reasonable person would consent to being a subject in the study and use that as a warrant either for carrying out the investigation or as a basis for modifying it.

Perhaps a more promising solution is to obtain *prior general consent* from subjects in advance of their actual participation. This is a form of consent that would be based on subjects' knowing the general types of procedures used in psychological investigations, but without their knowing what specific manipulations would be employed in the particular experiment in which they would take part. The first step would be to create a pool of volunteers to serve in psychology experiments. Before volunteering to join the pool people would be told explicitly that sometimes subjects are misinformed about the purposes of an experiment, and that sometimes emotional stresses arise in the course of an experiment. They would be given a chance to exclude themselves from any study using deception or involving stress *if they so wished*. Only persons who had indicated a willingness to participate in experiments involving deception or stress would, in the course of the year, be recruited for experiments that involved these elements. Such a procedure might reconcile the technical need for misinformation with the ethical problem of informing subjects.

Finally, since I emphasize the experience of the person subjected to procedures as the ultimate basis for judging whether an experiment should continue or not, I wonder whether participants in such experiments might not routinely be given monitoring cards which they would fill out and submit to an independent monitoring source while an experiment is in progress. An appropriate monitoring source might be a special committee of the professional organization, or the human subjects' committee of the institution where the experiment is carried out. Such a procedure would have the advantage of allowing the subject to express reactions about an experiment in which he has just participated, and by his comments the subject himself would help determine whether the experiment is allowable or not. In the long run, I believe it is the subject's reaction and his experience that needs to be given its due weight in any discussion of ethics, and this mechanism will help achieve this aim.

REFERENCES

1   Herbert Kelman, "Remarks made at the American Psychological Association," New Orleans, 1974.
2   Solomon E. Asch, *Social Psychology* (New York: Prentice Hall, 1952).
3   Elinor Mannucci, *Potential Subjects View Psychology Experiments: An Ethical Inquiry.* Unpublished Doctoral Dissertation. The City University of New York, 1977.
4   Bibb Latané and John Darley, *The Unresponsive Bystander: Why Doesn't He Help?* (New York: Appleton, 1970).
5   Stanley Milgram, *Obedience to Authority: An Experimental View* (New York: Harper and Row, 1974).
6   Stanley Milgram, "Issues in the Study of Obedience: A Reply to Baumrind," *American Psychologist* 19 (1964), 848-52.
7   Philip Zimbardo, "The Mind is a Formidable Jailer: A Pirandellian Prison," *The New York Times Magazine* (April 8, 1973), p. 38.
8   Kelman, "Remarks."

NO

Thomas Murray

LEARNING TO DECEIVE

In 1968 Paul Goodman, the radical social critic, came to Temple University, introduced himself as a social psychologist, and spoke eloquently against the war in Vietnam. None of this is surprising except for Goodman's self-identification as a social psychologist. Perhaps it should have struck a discordant note in the minds of his audience, but to those of us whose image of social psychology came from the uncritical textbooks of the sixties, a person of Goodman's commitments fits our image of what a social psycholgist ought to be. To unsophisticated undergraduates social psychology seemed to be *the* relevant discipline. What other groups of scientists devoted their lives to research on prejudice, conformity, obedience to destructive authority, propaganda, conflict resolution, or any of a multitude of topics that seemed to penetrate to the heart of war, injustice, and other evils?

It was only natural for a college graduate in that same year, idealistic and naive, to enter a graduate program in social psychology as a way to honor simultaneously intellect and justice. I enrolled, filled with enthusiasm and hope. Enlightenment, in the form of disillusionment, came slowly. In a discipline like social psychology that values "hands-on" research, the real education takes place not in the seminar room but in the laboratory. There the skills of the profession are transmitted, the real work done, and the appropriate views learned. It is those practiced views, and their impact on those who adopt them, that I want to explore here.

THE GROWTH OF DISCIPLINE

The history of social psychology offers some clues as to how it reached its stance on laboratory work. The widely acknowledged founder of experimental social psychology was Kurt Lewin, whose career spanned the twenties to the fifties. In his vision of the science, social progress would advance hand in hand with social theory. His famous adage, "There is nothing so practical as a good theory," soon came to be translated into something more like "Take care of

Reprinted by permission from the *Hastings Center Report*, 10:2, April 1980. Copyright ©1980, the Hastings Center.

theory and practical matters will take care of themselves." The emphasis was on doing good, respectable science; and the *sine qua non* of scientific respectability was the experimental method and its historical setting, the laboratory.

So dawned the age of the social laboratory and its pinnacle—the highly charged, dramatic, deception experiment.

An important part of the socialization of a professional is exposure to examples of excellence. Some of the examples offered to graduate students in my program (a representative one, I think) were Stanley Schachter's experiments on emotionality, Leonard Berkowitz on aggression, Bibb Latané and John Darley on helping in emergencies.[1] What these research programs and their kin had in common beside the fact that they were unusually well done were at least two things: the experiences of the subjects of the studies were intense and dramatic; and the deceptions employed were elaborate and skillfully managed.

By the sixties social psychologists had grown wary of Lewin's boundless faith in democracy, and were less worried about the immediate practicality of their research; but they remembered one lesson above all—whatever you do, do it with style and flair. Within the discipline the suspicion was growing that the acclaim a study received might have as much to do with the ingenuity and panache of the deception as with the importance of the scientific question. The tendency to choose flash over substance became so serious that a respected social psychologist, Kenneth Ring, took the discipline to task for what he called "frivolous values."[2] But these worries were largely ignored. Deception was securely entrenched as a methodology; not the only one certainly, but predominant in a number of research

areas.* This was the state of the discipline in the mid-1960s, although one would not have known it from the typical undergraduate textbook.

Perhaps my description of the discipline suggests an image of the deception researcher as a cool manipulator, utterly insensitive to the feelings of his or her subjects. That description fits very few social psychologists. The individuals with whom I worked closely were principled and responsible people, concerned with doing the right things. Their behavior would be much easier to understand, and much less interesting, had they been callous and cynical. Certainly I met the latter type, but I never worked with them directly.

Consider the problem this way: explain how otherwise good people, at least no worse than the run of academics, come routinely to frighten, provoke, insult, depress, and generally lie to the subjects of their experiments. And what is the impact of their views in practice on themselves and on their conception of human nature outside of the laboratory? To my knowledge, there are no authoritative studies on the personalities of social psychologists, their values, or their beliefs about human nature—a curious gap for a discipline so interested in behavior and motivation.

The question then is: does deception research harm the researcher? All forms of work have their hazards. Are there any hazards unique to or especially acute for

---

*Studies of the incidence of deception research are difficult to interpret. They typically take a sample of journals known to publish mostly social psychological research and classify the studies into those that employ deception as a major part of the procedure, and those that do not. Results vary widely, depending on the journals sampled and the criteria for classifying a procedure as a "deception." For the sixties they range from 16 percent to 38 percent. But in some research areas—conformity and attitude change studies, for example—deception was used in 81 percent and 72 percent of the studies, respectively. These areas, and related ones, also carried with them the highest prestige within the discipline.

the scientist who routinely deceives as a part of his or her profession? Perhaps a "case history"—an autobiographical one in this instance—can illuminate the kinds of harms that arise in deception research, without of course testifying to their extent. As just this sort of "case history," I offer my own experience as a graduate student and neophyte deception researcher.

A STUDY IN HELPING BEHAVIOR

The first deception study in which I participated was on helping behavior in emergencies. We played out an elaborate scenario for each individual subject with minor variations. The variations allowed us to create five separate conditions or "treatments" within the experiment, varying in the likelihood that they would inhibit helping responses. Our subjects were greeted by a phony "experimenter," taken through an elaborate cover story (one that by all the usual criteria worked very well), and asked to sit in a tiny booth watching a TV monitor. Within a very few minutes, they witnessed the "experimenter," apparently alone in another room, receive what looked like a severe electric shock and collapse on the floor, out of camera range. My job was to time the subjects—how long would it take them to call for help or otherwise come to the "experimenter's" aid? If they made no move to seek help within six minutes, I retrieved them from their booths. Then, with the study essentially over, I began my real work—"debriefing" the subject.

Whether or not the person "helped"— in the vernacular of the research report— I "revealed the true purpose of the study, answered all questions honestly, and remained with the subject until all negative effects of participation had been removed." Not quite. While I did reveal the true

purpose of the study, I did not always answer all questions honestly; and I seriously doubt that I, or anyone else, could have removed all negative effects of participation.

Those people who offered help—almost always in the first two minutes—were a pleasure to talk with afterwards. They praised the experiment, my cleverness, and social psychology in general. But why shouldn't they? They had been put to the test, and they had passed! When another human being was in need, they responded. They left the debriefing confident.

However, my experiences with subjects who did not respond within six minutes was another matter. I quickly began to dread the movement of the stopwatch hands. I knew that when the six minutes had passed I would have to face someone who might be trembling, who might have trouble talking, and who would probably have fabricated some fantastic explanation of what had happened to the "victim." Among the 99 subjects I put through the procedure, I saw individuals whose faces were drained of color, who were reduced to stuttering, or who could barely force words through their clenched teeth. These subjects had many versions of what had happened: the "victim" had sneezed, or tripped, or just maybe there was something wrong. Virtually every subject who had not responded showed some anxiety.

Of course, I had to explain the study. What do you tell people who sat idly by, or at least who felt that they had done so, while another human being was in possible danger? When I told many of the people who did not help that they were in an experimental condition designed to inhibit helping, it seemed to make them feel better. However, when I debriefed subjects who had failed to help even though they were *not* in a condition designed to inhibit helping, I found myself lying, saying that they were in a help-inhibiting situation.

When they congratulate you for running such an ingenious and significant experiment, as they invariably do, you try to forget the queasiness in their smiles, and the uncertainty in their handshakes. You try to convince yourself that, yes, all harmful effects have been removed. But I did not believe it then, and I do not today. If your experiment is good, according to the canons of experimental design in social psychology, it is realistic. If you are not getting people's "real" responses to your simulations of reality, then you have no claim to be doing good science. The more skillful you are at simulating reality, the more accurately your subjects can infer how they are likely to act in the larger social world from the way they have acted in your laboratory. To the extent that my simulated emergency was realistic, my nonresponding subjects could make the inference that they were *not* the sort of person who acts courageously to help others in a crisis. And I doubt that my attempts to reassure them, including my willingness to encourage their rationalizations, could really undo all the damage to their self-esteem.

The social psychologist who wants to study some humanly significant area of human behavior with a deception paradigm comes squarely up against a paradox: the more "real"—hence, valuable—the study, the greater the likelihood that someone's self-image will be altered unfavorably. This paradox appears as a moral problem only if you believe that there is something ethically objectionable about social scientists, in Diana Baumrind's phrase, "inflicting insight" on their unwitting subjects. Others, Stanley Milgram for one, see this as merely telling subjects some truth about themselves.[3]

But this already presumes that the scientist knows in just what respects the study *is* "real," and can explain it fully to the subjects, so that the subjects do not assume better—or worse—of themselves than is warranted. The first presumption is virtually impossible to satisfy; and there is evidence that the second may be wrong. That I might be making some individuals, volunteers in innocence and ignorance, judge themselves cowardly or callous, troubled me deeply. Before I began the work, I was warned that debriefing subjects after a procedure like the one we used would be like six weeks of psychotherapy packed into a half-hour. I had no idea how appropriate the warning would be.

One further incident brought home to me the potential effects of deception manipulations on subjects. Sometime after the helping research, I attended a meeting to discuss a proposed research project which was to use the now notorious "self-esteem manipulation." It is an extremely clever use of a principle well known to fortune-tellers—that within very wide limits, people will believe almost anything reported to them about themselves, as long as it comes from an "authoritative" source with some special claim to knowledge. Subjects take a phony personality test supposedly in the final stage of validation. When they return a couple of weeks later, they are handed an envelope containing a report of their "results." There are only two reports—one favorable, one unfavorable—and they are handed out on a random basis. What you do on the "test" has absolutely no relationship to the profile you receive. If you receive the positive profile, you read a flattering set of comments on the warmth of your personality, the depth of your friendships, your sincerity, honesty, maturity, and integrity. It ends with a sentence

213

like: "On the whole, this is one of the most favorable profiles we have ever encountered." If, by chance, you receive the negative profile, you read about your coldness, shallowness, insincerity, lack of principle, immaturity, and lack of integration. It concludes with: "On the whole, this is one of the most unfavorable profiles we have ever encountered."

The purpose of this charade is to manipulate the individual's self-esteem in a controlled fashion, so that the effects of high vs. low self-esteem on some other variables can be systematically studied. To my knowledge, this manipulation is no longer in use, but a decade ago it was popular. At that time I protested. I argued that its scientific validity was suspect: it was at least plausible that the sort of "self-esteem" affected by the manipulation was different in action from the normal underlying level of self-esteem; that what was really being studied by the "self-esteem manipulation" was the effect of being told you were a complete loser. No wonder that people with experimentally induced "low self-esteem" then performed poorly on a wide range of tasks! My methodological objections carried little weight. My ethical objection—that it was wrong to fraudulently alter, even temporarily, a person's self-perception—carried no weight at all. It was irrelevant.

For years I felt my misgivings about deception research were the product of an overly scrupulous mind. The weight of opinion in my profession rested clearly on the side of deception research, though there were notable exceptions even then.[4] But deception research has come under increasingly strong attack in recent years. And I now find myself not so alone.

My case is undoubtedly extreme. But it is not unprecedented. There are examples of virulent attacks on deception research by former social psychologists, for example, Thorne Shipley[5] and Donald Warwick.[6] There are also an unknown number of would-be social psychologists who quietly retired from the field because they were unable to put their wholehearted efforts into deception research, and unwilling or unable to develop other research methods. Even though Alan Elms, a graduate student who assisted Milgram in his now famous research on "obedience," defends the use of deception, he has foresworn it in his own research.[7] How many young and idealistic graduate students have found themselves choosing between lying to a subject and adding to the anxiety caused by a deception, between becoming a professional liar and taking up a new profession? And what compromises must be made to allow a person to deceive in the name of science?

It should not be hard for the reader to empathize with the social psychologist contemplating the use of deception. You want to study some pressing problem; you believe that the controlled laboratory setting is the best place to disentangle the complex threads of social phenomena and get at the truth; and the only way you know of duplicating the real world in your laboratory is through elaborate deceptions. Nowhere in your reasoning does callousness or cynicism appear; nowhere do you think of your subjects as "marks" or dupes. You want to do good, science is the surest road to knowledge; therefore, you are doing good. Since the problem you want to study is likely some socially troublesome issue, by studying it, and thereby contributing to its resolution, you are doing doubly good. How could anyone have the temerity to accuse you of harming your subjects, when your intentions are so obviously laudable?

Social psychologists, like psychoanalysts, have specialized in the study of rationalization and self-justification. They, more than anyone, ought to be able to recognize the powerful pressures on them to justify deception research. To adjure deception research now would be tantamount to confessing to past sins; it would be abandoning the tool many know best; it would make impossible many of the most interesting and impressive (and most highly rewarded) studies. It would require surrender of the singularly unique contribution of social psychology to the catalogue of social research methods.

The argument over the future of deception research must begin with a clearheaded assessment of the reality and importance of intrusions on subjects' wellbeing and substantive rights. Ultimately, the victor will be decided by government regulations. But beyond that we need to consider the costs of deception research to the individual scientist and his or her professional community.

To begin with the latter, I find it difficult to believe that social psychologists are proud of their image as the tricksters of science. (There is even a tape of selected vignettes from the "Candid Camera" show especially designed to illustrate social psychological principles. Both the television show and the discipline have specialized in getting people to reveal their foibles through elaborately staged and carefully recorded scenarios.) The word has certainly gotten around on campuses so that a large percentage of students *expect* to be deceived in psychology experiments, although they do not necessarily consider deception bad.[8] Some regard that appraisal as a warrant for the continued use of deception; others, myself included, as a warning. I have heard social psychology spoken of scornfully by other scientists and

by humanists. But these are all externalities. What psychic price does the individual social psychologist pay?

I know too many principled people who are social psychologists to make any hasty generalizations. And perhaps the mild cynicism they exhibit is no worse than the typical academic's. But do any of the values and presumptions they live with in their identity as researcher spill over into the rest of their lives? In trying to make our laboratory so much like the world, do we sometimes succeed in making our world like the laboratory? When we learn to stage events and manage impressions, are we led to do the same with our other relationships? Do we eventually come to see people as so easily duped outside the laboratory as inside it? And if our research induces people to behave inhumanely, do we come to believe that that is indeed the way people are? Because so much of social psychological research leads people to behave irrationally (if they behaved reasonably and rationally, what need would there be for the science?), do we come to see people as fundamentally irrational? In short, do we come to see people in general as easily manipulable, foolish, and not especially nice, as a result of our characteristic procedures?

The deception researcher's personal dilemma is this: either one successfully dissociates the carefully crafted manipulativeness that characterizes the relationship with research subjects from relationships with people outside the laboratory, or one does not. In the first case, we should worry about the impact of the inauthentic relationship on the subject, and about the researcher's learning to systematically shut off ethically central aspects of his or her personality, as for example, learning to lie with a completely straight face *and* a clear conscience. The very ability to dissociate

215

completely parts of one's life would seem to threaten one's psychological integration as well as one's personal integrity. In the second case, it follows analytically that one's relationships outside the laboratory are colored by the way one treats subjects. Neither option looks morally attractive.

It could be said that I have misrepresented the nature of the subject-experimenter relationship; specifically, I have left out the debriefing where the two people face each other honestly, and try to confront the feelings aroused by what each has done. Indeed, I suspect this does happen with some extraordinary researchers, deepening their humanity and their strength as moral actors. But I think it is the rare exception to the discouraging rule. The vast majority of social psychologists receive only the most superficial training on how to conduct a compassionate debriefing. Debriefings are more often viewed as discharging a responsibility (often an unpleasant one), an opportunity to collect additional data, or even as a chance for a further manipulation! Deception researchers are not trained to recognize signs of anxiety in their subjects, nor to deal with them should they appear. Any special sensitivity of researcher to subject is likely to be the result of individual talent, or of clinical training which is *not* routinely part of a social psychologist's graduate experience.

One final cost of deception research requires discussion. What kind of science can grow from a discipline that relies on systematically deceiving its subjects? Here I am not questioning its moral value but rather its scientific value. Defenders of deception research regularly argue that if you were to tell subjects what you were really studying, then their responses would be somehow "unnatural." It is a point well taken, although the realm to which it is applicable may be smaller than originally thought. But, implicit in that very argument is the understanding that human subjects are not the passive recipients of external manipulations; that their responses are mediated by meanings and expectations.

And if, as is demonstrably the case, many, perhaps the majority, of our subjects expect to be deceived, do we have a science of "how-people-behave-when-they-don't-trust-the-authority-figure-who-is-telling-them-what-is-what" and no more? The people who become our "subjects" do not surrender their curiosity when they enter the lab. Nor do they lose their interest in interpersonal relationships, including that potential one with the experimenter. To assume that they do either, or that by employing deception we are somehow escaping the complex task of understanding the role of setting, expectations, and other persons, is naive and in the long run destructive to our goal of developing a robust science.

How might social psychology adapt were its practitioners to abandon or severely curtail the use of deception, or if we were to accept more complex models of persons-as-subjects? I believe the results would be intellectually invigorating as well as morally defensible. In my criticism of the received wisdom I am certainly not suggesting that we don rose-colored spectacles. Rather I am arguing that we may now be wearing dark glasses. Deception research may be neither good for the science nor good for the scientist.

POSTSCRIPT

CAN DECEPTION IN RESEARCH BE JUSTIFIED?

The American Psychological Association's Ethical Principles, as revised in 1981, permit deception in research but only under certain conditions: The research problem must be important; deception must be necessary in order to carry out the study; subjects must consider it reasonable after they have been debriefed; subjects must have the right to withdraw freely; and the after-effects must be minimized by the researcher. The latest (1981) federal regulations governing research with human subjects do not specifically mention deception. However, they do state that the requirements for informed consent can be waived or altered "if the research could not practicably be carried out without the waiver or alteration." This provision has been widely interpreted as a way of permitting deception research to be approved by an institutional review board, a committee that considers the ethical aspects of research conducted at the institution.

A study published in the *American Psychologist* (January 1985) concluded that the practice of deception in social science research has not been diminished by ethical regulations. In fact the percentage of studies employing deception increased, as did the length of the deception. However, more subjects were being debriefed.

The results of Stanley Milgram's experiments and a fuller description of his method can be found in his book *Obedience to Authority: An Experimental View* (Harper & Row, 1974). For another controversial case of deception research involving clandestine observations of homosexual activity in a public restroom, see Laud Humphrey's, *Tearoom Trade* (Aldine, 1970). A generally sympathetic account is "Research through Deception" by Morton Hunt, *New York Times Magazine* (September 12, 1982). For critiques of deception by social scientists, see Donald Warwick, "Social Scientists Ought to Stop Lying," *Psychology Today* (February 1975), and Diana Baumrind, "Research Using Intentional Deception: Ethical Issues Revisited," *American Psychologist* (February 1985). Also see Joan E. Sieber, editor, *The Ethics of Social Research: Surveys and Experiments* (Springer-Verlag, 1982); and Tom L. Beauchamp et al., editors, *Ethical Issues in Social Science Research* (Johns Hopkins, 1982).

ISSUE 13

WAS IT ETHICAL TO IMPLANT A BABOON HEART IN BABY FAE?

YES: Jack W. Provonsha, from "The Best Available Therapy," from SCOPE, published by Loma Linda University, January-March 1985

NO: George J. Annas, from "Baby Fae: The 'Anything Goes' School of Human Experimentation," *Hastings Center Report* 15 (February 1985)

ISSUE SUMMARY

YES: Minister and physician Jack W. Provonsha claims that because of new information about organ rejection and better immunosuppressant drugs, implanting a baboon heart in Baby Fae offered a real measure of hope to save her life.
NO: Attorney George J. Annas maintains that the experiment on Baby Fae did not receive adequate ethical review and appropriate consent and that it was unjustified and premature.

On October 26, 1984, Dr. Leonard Bailey and his team at Loma Linda University Medical Center, Loma Linda, California, implanted a baboon heart in a 14-day-old infant who became known as Baby Fae. She had been born with hypoplastic left heart syndrome, a fatal condition in which the left side of the heart is much smaller than the right and is unable to pump sufficient blood to sustain life for more than a few weeks. This rare defect occurs about once in every 12,000 live births; it accounts for about a quarter of all cardiac deaths in newborns.

Baby Fae was not the first person to receive a vital organ from a non-human primate, but she was the first newborn. Previous attempts at xenografts (cross-species transplants) had been unsuccessful in the 1960s. But Dr. Bailey believed that there might be a better chance at success with a newborn, whose underdeveloped immune system might not reject the transplant. In addition, the use of a new drug, cyclosporine, in human transplants offered some hope of preventing organ rejection, the most serious side effect of transplantation.

As soon as the transplant was announced, however, it provoked widespread controversy. Critics asked: Was there sufficient evidence from animal experimentation to justify using this procedure in a human? Who consented for the infant and what were they told? Was it ethical to sacrifice a baboon for an experiment on a human?

The debate about Baby Fae raged for the 21 days she lived after the transplant, and beyond. It raises many general questions about human experimentation, such as the criteria necessary to try something for the first time, and the balance of risks and benefits to the subject. All federally funded research protocols are now reviewed by Institutional Review Boards (IRBs) in local institutions; Loma Linda's IRB reviewed this protocol, even though the research was privately funded. But was the review adequate?

The questions are made even more difficult because Baby Fae was a newborn, unable to consent for herself. When is it ethical to experiment on a child, particularly a dying one?

All these larger debates are echoed in the following selections. Jack W. Provonsha, a minister and physician associated with Loma Linda, defends the baboon heart implant on the grounds that "as much experimental preparation had been made as possible using animal models" and that Baby Fae faced certain death unless something drastic was done to correct her heart defect. Although he acknowledges that it is too soon to know whether the information gained augurs well for the future, he says that "those involved have acted with ethical responsibility in the past and the present." George J. Annas vehemently disagrees. He believes that the experiment on Baby Fae—"an impoverished, terminally ill newborn"—was unjustified on scientific and ethical grounds.

YES

Jack W. Provonsha

THE BEST AVAILABLE THERAPY

One of the goals of medical research is to discover tolerable, practical alternatives to untimely death—tolerable, because there are worse conditions than death (medicine is concerned not only with the quantity, but with the quality of life)—practical, because while theoretically possible some alternatives may not in fact be available. The investigation that preceded it and the actual transplantation of a seven-month-old baboon heart into Baby Fae's chest on October 26 were carried out with this larger purpose in mind, and it is important to remember this when reviewing the controversial Baby Fae case.

Organ replacement either by the transplant of organs from donor sources or by mechanical devices is an example of attempts to achieve this therapeutic goal. Unfortunately, for the transplant of organs there are not, and probably will never be, enough human donors available to supply the need. This is especially true for the neonate because of special difficulties peculiar to that period of life. For one thing, neonates are rarely involved in the death by accident or violence that constitutes the primary source of donor organs for older members of the population. Finding a newborn who has suffered brain-death but possesses a healthy heart undamaged by the circumstances often associated with neonatal brain-death, and is of the right size and tissue type, and in the right geographic location so that transport time does not compromise the organ, and for whom proxy donor consent has properly been given, present a complex of difficulties (further compounded if the recipient is already moribund) that render availability unlikely. Add to this the difficulty experienced in diagnosing isolated brain-death in the newborn, and one comes to see the practical limits of the allograft alternative for newborns. If an allograft were found, it would seem an extraordinary coincidence almost guaranteeing that tissue-type selection would be limited. Cardiac allografts do not at present appear to provide the practical alternative to the untimely death we seek. Practical mechanical hearts still remain a distant vision, and no one that I know of is preparing one for neonates.

Two other alternatives must therefore be considered. One of these is the Norwood procedure—a several stage surgical effort to rearrange the structures of the hypoplastic left heart so as to permit the right ventrical to carry the load of the missing left. The procedure is still highly experimental with a prohibitive mortality rate and of dubious long-range outcome—including a questionable quality of life. A successful surgical result provides somewhat greater longevity, but with a critically limited heart for the remainder of the child's life.

The only other present alternative is the xenograft route taken by Dr. Leonard Bailey at Loma Linda. The practicality of this approach derives from the fact that donor organs are readily available, that is if one uses baboons (most of the other larger primates are protected species). There are other advantages. One does not have to wait for brain-death to occur before harvesting baboon hearts. This virtually guarantees healthy, functional donor organs. The proper size can easily be selected, and one has some control over time factors both for donor transport and adequate tissue testing.

The main practical drawback is, of course, xenograft rejection and here the precedents are not encouraging, to say the least. A fair number of xenograft transplants have been attempted in the past with dismal results in every instance.

There are some interesting innovations in the case of Baby Fae, however, raising the possibility of a different outcome. First, the immunological investigation of potential animal donors has proceded far beyond anything done previously. Dr. Bailey and his associates have been studying xenograft techniques on animal models, chiefly sheep and goats—with varying degrees of success and with the accumulation of a large body of experimental data. The team's work included extensive tissue typing studies in baboons and included the profusion of a baboon heart with human blood—incidentally without apparent evidence of rejection.

What remained was the xenograft to a human host. In looking for a human model, the hypoplastic left heart syndrome was chosen because it was within Dr. Bailey's competence as a pediatric thorasic surgeon and because the condition untreated was uniformly lethal. Success would, of course, have much broader implications. Satisfaction of the criteria noted at the beginning seemed assured. The animal studies indicated that the procedure was well-tolerated. As confirmation, Baby Fae's

221

condition post-op was obviously not an intolerable one. We have noted its practicality above.

One of the startling results of this research was the finding of a much greater histo-comparability (the key figures seem to prefer this term to histo-compatability) between humans and at least some baboons than had previously been expected. Moreover, never had an attempt been made on so young a patient with the possible benefit of an immature immunological system and its diminished tendency to reject.

Another difference was cyclosporine-A, a newer immunosuppressive drug that has made a great deal of difference to transplant technology. These three factors constituted a basis for hope that this alternative might offer a reasonable possiblity of success—even a greater possiblity than any of the other options including the human allograft—in the rare instance that one were really available. (A human source is obviously no guarantee against rejection. Allografts are also rejected.) The other alternative was certain death, and Baby Fae came close to selecting it more than once prior to surgery.

What we have had then, in the Baby Fae case, was a slightly premature child facing certain death unless something drastic were done to correct her congenital heart defect. There were four options, all but the first highly experimental and none of them good. (1) Death, (2) the Norwood procedure, (3) a human allograft, and (4) a baboon xenograft. The ethical requirement that the incompetent patient's well-being take priority over purely experimental purposes demanded that the best available option be selected even if this interfered temporarily with experimental goals.

Option (1) death, was unacceptable by all of the tenets of medicine, providing a reasonable quality of life was a possibility. (2) The Norwood procedure had serious problems including an unacceptably high mortality rate and a reduced quality of life. (3) A human allograft was impractical as a solution to the larger organ transplant problem and presented specific insurmountable difficulties for the newborn which leaves us with (4), the baboon xenograft. In this case, because of newer information and better immuno-suppressant drugs, while there remain large questions, there was provided a real measure of hope. If it were successful, it would not only offer a practical solution to the Baby Faes among us but a host of other possiblities down the line. On balance, (4), as questionable as it was, offered at least as great, and possibly greater therapeutic hope than either (2) or (3). We would not know if the xenograft were not attempted.

As much experimental preparation had been made as possible using animal models. Proper consent was apparently provided including the protection of the incompetent. Therapeutic goals were sought rather than purely experimental ones; that is, that the baby was considered to be more important than the experiment.

Baby Fae lived almost 3 weeks after surgery, apparently at least two good weeks. This was much longer than any other xenograft had ever survived. And when she died she apparently died the death of an allograft rejection rather than that of a xenograft. An enormous amount of information has been accumulated that may augur well for the future. Was it worth it? Only the future will tell us for sure. But at least it seems that those involved have acted with ethical responsibility in the past and the present.

NO

George J. Annas

BABY FAE: THE "ANYTHING GOES" SCHOOL OF HUMAN EXPERIMENTATION

Was Baby Fae a brave medical pioneer whose parents chose the only possible way to save her life, or was she a pathetic sacrificial victim whose dying was exploited and prolonged on the altar of scientific progress? To answer this question we need to examine the historical context of this experiment, together with the actions and expressed motives of the parents and physicians.

In an exclusive interview in *American Medical News* ten days after he had transplanted the heart of a baboon into Baby Fae, Dr. Leonard Bailey described Dr. James D. Hardy as "my silent champion." Speaking of Dr. Hardy's transplant of a chimpanzee heart into a human being in 1964, he said, "He's an idol of mine because he followed through and did what he should have done . . . he took a gamble to try to save a human life."[1]

Dr. Hardy, of the University of Mississippi, did the world's first lung transplant on a poor, uneducated, dying patient who was serving a life sentence for murder. John Richard Russell survived the transplant for seventeen days, and died as a result of kidney problems that were expected to kill him in any event. Less than seven months later, in January 1964, Dr. Hardy performed the world's first heart transplant on a human being, using the heart of a chimpanzee. The recipient of the chimpanzee heart, Boyd Rush, did not consent to the procedure. Like Mr. Russell, he was dying and poor. Although not a prisoner, he was particularly vulnerable because he was a deaf-mute. He was brought to the hospital unconscious and never regained consciousness. A search for relatives turned up only a stepsister who was persuaded to sign a consent form authorizing "the insertion of a suitable heart transplant" if this should prove necessary. The form made no mention of a primate heart; in later written reports Dr. Hardy contended that he had discussed the procedure in detail with *relatives*, although there was only one. Mr. Rush survived two hours with the chimpanzee heart.

Dr. Hardy's justifications for using the chimpanzee heart were the difficulty of obtaining a human heart and the apparent success of Dr. Keith Reemtsma in transplanting chimpanzee kidneys into Jefferson Davis at New Orleans Charity Hos-

Reprinted by permission from the *Hastings Center Report*, 15, February 1985. Copyright © 1985 by the Hastings Center.

pital. Mr. Davis was a forty-three-year-old poor black man who was dying of glomerulonephritis. Davis describes his consent in this transcript of a conversation with his doctors after the operation:

> You told me that's one chance out of a thousand. I said I didn't have no choice. . . . You told me it gonna be animal kidneys. Well, I ain't had no choice.[2]

The operation took place on November 5, 1963; the patient was doing well on November 18 when he was visited by Dr. Hardy. On December 18 he was released to spend Christmas at home. Two days later he was back in the hospital, and on January 6, 1964, he died.

Whatever else one wants to say about these transplants, it is doubtful that anyone would seriously attempt to justify either the consent procedures or the patient selection procedures. Both experiments took advantage of poor, illiterate, and dying patients for their own research ends. Both seem to have violated the major precepts of the Nuremberg Code regarding voluntary, competent, informed, and understanding consent; sufficient prior animal experimentation; and an *a priori* reason to expect death as a result of the experiment.

The parallels are striking. Like Russell, Rush, and Davis, Baby Fae was terminally ill; her dying status was used against her as the primary justification for the experiment. We recognize that children, prisoners, and mental patients are at special risk for exploitation, but the terminally ill are even more so, with their dying status itself used as an excuse to justify otherwise unjustifiable research. Like these previous subjects, Baby Fae was also impoverished; subjects in xenograft experiments have "traditionally" been drawn from this population. Finally, as a newborn, she was even more vulnerable to exploitation. Three issues merit specific dis-

cussion: (1) the reasonableness of this experiment on children; (2) the adequacy of IRB review; and (3) the quality of the consent.

THE REASONABLENESS OF THE EXPERIMENT

While different accounts have been given, it seems fair to accept the formulation by immunologist Dr. Sandra Nehlsen-Cannarella: "Our hypothesis is that a newborn can, with a combination of its underdeveloped immune system and the aid of the anti-suppressive drug, cyclosporine, accept the heart of a baboon if we can find one with tissue of high enough comparability."[1] Questions that need answers are: Is there sufficient animal evidence to support this "underdeveloped immune system" hypothesis as reasonable in the human? Does the evidence give any reason to anticipate benefit to the infant? And is there any justification for experimenting on infants before we experiment on adults who can consent for themselves? The answer to all three questions seems to be no.

Only two new relevant scientific developments have occurred since the 1963-64 experiments of Reemtsma and Hardy: better tissue-matching procedures and cyclosporine. Both of these, however, are equally applicable to adults. Only the "underdeveloped immune system" theory, which posits that transplants are more likely to succeed if done in infants with underdeveloped immune systems, is applicable to newborns, and this could be tested equally well with a human heart. Without this type of prior work we are engaged, as one of my physician colleagues puts it, in "dog lab" experiments, using children as means to test a hypothesis rather than as ends in themselves. Without adult testing, there could be no reasonable anticipation of benefit for this child; the best that could be hoped for is that the parents would bury a very young child instead of an infant. There should be no more xenografts on children until they have proven successful on adults.

THE ADEQUACY OF IRB REVIEW

Since the Loma Linda IRB seems to have dealt with these concerns inadequately, we must question whether the IRB mechanism is able to protect human subjects involved in first-of-their-kind organ transplants. The record is not very good. The Utah IRB failed to protect Dr. Barney Clark from being used as a means to promote the artificial heart.[3] Likewise, the Humana Heart Institute IRB seems to have been more interested in promoting its own institutional concerns than in protecting William Schroeder. For example, its consent form requires the subject to sign over all rights he or his heirs or other parties might have in "photographs, slides, films, video tapes, recordings or other materials that may be used in newspaper, magazine articles, television, radio broadcasts, movies or any other media or means of dissemination." Very little is known about the Loma Linda IRB and its process. According to its chairman, Dr. Richard Sheldon, the twenty-three-member IRB first received the protocol in August 1983 and approved it later that year. Dr. Bailey was told to present any changes in it to the IRB when a suitable candidate was available. These were presented and approved by a nine to seven vote, two days before Baby Fae's transplant.

Some general observations about IRBs may explain their failure in these cases. First, IRBs are composed primarily (sometimes almost exclusively) of employees and staff of the research institute itself. When that institute, in addition to its basic research mission, has another common set of beliefs, based on a shared religion like Mormonism or Seventh Day Adventism, or a secular belief in the profit motive, there is a disturbing homogeneity in the IRB. This is likely to lead to approval of a project by a researcher who also shares the same belief system.

Second, IRBs are way over their heads in this type of surgical innovation. There is no history of successful IRB review of first-of-their-kind kidney, liver, or heart transplants. Ross Woolley has described the Utah IRB that approved the Barney Clark experiment as a "bunch of folks who get together and stumble around and do our thing." More courteously, Albert Jonsen, professor of ethics at The University of California School of Medicine in San Francisco, described the plight of the same IRB as akin to being "asked to build a Boeing 747 with Wright Brothers parts." Homogeneous IRBs without experience in transplant innovation are no match for surgical "pioneers."

THE CONSENT PROCESS

On day ten after Baby Fae's transplant Dr. Bailey said:

> In the best scenario, Baby Fae will celebrate her 21st birthday without the need for further surgery. That possibility exists.

This was, in fact, never a realistic or reasonable expectation, and raises serious questions both about Dr. Bailey's ability to separate science from emotion, and what exactly he led the parents of Baby Fae to expect. He seemed more honest when he described the experiment as a "tremendous victory" after Baby Fae's death. But this could only mean that the experiment itself was the primary end, and that therapy was never a realistic goal.

As of this writing the Baby Fae consent form remains a Loma Linda Top Secret Document. But the process is much more important than the form, and it has been described by the principals. Minimally, there should have been an independent patient selection committee to screen candidates to ensure that the parents could not easily be taken advantage of, could supply the child with sufficient stable support to make long-term survival possible, were aware of all reasonable alternatives in a timely manner, and were not financially constrained in their decision making.

Baby Fae's parents had a two-and-a-half-year-old son, had been living together for about four years, had never married, and had been separated for the few months prior to Baby Fae's birth. Her mother is a high school dropout who was forced to depend on Aid to Families with Dependent Children at the time of the birth of Baby Fae. Baby Fae's father had three children by a previous marriage and describes himself as a middle-aged adolescent. He was not present at the birth of Baby Fae and did not learn about it until three days later. Both felt guilty about Baby Fae's condition, and wanted to do "anything" that might "save her life."

Dr. Bailey describes the crux of the consent process as a conversation with the parents from about midnight until 7 A.M. on October 20. In Dr. Bailey's words:

> Apparently, the parents had spent three or four hours in debate at home [before admitting the baby] and now, from midnight until well into the next morning, I spent hours talking to them very candidly and very frankly. While Baby Fae was resting in bed, I showed them a film and I gave them a slide show, explaining our research and our belief why a baboon heart might work.

This account, given slightly more than two weeks after the transplant, is in error. Apparently Dr. Bailey is following Dr. Hardy's precedent of exaggerating the number of "relatives" involved in the consent process. What really happened is recounted by the couple in their exclusive interview in *People* magazine. Present at the midnight explanation were not "the parents," but the mother,

the grandmother, and a male friend of the mother who was staying at her home at the time of Baby Fae's birth. Baby Fae's father was *not* in attendance, although he says, "I would have been there at the meeting with Dr. Bailey if I'd known it was going to turn into a seven-hour discussion." Nonetheless, even though he missed the explanations about what was going to happen to his daughter, "when it came time to sign the agreements, I was up there."[4]

It is unclear that either of the parents ever read or understood the consent forms, but it is evident that the father was not involved in any meaningful way in the consent process.

LESSONS OF THE CASE

This inadequately reviewed, inappropriately consented to, premature experiment on an impoverished, terminally ill newborn was unjustified. It differs from the xenograft experiments of the early 1960s only in the fact that there was prior review of the proposal by an IRB. But this distinction did not make a difference for Baby Fae. She remained unprotected from ruthless experimentation in which her only role was that of a victim.

Dr. David B. Hinshaw, the Loma Linda spokesman, understood part of the problem. In responding to news reports that the hospital might have taken advantage of a couple in "difficult circumstances to wrest things from them in terms of experimental procedures," he said that if this was true, "The whole basis of medicine in Western civilization is challenged and attacked at its very roots."[5] This is an overstatement. Culpability lies at Loma Linda.

Some will find this indictment too harsh. It may be (although none of us can yet know) that the IRB followed the NIH rules on research involving children to the letter, and that the experiment *could* be fit into the federal regulations by claiming that Baby Fae's terminally ill status was justification for an attempt to save her life. But if the federal regulations cannot prevent this type of gross exploitation of the terminally ill, they must be revised. We may need a "national review board" to deal with such complex matters as artificial hearts, xenographs, genetic engineering, and new reproductive technologies. That Loma Linda might be able to legally "get away with" what they have done demonstrates the need for reform and reassertion of the principles of the Nuremberg Code.

As philosopher Alasdair MacIntyre told a recent graduating class of Boston University School of Medicine, there are two ways to be a bad doctor. One is to break the rules; the other is to follow all the rules to the letter and to assume that by so doing you are being "good." The same can be said of IRBs. We owe experimental subjects more than the cold "letter of the law."

The *Loma Linda University Observer*, the campus newspaper, ran two headline stories on November 13, 1984, two days before Baby Fae's death. The first headline read ". . . And the beat goes on for Baby Fae"; the second, which covered an unconnected social event, could have more aptly captioned the Baby Fae story: " 'Almost Anything Goes' comes to Loma Linda."

NOTES

1. This and later quotes by Dr. Bailey appear in Dennis L. Breo, "Interview with 'Baby Fae's' Surgeon: Therapeutic Intent was Topmost," *American Medical News*, Nov. 16, 1984, p. 1.

2. Material about Dr. Hardy is drawn from Jurgen Thorwald, *The Patients* (New York: Harcourt Brace Jovanovich, 1972).

3. George J. Annas, "Consent to the Artificial Heart: The Lion and the Crocodiles," *Hastings Center Report*, April 1983, pp. 20-22.

4. Information and quotes concerning Baby Fae's parents are taken from Eleanor Hoover, "Baby Fae: A Child Loved and Lost," *People*, Dec. 3, 1984, pp. 49-63. The second part of the interview appeared in the Dec. 10 issue.

5. *New York Times*, Nov. 15, 1984, p. A27.

POSTSCRIPT

WAS IT ETHICAL TO IMPLANT
A BABOON HEART IN BABY FAE?

Following the controversy surrounding the Baby Fae case, the National Institutes of Health (NIH) sent a team to Loma Linda University Medical Center to review the research review procedures that were followed. The team concluded that the IRB review of the xenograft protocol followed federal regulations. However, it identified some shortcomings in the consent document: it failed to include an explanation of what compensation and medical treatment was available if injury occurred; it overstated the expected benefits of the procedure by claiming that "long-term survival" is an expected possibility; and it stated that sizematched human hearts were not available, although no search had been conducted or considered.

No further xenografts have been performed, although Dr. Bailey believes that the procedure deserves further trial. In retrospect, Dr. Provonsha still believes that the consent given by Baby Fae's mother was as "well-informed as humanly possible." However, he says that "until we have thoroughly learned all our lessons from Baby Fae we shouldn't proceed with another xenograft." Since the Baby Fae case, Dr. Bailey has performed several human heart transplants in newborns. His report of the Baby Fae case was published in the *Journal of the American Medical Association* (December 20, 1985). The same issue contains other articles on xenografts. The full account of the NIH site visit was published in *IRB: A Review of Human Subjects Research,* March/April 1985, along with other articles on the case. See also "The Subject Is Baby Fae," *Hastings Center Report,* February 1985.

ISSUE 14

SHOULD FETAL RESEARCH INVOLVING MORE THAN MINIMAL RISK BE BANNED?

YES: Seymour Siegel, "A Bias for Life," from Appendix, *Research on the Fetus,* National Commission for the Protection of Human Subjects of Biomedical and Behavioral Research (Washington, D.C., 1976)

NO: John C. Fletcher and Joseph D. Schulman, from "Fetal Research: The State of the Question," *Hastings Center Report,* April 1985

ISSUE SUMMARY

YES: Applying the general principle of a "bias for life" to fetuses, theologian Seymour Siegel concludes that no experimental procedures likely to harm a fetus, even when it is to be aborted, are justifiable.
NO: Ethicist John C. Fletcher and physician Joseph D. Schulman argue that current guidelines on fetal research need to be re-examined in the light of new knowledge and new therapeutic possibilities. More risks might be allowed in carefully designed studies.

Concern about fetal research arose in the aftermath of the 1973 US Supreme Court decision legalizing abortion (see Issue 1). Before *Roe* v. *Wade,* fetal research had been conducted with little apparent public concern. But reports of research conducted by Scandinavian researchers using live, post-abortion fetuses fueled a hot and emotional debate in this country and led to a moratorium imposed by the National Institutes of Health (NIH) on any research involving a living fetus before or after abortion. Spurred by public protests, in 1975 Congress established the National Commission for the Protection of Human Subjects of Biomedical and Behavioral Research to examine the ethical issues surrounding experimentation. The first topic on its agenda was fetal research.

The legislation creating the National Commission continued the ban on fetal research, except when it was intended to ensure the survival of a fetus. The Commission heard testimony on the kinds of fetal research then in progress, and on the ethical, legal, and religious views of the practice. One of the important questions raised by the Commission was: Is the fetus a person? The views ranged from the testimony of Protestant theologian Joseph Fletcher ("The fetus is an object, not a subject—a nonpersonal organism") to the official dissent to the final report by Commissioner David Louisell ("I would, therefore, turn aside any approval, even in science's name, that would by euphemism or other verbal device, subject any unconsenting human being, born or unborn, to harmful research, even that intended to be good for society"). The Commission adopted the intermediate view that the fetus is in a distinctive moral category—not a fully developed human being but close to it.

Research that would impose little or no risk to the fetus or that was intended to benefit the fetus posed few ethical difficulties for the Commission. However, irreconcilable differences arose when abortion entered the picture. Research using about-to-be-aborted fetuses might be intended, for example, to determine the harmful or beneficial effects on the fetus of drugs given to the pregnant woman during pregnancy or labor. Other types of research might be harmful to the fetus and could not ethically be performed on a fetus that is destined to be delivered at term. The Commission (with Dr. Louisell dissenting) approved minimal-risk research if abortion was anticipated but required the approval of a national ethical review body for more than minimal risk.

The Commission's recommendations, with some modifications, were incorporated into the federal regulations governing human subject research in 1975 and have remained essentially unchanged since then. The Department of Health, Education and Welfare (now the Department of Health and Human Services) did establish a national Ethics Advisory Board as recommended by the Commission, but it was disbanded in 1980 when the President's Commission for the Study of Ethical Problems in Medicine and Biomedical and Behavioral Research was established.

The controversy over fetal research languished for several years. It has recently recurred, however, spurred by two different interests. Several attempts to ban fetal research entirely, so far unsuccessful, have been made by pro-life forces in Congress. On the other hand, many researchers and policy makers are calling for a new look at the current regulations, which they consider too restrictive in the light of new therapeutic possibilities.

In a selection from his testimony to the National Commission, Seymour Siegel illustrates the concern for fetal rights that underlies the present policies. John C. Fletcher and Joseph D. Schulman argue that the time has come to reevaluate the regulations in order to promote research that can provide benefits to individuals and society.

YES

Seymour Siegel

A BIAS FOR LIFE

The most general principle which should inform our decisions . . . is a "bias for life." This "bias" is the foundation of the Judeo-Christian world view as well as the motivating force which undergirds medical research and practice. It flows, for most people, from a theistic belief. However, it has been and can be affirmed by those whose views of reality do not include the existence of God. The "bias for life" requires that all individuals—most especially those involved in the healing arts—should direct their efforts toward the sustaining of life where it exists; that means and procedures which tend to terminate life or to harm it are unethical; and that where there is a doubt, the benefit of that doubt should always be on the side of life. Another implication of this "bias" is that any individual life which claims our efforts and attention, and which is before us at this moment, has precedence over life that might come afterwards. In certain situations, individuals are called upon to sacrifice their lives or their comfort for future generations. This is part of our character as members of the human race tied to those who came before us and to those who will come after us. However, the burden of proof is always upon those who wish to subordinate the interests of the individual presently before us for the sake of those who will come later. Experiments for the "good of medicine" or for the "progress of knowledge" are not automatically legitimated, if they cause harm to people now, because someone in the future might benefit. What comes in the future is what the Talmudic literature calls "the secrets of the Almighty." This does not mean that we have no responsibility toward the future. However, we have a greater responsibility to those who are now in our care. These reflections do not, of course, preclude the scientist's search. These are intended to make him more cautious in his search.

This "bias for life" is exercised whatever the status of the life before us is. The fact that the life is certainly to be terminated, that it is flawed, or doomed does not preclude the activation of the "bias." This idea is expressed in the 1973 U.S. Guidelines published by the Department of Health, Education and

From, "A Bias for Life," Appendix in *Research on the Fetus,* National Commission for the Protection of Human Subjects of Biomedical and Behavioral Research, Department of Health, Education and Welfare, Washington, DC., 1976.

Welfare: "Respect for the dignity of human life must not be compromised whatever the age, circumstance, [or] *life expectation of the individual.*" [Emphasis mine.]

The Indeterminancy of the Future

Even the most expert scientific intelligence cannot predict the future with certainty. This is especially true of medical science. Medical science is replete with instances where certain experiments and treatments were administered to human subjects with the expectation that these procedures would be positive in their effect—only to turn out to be harmful. That means that when a decision is made to permit experimentation on human subjects, there must be present the utmost caution. Some of the experiments proposed would involve the mother as well as the fetus. It is not impossible to predict that these very procedures would have so changed the mother's organism as to preclude further births or to have other untoward effects.

In speaking of the future effects of experimentation we should not overlook the social consequences of policies in this area. Already the public is beginning to believe that physicians are not merely the saviors of human life—but also its destroyers. While this allegation is, of course, unfair, it is still important to keep the social effects in mind when making policy in this very sensitive field. This century has seen the consequences of the breach of the notion of the sanctity of life. The Nazi horrors began with the legitimation of the destruction of "useless" life and concluded with the most horrible phenomenon of this or any other century. The ethicist, Le-Roy Walters, has stated: "An unexamined premise of both the British and the American policy statements on fetal experimentation is that the consequences of such research will be medical and that they will be good . . . it is equally plausible to argue that serious social consequences will follow such experimentation and that these consequences will be mixed, at best."

The Nub of the Problem: The Fetus

In approaching our problem, the nub of the issue is the status of the fetus. This problem can be approached medically, metaphysically and ethically. It would seem that the two extreme positions which have been expressed in the literature and public debate on this issue—though having much to commend them—do not seem plausible.

The fetus does not seem to be identical with an infant. This is the view of many religious and ethical traditions—including the rabbinic tradition. It is supported also by common sense. The fetus has no independent life-system and is literally tied to the mother. It has not developed the social and personal qualities generally assumed to be part of being a full human being. This is not a self-evident principle. B.A. Brody, in a recent article says: "the status of the fetus and of whether destroying the fetus constitutes the taking of a human life . . . seems difficult, if not impossible to resolve upon rational grounds." Yet, it would seem that the weight of common sense is on the side of those who wish to distinguish ontologically and ethically between a born infant and a fetus. This means that feticide is not the same as homicide—that is, before viability.

However, this does not mean that from an ethical standpoint there is no difference between a fetus and a tooth or a fingernail of the mother—to be disposed of as the mother wishes. It is indeed part of the mother's body—but a unique part of the mother's body. It is the only part of the mother's body which is destined to leave the mother's body in order to take upon itself individual and independent existence as a human being. This special status gives the fetus certain rights that other organs of the mother do not possess. This is expressed in the fact that Western religious thought has "ascribed a high value to prenatal human life." Nor should we forget that even if we were to conceive of the fetus as merely a limb of the mother, this does not imply that society has no responsibility for what the mother does with her limbs. No civilized community would allow individuals to capriciously cut off limbs from their own bodies—even if they wished to do so. Of course, limbs can be amputated for the sake of the whole individual. But this must be justified by the "interests" of the individual, and this "interest" must stand the test of common sense as well as medical opinion.

What then is the status of the fetus, if it is not a whole individual or mere tissue. The answer must be that the status of the fetus is that of "potential human life." Both Aristotle and Thomas Aquinas and many medieval thinkers saw human life as a developing process from step to step. In the case of the ancients it was from vegetative to animal to rational levels. However, it is clear that successive stages of human ontogeny contain within themselves the future stages. That is to say, that all "higher" stages are present *in potentia* in the "lower" stages.

The character of the fetus as "potentially human" raises it above the level of "mere tissue." It therefore evokes within us a sense of responsibility for its welfare as well as the welfare of the mother. Because it is not yet fully human, the fetus has less rights than it would have if it were fully born. When the fetus presents a threat to the mother's life or to the lives of its potential siblings, then the mother has a right to protect herself against the fetus. That is why most religious traditions permit abortion under some circumstances. When one harms the fetus, however, "potential life is being thwarted."

The Rights of the Fetus

The fetus, then, has potential human qualities and therefore it has rights. These rights are encapsulated in the demand it can make upon us to benefit from our "bias toward life." This "bias," which makes us responsible to guard and preserve life where it exists, this responsibility to preserve the life of the fetus, is not an absolute responsibility. In most civilized societies war is legitimate even though it means the inevitable loss of life. But it is used to serve a larger and more comprehensive aim of the society—its self-protection. In the same way the fetus' right to our concern for its life is mitigated when the fetus threatens someone elses life or health—his mother's or his prospective sibling's. However, when there is no threat then the fetus' potential humanity and his present life signs entitle him to benefit from the ethical imperative to protect and revere life. This means that even before viability and even when *in utero* the fetus has a right to expect those who interfere with his own life-system to do so out of a consideration for the fetus' well-being or the health of his mother. Those who do interfere with his life-system—physicians, experimenters, or others—are ethically permitted to do so only to help the fetus sustain his life-system (unless, of course, he is a threat to the mother or his prospective family). It must be stressed that this consideration involves all fetuses— whether viable or not. To declare that a fetus or abortus is not viable is never the same thing as to declare that a living previable fetus/abortus has died.

This does not mean that any kind of experimentation is prohibited. Experiments, even when nontherapeutic, could be carried on which present no discernible harm to either the mother or the fetus. Though the fetus can hardly give consent to such experiments, those who are his guardians can give consent. Andre Hellegers has described the many important experiments which could be carried on within these guidelines, especially those related to amniocentesis.

It would be most unfortunate if the respect for the life of the fetus were related to the fact that he is soon to be aborted. Both the British and the American guideliness are insistent that a fetus *in utero* should not be the subject of procedures which can cause him harm even when he is destined to oblivion through abortion. Paul Ramsey warns against skewing the medical ethical issue involved here by the abortion issue. It is possible to be against fetal research *in utero* even when favoring abortion. The analogy has been drawn to a condemned prisoner who is facing execution, or someone who is *in extremis*. Medical ethical practice would condemn experiments on such individuals, even if they were to redound to the benefit of scientific progress, unless such experiments or procedures were designed to help the patient in some way. "Still I suggest that someone who believes that it would be wrong to do nontherapeutic research on children, on the unconscious or the dying patient, or on the condemned, may have settled negatively the question of the morality of fetal research."

The Fetus In Utero

Therefore the interventions that would be sanctioned when the fetus is *in utero* would be those which (1) help the mother, (2) are harmless to the fetus, or which (3)

are designed to help the fetus in his own life-system. The latter would be licit even if it resulted in negative outcomes—for it is ethical to undergo procedures which have a good chance of success even when some risk is involved.

The view expressed here reflects the prevailing opinion that "no procedures be carried out during pregnancy with the deliberate intent of ascertaining the harm they might do to the fetus." (Peel Commission.)

Furthermore, it has been suggested that permission to initiate procedures which will harm the fetus, even when there is an announced intention of abortion, makes it impossible for the parent to change his or her mind about the fate of the fetus. The possibility of reversal of decision about abortion should remain to the last possible moment. This is a convincing argument to my mind.

The assertion that there might be a different ethical consideration in reference to experiments carried out in the course of the abortion does not, in my mind, merit approval. The circumstances of life do not mitigate the right to benefit from our bias for life. To cite the analogy used above— even when the rope is around the neck of the condemned prisoner he cannot be used for any procedure except that which is designed to bring him comfort or well-being.

The Fetus Ex Utero

The living fetus *ex utero*, even when not viable, would seem to have more rights than the fetus *in utero*. When the fetus has been severed from his mother's body, he can no longer pose a threat to her. There is no issue of the woman doing with her body as she wishes, or the right of privacy, or the consideration of the mother's health. It would seem, therefore, that the fetus' right to enjoy our bias for life would be enhanced when he passes out of the mother's uterus. Life is valuable wherever it exists. As such it evokes our responsibility. The fact that the abortus is sure to die—it is, after all, nonviable—does not mean that our concern for the life is diminished. Because it will never be a real child, it is not, nevertheless, right to consider it "nothing more than a piece of tissue."

We should understand "live" to include the presence of a heartbeat or any other discernible sign of life. For example the Louisiana statute on the matter reads: "A human being is liveborn, or there is a live-birth, whenever there is the complete expulsion or extraction from the mother of a human embryo or fetus, irrespective of the duration of the pregnancy, which after such separation breathes or shows any other evidence of life such as beating of the heart, pulsation of the umbilical cord or movement of voluntary muscles, whether or not the umbilical cord has been cut or the placenta is attached."

The prohibition against experimental procedures on live abortuses should, as the published guidelines suggest, concern both the artificial prolongation of life systems such as heartbeats for the purpose of observation or the stopping of any of the life signs. This does not mean that all experiments are prohibited. Only those should be prohibited that do discernible harm to the abortus. However, any procedure which breaches the dignity of the abortus such as prolongation of life-systems or destruction of existing life-systems should be prohibited. These considerations are in line with the guidelines suggested by both the Peel Commission and the regulations proposed by the Department of Health, Education and Welfare.

Fetal Death

The question of when can an abortus be presumed to be dead is a crucial issues. There are those, who were cited above, who believe that in regard to prehumans, the only meaningful distinction is viability or nonviability. For the reasons cited above, this approach is against the ethical canons of medicine—which make no distinction of the prospects of the subject in regard to his right to be treated with dignity and concern. While the dividing line between viability and nonviability is crucial, the dividing line between death and life is even more crucial. It is life—real and potential as well as being part of the human species—that has an ethical claim upon us.

The best approach to this problem is that suggested by Professor Paul Ramsey, "the difference between life and death of a human fetus/abortus should be determined substantially in the same way physicians use in making other pronouncements of death." He quotes Doctor Bernard Nathanson, who gave the only intellectually coherent reply that can be given to the question put to us by the Commission:

> "The Harvard Criteria for the pronouncement of death assert that if the subject is unresponsive to external stimuli (e.g., pain), if the deep reflexes are absent, if there are no spontaneous movements or respiratory efforts, if the electroencephalogram reveals no activity of the brain, one may conclude that the patient is dead. If any or all of these criteria are absent—and the fetus does respond to pain, makes respiratory efforts, moves spontaneously and has electroencephalographic activity—life must be present."

These signs of life do not make the abortus into a viable infant. But they do make it possible for the abortus to enjoy the fruits of our "bias for life." It is interesting that the proposed DHEW guidelines do not present criteria for fetal death. The Peel Commission defines death as "the state in which the fetus shows none of the signs of life and is incapable of being made to function as a self-sustaining whole." These criteria have been criticized by LeRoy Walters as being too vague. The last criterion, for example (being made to function as a self-sustaining whole) might determine that infants are dead. The idea of "signs of life," without designating what these "signs" are, also is too vague. LeRoy Walters writes: "As a general formal requirement for defining fetal death, I would suggest that any criteria developed for determining death in human adults should be applied, insofar as it is technically feasible, to the fetus. This requirement of simple biological consistency would rule out in advance the special pleading contained in hypothetical claims that the fetus is dead because it is about to die or that the fetus was never really alive."

Consent

The concept of informed consent is essential in formulating guidelines for experiments on human subjects. In the case of fetuses, this concept has doubtful application. The fetus obviously cannot give consent. The consent of the parents is made questionable by the fact that they have decided to terminate their relationship to the fetus by consenting to an abortion. The concept of consent is related to the concept of responsibility. Those who give consent must in some way be ready to bear the consequences of their decision.

In the case of abortuses and fetuses this has doubtful applicability. Therefore, it would seem that for the experiments that are legitimated, a special board should give the requisite consent. This board would closely scrutinize the proposed procedure and determine that there is no real risk in carrying it out, that all precautions had been taken, and that there be strict separation between the physician doing the abortion and the researcher.

Proposed Guidelines

In light of the above it is recommended that:

A. Research and experimentation on fetuses be limited to procedures which will present no harm or which have as their aim the enhancement of the life-systems of the subjects.

B. No procedures be permitted which are likely to harm the fetus, even when the abortion decision has already been made, and even where the abortion procedure has been initiated or is in progress.

C. When the fetus is *ex utero* and alive, no procedures should be permitted which do not have as their primary aim the enhancement of the life-systems of the fetus, unless such procedures present no risk to the subject. This prohibition would also apply to the artificial sustaining of life-systems for the sole reason of experimentation.

D. Criteria for determining death in the fetus be the same as the criteria applied to viable fetuses and other human individuals.

NO

John C. Fletcher and Joseph D. Schulman

FETAL RESEARCH: THE STATE OF THE QUESTION

Public policies, including policies about ethics, require a good heart (sound principles) and two good hands (sound institutional controls) to succeed. We believe that most investigators who conduct fetal research share our basic thesis: the 1975 federal regulations for fetal research "conducted by the Department of Health and Human Services (DHHS) or funded in whole or in part by a Department grant, contract, cooperative agreement or fellowship" were constructed on the soundest ethical principles: equality of protection for all research subjects; and the benefits to individuals and society that may be realized by research activities.[1]

Further, to resolve conflicts between these principles, the guidelines were set within a system of institutional controls with interaction between local and national levels. Unfortunately, since 1980 one of the hands of federal fetal research policy has been paralyzed by the lack of an Ethics Advisory Board (EAB). The other hand of policy, the local institutional review board (IRB), is now the only locus of practical control in fetal research. Consequently, fetal research in the United States is now reviewed only at the local level and receives support primarily from the private realm.

Our goal is the development of a set of public policies, ethically and institutionally coherent, to protect those toward whom research may be directed: the human embryo before and after implantation, the pregnant woman, the developing fetus inside or outside the uterus, and the infant in the perinatal period. (The "fetus" is defined in the regulations as "the product of conception from the time of implantation . . . until a determination is made . . . that it is viable" [45 CFR 46.203 (C)]. Here we discuss mainly fetal research, although we do pay some attention to the need for research with the human embryo. . . .

The Commission, with one notable dissent by David Louisell on categories (4) and (5), encouraged federal support of six categories of fetal research, conditional on IRB approval, informed consent of the mother, and the nonobjection of the father:

Reprinted by permission from the *Hastings Center Report*, April 1985. Copyright © 1985 by the Hastings Center.

1. *Therapeutic research directed toward the fetus*, within appropriate medical standards;

2. *Therapeutic research directed toward the pregnant woman*, provided the research imposed minimal risk or no risk to the fetus; altered in the regulations to "fetus will be placed at risk only to the minimum extent necessary to meet" the health needs of the mother, [46.207 (a) (1)];

3. *Nontherapeutic research directed toward the pregnant woman*, if the risk to the fetus is minimal;

4. *Nontherapeutic research directed toward the fetus in utero* either: (a) not anticipating abortion, if risk to the fetus is minimal, and the knowledge is unobtainable by other means; or (b) anticipating abortion, if risk to the fetus is minimal; approval of a national ethical review body was required if such research presents "special problems related to the interpretation or application of these guidelines";

5. *Nontherapeutic research directed toward the fetus during the abortion procedure and nontherapeutic research directed toward the nonviable fetus ex utero*, provided that the fetus is less than twenty weeks gestational age, no significant changes in the interests of research alone are introduced into the abortion procedure, and no attempt is made to alter the duration of the life of the fetus; like the fourth category, only with approval by a national ethical review body, if problems arise about the interpretation of minimal or added risk.

6. *Research directed toward the possibly viable fetus*, provided that no additional risk to the infant will be imposed by the research, and that the knowledge is unobtainable by other means.

Except for the removal of the twenty weeks gestational age provision in the fifth category, and a few elisions and minor rewordings, existing federal regulations still embody these key elements, though they do not use the language of "therapeutic" and "nontherapeutic" research. Instead, they describe activities "to meet the health of the particular fetus" or "the development of important biomedical knowledge which cannot be obtained by other means." However, neither the Commission's recommendations nor the current regulations defined minimal risk *specifically* for fetal research. A specific definition for minimal risk in research with children was developed by the Commission in 1975: "Minimal risk" means that risks of harm anticipated in the proposed research are not greater, considering probability and magnitude, than those ordinarily encountered in daily life or during the performance of routine medical or psychological examinations or tests, of healthy children."[2] In the regulations, the last frame of reference phrase of "healthy children" was omitted, and "physical" substituted for "medical" tests [45 CFR 46.102 (g)].

What frame of reference is supposed to be used for evaluating minimal risk of research with the fetus? The logical extension of the Commission's reasoning would be healthy, wanted fetuses, and the routine tests and examinations done on them. But how does one learn to do "routine" tests, unless by research, which at first involves risks of testing the new approach? This issue has never been resolved in the fetal regulations. Regulations to protect prisoners in research include a definition of minimal risk with the frame of reference being "healthy persons" [46.303 (d)].

Understandably, the most controverted issue faced by the Commission was the meaning of equal protection in nontherapeutic research with fetuses to be aborted. A maxim was developed from the

Golden Rule implications of the equality principle, that is, one ought to do or refrain from doing with a fetus to be aborted what one would likewise do or refrain from doing with a fetus to be delivered.

In the Commission discussions of this issue, most members favored a policy in which, if the research carried some risk but was acceptable to offer to fetuses to be carried to term, initial studies could be offered selectively to fetuses scheduled for abortion. However, if the research involves learning to do something new in prenatal diagnosis that carries a risk of fetal loss, should one *begin* to learn equally with both classes of fetuses or only with those to be aborted? The Commission's report (p. 67) admitted this moral dilemma, and left it unresolved with the further potential of national review:

> There is basic agreement among Commission members as to the validity of the equality principle. There is disagreement as to its application to individual fetuses and classes of fetuses. Anticipating that differences of interpretation will arise over the application of the basic principles of equality and the determination of 'minimal risk,' the Commission recommends review at the national level . . . the appropriate forum for determination of the scientific and public merit of such research. In addition, such review would facilitate public discussion of the sensitive issues surrounding the use of vulnerable nonconsenting subjects in research.

Thus the Commission intended the already intact system of independent local IRBs with the addition of one national Ethics Advisory Board as the *necessary* means to nurture and maintain the complex moral consensus they achieved.

THE ETHICS ADVISORY BOARD

The fetal research guidelines were adopted as federal guidelines on July 29,

1975. These regulations also required that proposals involving *in vitro* fertilization (IVF) be reviewed by an EAB which, among other duties, would advise the Secretary as to their acceptability. An EAB was not chartered until 1977, and not convened until 1978, so a *de facto* moratorium continued on federal support for fetal research involving minimal risks and also on IVF.

Meanwhile, in 1977, the NIH received an application for support of IVF research, which was approved by study section. In May 1978, the EAB agreed to review the proposal and the EAB published its recommendations and forwarded them to the Secretary in May 1979. Louise Brown, the first infant born after IVF and embryo transfer (ET), was delivered in July of the same year. The EAB recommended that DHEW support research involving IVF-ET to establish the safety and efficacy of the technique when used for the treatment of infertility.[3] Conditions placed upon approval included IRB approval, informed consent, a fourteen-day limit for sustaining embryos *in vitro*, and the use of gametes obtained only from lawfully married couples. These recommendations have yet to be approved by any of the subsequent DHHS Secretaries and no federal support of IVF research can yet be allowed.

The EAB considered only one proposal for fetal research after implantation. In 1978, investigators from the Charles R. Drew Postgraduate Medical School planned to assess the safety of fetoscopy for prenatal diagnosis of hemoglobinopathies in pregnant women who had elected abortion for reasons unrelated to the research. Working with data obtained from the earliest use of fetoscopy in the U.S., the EAB evaluated a situation in which risk of fetal loss was estimated to be at least five percent but was essentially unknown. The EAB did not insist on a rigorous application of the equality maxim in this case. Because of the importance of the biomedical information, unobtainable by any other method, the EAB recommended a waiver of provisions of the regulations involving minimal risk.[4] The EAB also stipulated that the timing of the planned abortions was not to be altered by the research. Secretary Califano granted such a waiver for this single research project in September 1979, but took no action on an EAB recommendation for a generic waiver for fetoscopy studies. Later in 1979, the first definitive review of the risk of fetal loss after fetoscopy showed that an initial rate of 10 percent might not be too high.[5]

A second fetoscopy proposal would have reached the EAB but did not. In 1980 NICHD's National Advisory Council approved funding for a proprosal from the University of California at San Francisco to obtain fetal blood samples from controls in a study of prenatal diagnosis in three genetic disorders (severe combined immunodeficiency disease, Wiskott-Aldrich syndrome, and glycogen storage disease, Type I). Fetal blood would be obtained by fetoscopy concurrently with abortion at mid-trimester to establish the feasibility of using fetal red blood cells for prenatal diagnosis of these disorders. However, the EAB was allowed to lapse by Secretary Harris when its charter and funding expired on September 30, 1980. No national review could be done, and the research has not been able to proceed. Mitchell Golbus, the principal investigator, says that his research on prenatal diagnosis for these disorders has been "seriously restricted" by lack of access to an EAB review in the same department where approval for his project was achieved.[6]

FETAL RESEARCH TODAY

We recently reviewed 183 research projects on high-risk pregnancies and fetal pathophysiology supported by NICHD, the primary source of federal support for fetal research. Other than two studies that employ ultrasound and one with antibiotic therapy, we could not find an example of human fetal research that approached the threshold of minimal risk. The latter study focuses on the question of whether bacterial infections in the female genital and urinary tracts cause premature labor and whether treatment with antibiotics prevents early labor. Studies of why labor starts suggest that an enzyme, phospholipase A2, that may stimulate contractions, could also be released by bacteria that cause genitourinary infections. Subjects will be women in the sixth month of pregnancy with any of three bacterial organisms but no other symptoms. Half will be treated with an antibiotic and half with a placebo until the thirty-eighth week of pregnancy or delivery, whichever occurs first, followed by assessment of the effect of treatment on prematurity and the infant's health.

In one of the ultrasound studies, the technique is being evaluated as a predictive test for respiratory distress syndrome (RDS) following delivery. In the second, it is used to study fetal heart, lung, and other functions as responses to hypoxia and the effects of smoking in pregnancy. In 1984 an NIH consensus development panel on diagnostic ultrasound imaging concluded that because some biological effects had been observed after ultrasound exposure in various experimental systems, the question of risks deserved more study and that "Data on clinical efficiency and safety do not allow a recommendation for routine screening at this time."[7] However, the panel listed twenty-seven clinically indicated uses of ultrasound, some of which parallel the uses in these two studies. By the standards set out by the panel, ultrasound examination falls well within the meaning of minimal risk applied to fetuses that may be at higher risk for RDS or for harms due to smoking. However, it would be more difficult, within current regulations, to test ultrasound for safety in studies with presumably healthy fetuses, since the examination can be challenged as a "routine" procedure for the fetus. Thus, some issues of minimal risks from questionably routine tests can only be settled by long-term studies of children who did and did not have such examinations.

All the other fetal pathophysiological studies currently funded by NICHD use animals. The high-risk pregnancy studies use only observational or health education techniques, for example, following the pregnancies of diabetic mothers for malformations or losses, and assisting the District of Columbia to identify mothers at risk for babies with low birthweight. These mothers are then given education and encouragement to stay in prenatal care.

Since 1980 some significant developments have occurred in fetal research. The single thread that runs through the story is that no initiatives in fetal research involving minimal risk have been federally conducted or supported, except for the ultrasound and antibiotic studies cited above, and one case of experimental fetal therapy cited below.

Fetal therapy: Experimental fetal surgery has been successfully used in a few centers to correct fetal obstructive uropathy and obstructive hydrocephalus, and will likely be tried soon for diaphragmatic hernia.[8] The initial plans were approved by local IRBs and financially supported by the institution or patient fees. Investigators in this new field published guidelines, including ethical considerations, for experimental fetal surgery.[9] Criteria for patient selection and a multidisciplinary team satisfied the "appropriate medical standards" required by the regulations.

Investigators in the NICHD attempted innovative steroid therapy for congenital adrenal hyperplasia in one pregnancy.[10] Their findings confirmed the feasibility of this therapy. The process for institutional review and bioethical consultation for this NIH case was also reported.[11]

Prenatal diagnosis: The most significant advance since amniocentesis is chorionic villus sampling (CVS). With CVS, cells genetically identical to fetal cells can be obtained for study and diagnosis without puncture of the uterus and amniotic sac. CVS is usually done today between nine and eleven weeks of pregnancy.[12]

Guided by ultrasound, the physician inserts a plastic or metal cannula into the cervix and directs it to the *chorion frondosum,* a villous part of the embryonic membrane that enters the developing placenta. Small amounts of tissue are removed for direct analysis of chromosomes or subsequent tests for other genetic disorders. The early timing of CVS is a major advantage, because in most cases the negative result relieves the anxiety of parents at higher risk much sooner than is possible with amniocentesis. After a positive finding, usually followed by an elective abortion, the early timing avoids the higher physical and emotional risks of midtrimester abortion. Emotional and moral differences between earlier and later abortion for genetic reasons also need careful study. The emotionally painful experience for mother and family of later abortions after amniocentesis has been well documented.[13]

Physicians in the U.S. brought CVS through an early research stage into the first phase of clinical practice without any federal support, although their initial studies were approved locally by IRBs. A few investigators working in states with laws banning any nontherapeutic research on the fetus to be aborted used cases of blighted ovum for the earliest studies. However, most of the initial feasibility studies obtained villi for diagnosis in the context of elective abortions. Women who had decided for first-trimester abortions were asked to participate in the research only after the procedure had been scheduled. Other than anecdotal reports, we have no record of IRB discussion of research risks to these fetuses to be aborted, or what frame of reference was used to discuss such risks. We suspect that the equality maxim could not have been applied literally in the actual choices made. The fact that CVS was already being widely used in Europe for diagnostic cases might have helped to balance the choice to allow physicians to learn to do a procedure that would eventually be beneficial to pregnant women. First-trimester diagnosis also carries a potential for earlier and more effective fetal therapy for some conditions. Presumably IRB members felt that CVS research was ethically acceptable within the intent of the regulations.

If an EAB had been available for national review of an application for early CVS research, the scientific and ethical considerations could have been shared, and perhaps improved, by many more persons. Further, the fetal regulations could have been put to another test, especially on the relevant framework for nontherapeutic research involving "minimal risk" for the human fetus. But no applications for federal support were made for three reasons. First, investigators knew an EAB review would be needed to waive "minimal risk" considerations by an EAB

that did not exist. Second, they could proceed with IRB approval alone without federal support. Third, they felt a need to move promptly to evaluate a method of diagnosis already being requested by patients.

How would an EAB have evaluated the risks of CVS to the fetus to be aborted and the value of the information to be gained? Data were scanty in the U.S. at the time (1982-1983), but publications about use in diagnostic cases were out from China,[14] the Soviet Union,[15] Great Britain,[16] and available from Italy.[17] The risk of fetal loss was probably below what a previous EAB had approved in fetoscopy studies. Even without this precedent, a series of phased feasibility *and* early diagnostic studies could have been approved in the interest of speeding delivery of a test that might benefit the health of mothers in the highest risk groups by providing earlier diagnosis. If an FAB took only fetal interests into account and used the equality maxim rigorously, the only feasibility study that could have been approved would have had to involve both fetuses to be aborted and fetuses at risk for genetic disorders randomly in the same study.

We believe, at the point of considering this alternative, an EAB would have considered its earlier willingness first to expose fetuses to be aborted followed by fetuses to be delivered in the same study series. In the debate, opportunities would have arisen to examine the concept of minimal risk with more specificity to fetal research. It seems to us inherently contradictory to derive a definition of minimal risk in a framework intended to apply to healthy *individuals* after birth, and to use the same definition in the context of the fetal-maternal unit. A more fitting and clearer definition is needed, based on presumably healthy mothers and fetuses, in the context of a "normal" pregnancy. However, only by constant examination of the shortcomings of the present expression of minimal risk in the light of actual research choices will the regulations be refined and improved.

What is known about the risks of fetal loss from CVS? Laird Jackson maintains a voluntary registry of fetal loss following CVS in diagnostic cases. At last report from 46 centers in Europe, Canada and the U.S., a total of 4,054 diagnostic procedures had been done (1,609 deliveries) with a maximum fetal loss rate of 4.1 percent.[18] Some fetal losses due to spontaneous abortions that would occur anyway and losses due to CVS are mixed in this figure. In the most experienced centers, like Jefferson Medical College, the loss rate is less than 2 percent (1.8 percent).

By a cooperative agreement, NICHD is now supporting the costs of data collection in a seven-center randomized trial to compare the safety and accuracy of CVS with amniocentesis.[19] Most patients to be enrolled will be women between the age of 35 and 39 whose pregnancies are at higher risk for chromosomal disorders. The patients will be randomized; those who do not agree to randomization will choose the procedure they prefer and will be included in some phases of the study. The costs of the procedures will be reimbursed by patient fees. This study, now in a stage in which patients are being admitted, will require about three years to complete.

Testing maternal serum for elevated levels of alpha-fetoprotein (AFP), an indication for higher risk of neural tube defects, began in Great Britain in the late 1970s in conjunction with analysis of AFP in amniotic fluid for a definitive fetal diagnosis. Although tests are now widely used here, no systematic study to evaluate the feasibility or safety of AFP screening in prenatal diagnosis was ever conducted in the United States. Indeed, a delay of several years took place in Food and Drug Administration action to release the test kits for commercial production. AFP-testing in maternal serum is an example of a significant step in prenatal diagnosis being introduced after exceptional delay and yet paradoxically without adequate studies of the capacity and competence of genetic centers to deliver the counseling and follow-up required.

Prevention of birth defects: Following encouraging but inconclusive reports in 1977 from Great Britain that vitamin supplementation around the time of conception reduces the recurrence of neural tube defects, the placebo-controlled randomized trial was begun there to answer the question conclusively.[20] One arm of the trial involved a dose of folic acid (a vitamin in the B vitamin complex) more than five times higher than the recommended daily allowance in pregnancy. Among the investigators who most favor a trial in the U.S. is Godfrey Oakley, Jr., of the Centers for Disease Control (CDC). Ethical issues in a proposed trial were extensively debated in NICHD; the agency was open to a trial that would involve only women at higher risk who had not taken vitamins and were not taking them at the time of recruitment.[21]

Oakley and others who favor a trial take the position that since current scientific evidence is not strong enough to support recommending vitamins to all women before conception, the most ethically desirable alternative is to conduct a trial. At this stage, CDC and the Spina Bifida Association of America have begun a collaborative study of the feasibility of conducting the trial. In particular, they will evaluate various recruitment mechanisms to determine how best to recruit subjects, and make a determination as to whether a full-scale trial is possible in the U.S.

Does the proposed trial, if feasible, meet the requirements of federal regulations? Two provisions apply here. First an IRB would have to determine that the fetuses on the higher dosage vitamin arm of the trial meet the requirements of 46.208 (a) (1) if that arm was seen to present greater than minimal risk: that is, would inclusion in this arm meet the health needs of the particular fetus? Second, an IRB would have to determine that the fetuses in the placebo arm met the requirements of 46.208 (a) (2), that is, that no greater than minimal risk was involved and that important biomedical knowledge was a likely outcome which could not be obtained in another way. Exact knowledge to answer these objections is unavailable. Indeed, the trial is designed to seek information about dose-relationships and recurrence rates. Literally applied, the regulations appear to prevent a trial that seeks scientific information in the context of a *possibly* therapeutic trial.

In our view, the best position from which to apply the regulations to the proposed trial is one that allows some attention to early, favorable results in uncontrolled trials but includes true uncertainty as to whether vitamin-taking around the time of conception will prove to reduce the recurrence of neural tube defects or do harm to the fetus at the higher dosage when rigorously tested. On this view, since the trial is at least partly designed to "meet the health needs" of the fetuses at higher risk for neural tube defects by testing the only mode of prevention other than abortion, and since the trial will distribute the risks (if any) equally to all fetuses in the trial (by random chance), each particular fetus will be placed at risk "only to the minimum extent necessary to meet such needs" [46.208

(a)]. We note, however, how difficult it is to study for the first time an important question that may involve ventures over the boundary of minimal risk.

Research with fetuses ex utero, including nonviable fetuses: A pressing long-range problem in fetal research is the development of methods to sustain the previable fetus (the spontaneous abortus less than twenty-four weeks) *ex utero* until it develops to the point of sufficient maturity for independent survival. These methods might be considered the development of an artificial uterine environment in the broadest sense, including the "artificial placenta" or new techniques to perfuse directly the previable fetus with nutrients or oxygen. Any work of this type, if successful, will be life-saving in cases of extreme prematurity. To *learn* to do such work and to test the technology would require research with nonviable fetuses, in our view, since it would be ethically objectionable to subject a possibly viable fetus to totally unproven techniques.

To carry out this research runs counter to [46.209 (b) (1)], "no nonviable fetus may be involved as a subject . . . unless vital functions of the fetus will not be artificially maintained." In our view, the regulations go too far in an effort to prevent recurrence of nontherapeutic research with nonviable fetuses that had no relevance to potential therapy. The nonviable fetus to be studied to "develop important biomedical knowledge which cannot be obtained by any other means" [46.209 (b) (3)] and which is clearly related to potentially life-saving therapy, should be anesthetized and the fetal experiment terminated at a specific predetermined point.

IVF: In testimony before Congress in August 1984, Gary Hodgen, Scientific Director of the Jones Institute for Reproductive Medicine in Norfolk, Va., summarized progress in IVF research. Hodgen, an expert in pregnancy and fertility research who resigned from the NIH in part because of the lack of opportunity to study human IVF, reported that the number of children born as a result of IVF-ET therapy exceeded 700 and more than 300 pregnancies were ongoing.[22] Over 200 IVF programs have been established, with perhaps fifty of these in the United States. No federal funds have been expended on research concerning the efficacy and safety of IVF-ET in its actual use. However, the first detailed follow-up study of children born after IVT-ET will be done with federal support. NICHD will soon begin such a project, through contract with a major IVF program.

Hodgen's statement about research goals with IVF included: (1) monitoring the safety and reliability of methods to freeze, store, and thaw human embryos for later transfer to infertile women, which avoids laparoscopy and prevents destruction of embryos already fertilized; (2) developing a safe method to freeze human eggs, since between five and ten can be obtained from most patients; (3) overcoming male infertility caused by oligospermia (too few living sperms) by IVF with induced fusion of egg and sperm or microsurgical placement of sperm in ooplasm; (4) developing tests predictive of the normalcy of each fertilized embryo, to avoid the risk of multiple pregnancies caused by implanting several embryos; (5) diagnosing chromosomal and/or genetic disorders in the preimplantation embryo; and (6) studying cell messengers in human embryos and their relation to normal embryonic genes, oncogenes, and development of cancer.

Officially appointed bodies were established in Great Britain[23] and Victoria, Australia[24] to review ethical, legal, and social considerations of IVF research with preimplantation human embryos that were not to be transferred. Both recommended research that would restrict studies to a limit of fourteen days after fertilization. The EAB report of 1979 anticipated this issue in allowing for research with fertilized embryos not used for ET. "The Board believes that such research, if performed as a corollary to research designed primarily to establish safety and efficacy of IVT-ET, would also be acceptable from an ethical standpoint" (EAB Report, p. 108). The EAB report also anticipated but did not take up the issue of fertilizing human ova for the purpose of research.

Clearly, an officially appointed national body in the United States needs to consider these questions in the context of our legal, ethical, and social traditions. The ideal group would be a newly convened EAB. A decision memorandum regarding establishment of an EAB is awaiting Secretarial approval. The former Assistant Secretary for Health, Edward Brandt, prior to his recent departure from office, recommended creation of an EAB. A new EAB should be asked, as its first assignment, to establish criteria according to which the Department will support research on human embryos not to be transferred.

THE CONSEQUENCES OF INACTION

Federal regulations on fetal research are ethically sound and widely respected by investigators. For a variety of reasons having to do with political and social conflict about the moral status of the human embryo and the fetus, federal support for an ethical review of research with virtually *any* risk to the human fetus ended in 1980 and has not resumed. The dangers of such a situation, foreseen by the framers of the guidelines, have already clearly emerged.

We close by simply listing some serious consequences of this situation and the policy choices before those who can change it. First, a gulf has been created between local and national considerations of fetal research. The gulf is harmful to science and ethics. The NIH is being prevented, to quote Hodgen's testimony, from its "natural roles . . . in peer review of research, debate of relevant scientific, ethical and legal issues, and provision of funding for research excellence. . . ."

Second, support for fetal research has been divided. Research with risks to the fetus or mother is supported in the "private" realm. Unquestionably safe research is supported by federal sources. In no other realm of medicine and science does this situation exist. In effect, by the absence of an expert national review body for just such guidance, federal authorities cannot support research that may involve acceptable risks, as defined by federal guidelines, to achieve gains on behalf of seriously affected groups and individuals. Families at higher genetic risk, fetuses at higher risk, pregnant women, and infertile couples are being deprived of the potential benefits of research on problems that affect their life chances. The distribution of the benefits of federally supported research has become unjust in the process and, in our view, needs correction.

Third, the absence of an EAB has many unfortunate consequences. Missing is the mechanism seen by the Commission as vital for resolving conflicts of scientific opinion and ethical differences too great for any local IRB to assume. The public, broadly considered, is deprived of participation in choices of great significance. Further, if federal policies on research with human subjects are understood as a moral code, it is necessary to keep their provisions under critical evaluation. Moral codes that cannot be tested and examined in the light of actual choices usually wither and die, because they lose relevance to ever new scientific questions. A new EAB needs to be appointed to keep the specifics of the protections for human subjects under critical review. An EAB is also needed to implement the public partnership between national and local institutions that undergirded the original policy formulated in 1966 to require prior ethical review of research.[25]

Fourth, if and when an EAB is assembled, two provisions of the regulations on fetal research need careful study. A definition of minimal risk, with pregnancy, healthy mothers and "normal" fetuses as its frame of reference, needs to be drafted and debated in an open public forum. Moreover, the fetal research guidelines need to be reexamined in the light of the potential for fetal therapy and its relation to fetal diagnosis. The Commission report was drafted in a climate of concern to protect fetuses that were to be aborted. Now that more therapeutic possibilities are available, more risks might be allowed in early therapeutically designed studies. We include in this concern the research required to learn to save and nurture babies so small and compromised that they hover between the borderline of viable and nonviable.

After a period of almost ten years since the Commission debates, the ethics of fetal research needs to be reexamined by an Ethics Advisory Board, in the context of current possibilities in research from fertilization to delivery.

REFERENCES

1. Title 45, Code of Federal Regulations, Part 46—Protection of Human Subjects, Subpart B—Additional Protections Pertaining to Research Develop-

ment, and Related Activities Involving Fetuses, Pregnant Women, and Human In Vitro Fertilization (revised as of March 8, 1983). Available from Office of Protection from Research Risks, Bldg. 31, Room 4B-09, NIH, Bethesda, Md. 20205.

2. Commission, *Research Involving Children: Report and Recommendations,* DHEW Publication No. (OS) 77-0004, 1977; the specific reference to the earliest definition of minimal risk in *Federal Register* 40:33529, 1975.

3. Ethics Advisory Board of the U.S. Department of Health, Education and Welfare, "Report and Conclusions: DHEW Support of Research Involving In Vitro Fertilization and Embryo Transfer," (May 4, 1979); also, *Federal Register* 44:35, 1979.

4. Margaret Steinfels, "At the EAB, Same Members, New Ethical Problems," *Hastings Center Report* 5 (October, 1979), p. 2.

5. R. Benzie, M. J. Mahoney, D.V.I. Fairweather, et al., "Fetoscopy and Fetal Tissue Sampling," in John L. Hamerton and Nancy E. Simpson (eds.), Report of an International Workshop, *Prenatal Diagnosis* (Special Issue, December 1980), p. 32.

6. Personal Communication, December 17, 1984.

7. National Institutes of Health Consensus Development Conference, *Consensus Development Statement,* Vol. 5 (No. 1), 1984, Question 4. Available from Office of Medical Applications of Technology, Building 1, Room 216, NIH, Bethesda, MD 20205.

8. Michael R. Harrison, Mitchell S. Golbus, and Roy A. Filly, *Unborn Patient* (Orlando, FL: Grune & Stratton, 1984).

9. Michael R. Harrison, Roy A. Filly, Mitchell S. Golbus, et al., "Fetal Treatment 1982," *New England Journal of Medicine,* 307 (December 23, 1982), 1651-52.

10. Mark I. Evans, George P. Chrousos, Dean Mann, et al., "Pharmacologic Suppression of the Fetal Adrenal Gland in Utero: Attempted Prevention of Abnormal External Genital Masculinization in Suspected Congenital Adrenal Hyperplasia," *Journal of the American Medical Association,* 253 (Feb. 15, 1985), 1015-1020.

11. John C. Fletcher, "Emerging Ethical Issues in Fetal Therapy," in Kare Berg and Knut Erik Tranoy, *Research Ethics* (New York: Alan R. Liss, Inc. 1983), pp. 309-11.

12. Bruno Brambati, Giuseppe Simoni, and S. Fabro, (eds.), *Fetal Diagnosis During the First Trimester* (in press) Marcel Dekker, Inc.

13. Three studies have appeared in the literature. The latest is the most extensively documented. B.D. Blumberg, M.S. Golbus, and K.H. Hanson, "The Psychological Sequalae of Abortion Performed for a Genetic Indication," *American Journal of Obstetrics and Gynecology,* 122 (1975), 799-808; P. Donnai, N. Charles, and N. Harris, "Attitudes of Patients After

'Genetic' Termination of Pregnancy," *British Medical Journal,* 282 (1981), 621-22; N.J. Leschot, M. Verjaal and J.H. Leschot, On Prenatal Diagnosis (Doctoral Dissertation, Rodopi, University of Amsterdam, 1982), pp. 96-111.

14. Anshan Department of Obstetrics and Gynecology, "Fetal Sex Prediction by Sex Chromatin of Chorionic Villi Cells During Early Pregnancy," *Clinical Medical Journal* 1 (1975), 117-126.

15. Z. Kazy, I.S. Rozovsky, and V. Bakharev, "Chorion Biopsy in Early Pregnancy," *Prenatal Diagnosis* 2 (1982), 39-45.

16. R.H.T. Ward, B. Modell, et al., "Method of Sampling Chorionic Villi in First Trimester of Pregnancy Under Guidance of Real Time Ultrasound," *British Medical Journal* 286 (1983), 1542.

17. G. Simoni, B. Brambati, C. Danesino, et al., "Diagnostic Application of First Trimester Trophoblast Sampling in 100 Pregnancies," *Human Genetics,* 66 (1984), 252-59.

18. Laird Jackson (ed.), "CVS Newsletter," February 5, 1985), p. 2. Available through Division of Medical Genetics, Jefferson Medical College, Philadelphia, PA 19107.

19. Virginia Cowart, "NIH Considers Large-Scale Study to Evaluate Chorionic Villi Sampling," *Journal of the American Medical Association* 252 (July 6, 1984), 11-15.

20. R.W. Smithells, S. Sheppard, and C.J. Schorah, et al., "Possible Prevention of Neural Tube Defects by Periconceptual Vitamin Supplementation," *Lancet* 1 (1980), 339-44.

21. Mortimer B. Lipsett and John C. Fletcher, "Do Vitamins Prevent Neural Tube Defects (And Can We Find Out Ethically)?" *Hastings Center Report* (August 1983), pp. 5-8.

22. Gary D. Hodgen, "Testimony Before Subcommittee on Investigations and Oversight," Committee on Science and Technology, U.S. House of Representatives (August 8, 1984); Jeffrey L. Fox, "Scientist Quits NIH Over Fetal Rules," *Science* 223 (March 2, 1984), 916.

23. Department of Health and Social Security, *Report of the Committee of Inquiry into Human Fertilization and Embryology* (London: Her Majesty's Stationery Office 1984), p. 84.

24. Victoria, Committee to Consider the Social, Ethical, and Legal Issues Arising From In Vitro Fertilization, *Report on the Disposition of Embryos Produced by In Vitro Fertilization* (Melbourne: F.D. Atkinson Government Printer, August 1984), p. 60.

25. Surgeon General, Public Health Service, Department of Health, Education and Welfare, "Investigations Involving Human Subjects, Including Clinical Research: Requirements for Review to Insure the Rights and Welfare of Individuals," PPO 129, Revised Policy, July 1, 1966.

POSTSCRIPT

SHOULD FETAL RESEARCH INVOLVING MORE THAN MINIMAL RISK BE BANNED?

In November 1985 Congress passed a bill, over President Reagan's veto, establishing a Biomedical Ethics Board. It is mandated to "conduct a study of the nature, advisability, and biomedical and ethical implications of exercising any waiver of the risk standard" in the federal regulations governing fetal research. The Board is made up of six senators and six representatives, and it will appoint a Biomedical Ethics Advisory Committee of experts in various fields.

Following the public debates in the early 1970s, many states passed laws regulating fetal research. According to attorney Charles H. Baron, they are "anything but uniform." In fact, they range from very restrictive, as in Arizona (which bans every form of research not "strictly necessary" to diagnose a disease or condition), to very liberal, as in South Dakota and Tennessee (which permit fetal research of all sorts as long as the mother consents). See Charles H. Baron, "Fetal Research: The Question in the States," *Hastings Center Report,* April 1985.

A balanced account of the ethical problems of fetal research is found in Robert J. Levine, *Ethics and Regulation of Clinical Research,* 2nd edition (Urban & Schwarzenberg, 1986). A classic critique of fetal research is Paul Ramsey, *The Ethics of Fetal Research* (Yale University Press, 1975). Also see "Fetal Experimentation: A Symposium," *Human Life Review* (Fall 1975) for arguments that the National Commission did not go far enough in banning fetal research.

ISSUE 15

SHOULD ANIMAL EXPERIMENTATION BE STOPPED?

YES: Peter Singer, from "Tools for Research, or What the Public Doesn't Know It Is Paying For," *Animal Liberation* (New York: The New York Review, 1975)

NO: U.S. Congress, Office of Technology Assessment, from *Alternatives to Animal Use in Research, Testing, and Education* (Washington, D.C.: February 1986)

ISSUE SUMMARY

YES: Philosopher Peter Singer claims that much experimentation involving animals is brutal and serves no direct or urgent purpose for the benefit of humans and that alternative scientific methods can be used to achieve the same knowledge.
NO: The Office of Technology Assessment acknowledges the conflict of interest between the liberty that humans have to use animals for human ends and the need of animals to be free from suffering, but concludes that when suffering inflicted on animals is unavoidable to satisfy desirable human objectives, the human interest will be controlling.

In 1865 the great French physiologist Claude Bernard wrote: "Physicians already make too many dangerous experiments on man before carefully studying them in animals." In his insistence on adequate animal research before trying a new therapy on human beings, Bernard established a principle of research ethics that is still considered valid. But in the past few decades this principle has been challenged by another view—one that sees animals not as tools for human use and consumption but as moral agents in their own right. Animal experimentation, according to this theory, cannot be taken for granted but must be justified by ethical criteria at least as stringent as those that apply to research involving humans.

Philosophers traditionally have not ascribed any moral status to animals. Like St. Thomas Aquinas before him, Rene Descartes, a seventeenth-century French physiologist and philosopher, saw no ethical problem in experimention on animals. Descartes approved of cutting open a fully conscious animal because it was, he said, a machine more complex than a clock but no more capable of feeling pain. Immanuel Kant argued that animals need not be treated as ends in themselves because they lacked rationality.

Beginning in England in the nineteenth century, "anti-vivisectionists" or people who advocated the abolition of animal experimentation campaigned, with varying success, for laws to control scientific research. But the internal dissensions in the movement and its frequent lapses into sentimentality made it only partially effective. At most the vivisectionists achieved some legislation that mandated more humane treatment of animals used for research, but they never succeeded in abolishing the research (in fact such experimentation increased enormously in recent years) or even in establishing the need for justification of particular research projects.

The more recent movement to ban animal research, however, is both better organized politically and rests on a more rigorous philosophical basis. The movement, often called "animal liberation" or "animal rights," is similar in principle to the civil rights movement of the 1960s. Just as blacks, women, and other minorities sought recognition of their equal status, animal advocates have built a case for the equal status of animals.

Peter Singer, one of the leaders of this movement, has presented an eloquent case that we not only practice racism and sexism in our society—we practice "speciesism." That is, we assume that human beings are superior to other animals; we are prejudiced in favor of our own kind. Experimenting on animals and eating their flesh are the two major forms of speciesism in our society. Singer points out that some categories of human beings—infants and mentally retarded people—rate lower on a scale of intelligence, awareness, and self-consciousness than some animals. Yet we would not treat these individuals in the way we do animals. He argues that "all animals are equal" and the suffering of an animal is morally equal to the suffering of a human being.

Proponents of animal research counter that such views are fundamentally misguided, that human beings, with the capacity for rational thought and action, are indeed a superior species. They contend that, while animals deserve humane treatment, the good consequences of animal research (i.e., knowledge that will benefit human beings) outweigh the suffering of individual animals. No other research techniques can substitute for the reactions of live animals, they declare.

The following exerpt from Peter Singer's book *Animal Liberation* presents a gripping recital of actual animal experiments. Singer uses these examples to bolster his claim that such experimentation is unnecessary for scientific reasons and ought to be stopped. The Office of Technology Assessment, on the other hand, rebuts Singer's claim that animals have rights. They are morally entitled to be treated humanely, but whether they are entitled to more than that is unclear. Even though suffering should not be inflicted on animals needlessly, when it serves a desirable human interest, it can be justified.

YES Peter Singer

TOOLS FOR RESEARCH . . .
OR WHAT THE PUBLIC DOESN'T KNOW
IT IS PAYING FOR

In July 1973 Congressman Les Aspin of Wisconsin learned through an advertisement in an obscure newspaper that the United States Air Force was planning to purchase 200 beagle puppies, with vocal chords tied to prevent normal barking, for tests of poisonous gases. Shortly afterward it became known that the army was also proposing to use beagles—400 this time—in similar tests.

Aspin began a vigorous protest, supported by antivivisection societies. Advertisements were placed in major newspapers across the country. Letters from an outraged public began pouring in. An aide from the House of Representatives Armed Services Committee said that the committee received more mail on the beagles than it had received on any other subject since Truman sacked General MacArthur, while an internal Department of Defense memo released by Aspin said that the volume of mail the department had received was the greatest ever for any single event, surpassing even the mail on the bombings of North Vietnam and Cambodia.[1] After defending the experiments initially, the Defense Department then announced that it was postponing them, and looking into the possibility of replacing the beagles with other experimental animals.

All this amounted to a rather curious incident; curious because the public furor over this particular experiment implied a remarkable ignorance of the nature of quite standard experiments performed by the armed services, research establishments, universities, and commercial firms of many different kinds. True, the proposed air force and army experiments were designed so that many animals would suffer and die without any certainty that this suffering and death would save a single human life, or benefit humans in any way at all; but the same can be said for tens of thousands of other experiments performed in the United States alone each year. For instance, limiting ourselves for the moment just to experiments done on beagles, the following should, one might think, have provoked as much protest as those planned by the air force and the army:

At the Lovelace Foundation, Albuquerque, New Mexico, experimenters forced sixty-four beagles to inhale radioactive strontium 90 as part of a larger "Fission Product Inhalation Program" which began in 1961 and has been paid for by the US Atomic Energy Commission. In this particular experiment twenty-five of the dogs eventually died. One of the deaths occurred during an epileptic seizure; another from a brain hemorrhage. Other dogs, before death, became feverish and anemic, lost their appetites, had hemorrhages and bloody diarrhea.

The experiments, in their published report, compared their results with the results of other experiments at the University of Utah and at Argonne National Laboratory, in Illinois, in which beagles were injected with strontium 90. They concluded that the various experiments had led to similar results on the dose of strontium 90 needed to produce "early deaths" in 50 percent of a sample group of beagles, but that there was a difference in the number of deaths occurring later, because dogs injected with strontium 90 retain more of the radioactive substance than dogs forced to inhale it.[2]

At the University of Rochester School of Medicine a team of experimenters placed fifty beagles in wooden boxes and irradiated them with different levels of radiation by X-rays. Twenty-one of the dogs died between the ninth and thirty-ninth day after irradiation. The experimenters determined the dose at which 50 percent of the animals will die with "95 percent confidence." The irradiated dogs vomited, had diarrhea, and lost their appetites. Later they hemorrhaged from the mouth and the anus. In their report these experimenters summarized nine other experiments in which more than 700 beagles and other dogs were irradiated with X-rays, and they said that the injuries produced in their own experiments were "typical of those described for the dog."[3]

Experimenters working for the US Food and Drug Administration gave thirty beagles and thirty pigs large amounts of methoxychlor (a pesticide) in their food, seven days a week for six months, "in order to ensure tissue damage." Within eight weeks, eleven dogs showed signs of "abnormal behavior" including nervousness, salivation, muscle tremors, spasms, and convulsions. Dogs in convulsions breathed as rapidly as 200 times a minute before lack of oxygen caused them to collapse. Upon recovery from an episode of convulsion and collapse, the dogs were uncoordinated, apparently blind, and "any stimulus such as dropping a feed pan, squirting water, or touching the animals initiated another convulsion." After further experiments on an additional twenty beagles, the experimenters concluded that massive daily doses of methoxychlor produce different effects in dogs from those produced in pigs.[4]

These three examples should be enough to show that the air force beagle experiments were in no way exceptional. Note that all of these experiments, according to the experimenters' own reports, obviously caused the animals to suffer considerably before dying. No steps were taken to prevent this suffering, even when it was clear that the radiation or poison had made the animals extremely sick. Note, too, that these experiments are parts of series of similar experiments, repeated with only minor variations, that are being carried out all over the country. Note, finally, that these experiments do not save human lives. We already knew that strontium 90 was unhealthy before the beagles died; and the experimenters who poisoned dogs and pigs with methoxychlor knew beforehand that the large amounts they were feeding the animals (amounts no human would ever consume) would cause damage. In any case, as the differing results they obtained on dogs and pigs make clear, it is not possible to reach any firm conclusions about the effects of a substance on humans from tests on other species. The same is true of radioactive substances, and so the precision with which experimenters determine the dose necessary to make 50 percent of a sample group of beagles die has no application to humans.

Nor should we limit ourselves to dogs. People tend to care about dogs because they have dogs as pets; but other animals are as capable of suffering as dogs are. Dogs are only one species of many that are used in experiments. In Britain sentimental attachment to dogs and cats has gone so far that the law regulating experiments on animals requires an experimenter to obtain a special certificate for performing an experiment on unanesthetized dogs and cats; apes and monkeys, however, receive no such protection; nor, of course, does the common laboratory rat. Few people feel sympathy for rats. Yet the laboratory rat is an intelligent, gentle animal, the result of many generations of special breeding, and there can be no doubt that the rats are capable of suffering, and do suffer from the countless painful experiments performed on them.

The practice of experimenting on nonhuman animals as it exists today throughout the world reveals the brutal consequences of speciesism. Experiments are performed on animals that inflict severe

pain without the remotest prospect of significant benefits for humans or any other animals. These are not isolated instances, but part of a major industry. In Britain, where experimenters are required to report the number of experiments performed, official government figures show that around 5 million experiments on animals are now performed each year. In the United States there are no figures of comparable accuracy. . . .

An official of the US Department of Agriculture has stated that the number of rats and mice used annually for research purposes is estimated at 40 million.[5] In testimony before congressional committees in 1966, the Laboratory Animal Breeders Association estimated that the number of mice, rats, guinea pigs, hamsters, and rabbits used for experimental purposes in 1965 had totaled around 60 million; and they projected a figure of 97 million for these species by 1970. They estimated the number of dogs and cats used in 1965 as between 500,000 and 1 million.[6] A 1971 survey carried out by Rutgers University College of Agriculture and Environmental Sciences produced the following estimates of the number of animals used each year in U.S. laboratories: 85,000 primates, 500,000 dogs, 200,000 cats, 700,000 rabbits, 46,000 pigs, 23,000 sheep, 1.7 million birds, 45 million rodents, 15-20 million frogs, and 200,000 turtles, snakes, and lizards; a total of more than 63 million animals.[7]

These estimates are somewhat lower than the Laboratory Animal Breeders Association estimates for the species included in their survey for 1965; and much lower than their projections for 1970. These projections may, of course, have been over-optimistic expectations about the continued growth of the animal breeding industry, which had grown phenomenally in preceding years. Assuming then that the Rutgers University figures are a reasonable, and certainly not exaggerated, estimate, it is still clear that the official Animal Welfare Act report covers only a very small fraction of the animals experimented upon in the United States.

Of this vast number of experiments, only a few contribute to important medical research. Huge numbers of animals are used in university departments from Forestry to Psychology, and many more are used for commercial purposes, to test new cosmetics, shampoos, food coloring agents and other inessential items. All this can go on only because of our prejudice against taking seriously the suffering of a being that is not a member of our own species. The typical defender of experiments on animals does not deny that animals suffer. He cannot use this argument because he needs to stress the similarities between humans and other animals in order to claim that his experiment may have some relevance for human purposes. The researcher who forces rats to choose between starvation and electric shock to see if they develop ulcers (they do) does so because he knows that the rat has a nervous system very similar to man's, and presumably feels an electric shock in a similar way.

There has been opposition to experimenting on animals for a long time. This opposition has made little headway because experimenters, backed by commercial firms who profit by supplying laboratory animals and equipment, have been able to convince legislators and the public that opposition comes from sentimental cranks who consider the interests of animals more important than the interests of human beings. But to be opposed to what is going on now it is not necessary to insist that all experiments stop immediately. All

that we need to say is that experiments serving no direct and urgent purpose should stop immediately, and in the remaining areas of research, methods involving animals should be replaced as soon as possible by alternative methods not involving animals. . . .

In Britain almost 100 new cosmetics and toiletries come onto the market every *week,* and it has been estimated that up to a million animals die annually in research connected with cosmetics alone.[8] The figure for the United States is not known, but could well be much higher. To this must be added the enormous numbers of animals used to test inessential foodstuffs—new coloring agents, new sweeteners or other flavoring agents, new preservatives, and so on. Any company that wants permission to market such a new substance must lodge with the Food and Drug Administration evidence of the product's safety. This evidence consists of a thick file full of reports of the experimental poisoning of animals.

It is not only products intended for consumption that are tested. All kinds of industrial and household goods are fed to animals and tested on their eyes. A reference book, *Clinical Toxicology of Commercial Products,* provides data, mostly from animal experiments, on how poisonous hundreds of commercial products are. The products include: insecticides, antifreeze, brake fluids, bleaches, Christmas-tree sprays, church candles, oven-cleaners, deodorants, skin fresheners, bubble baths, depilatories, eye make-up, fire extinguishers, inks, suntan oils, nail polish, mascara, hair sprays, paints, and zipper lubricants.[9]

Whenever the testing on animals of products intended for human use is criticized, someone brings up the tragic "thalidomide babies" in support of the claim that thorough testing is needed to protect the general public. This example is worth investigating. The lesson to be learned from it is not what most people expect.

The first thing to remember is that thalidomide was not an essential, life-saving substance. It was a new kind of sleeping tablet, and while sleeping tablets may be more important than cosmetics, the animal suffering involved in testing a substance is in any case a high price to pay for the avoidance of sleeplessness. So doing without animal testing would not mean releasing substances like thalidomide untested; it would mean doing without it, and trying to become less dependent on drugs.

Second, and more important, is the fact that thalidomide *was* extensively tested on animals before it was released. These tests failed to show any abnormalities. Indeed, as the editor of a recent book on toxicology has stated: "the toxicity tests that had been carefully carried out on thalidomide without exception had demonstrated it to be an almost uniquely safe compound."[10] Even after the drug was suspected of causing deformities in human babies, tests on pregnant laboratory dogs, cats, rats, monkeys, hamsters, and chickens all failed to produce deformities. Only when a particular strain of rabbit was tried were deformities produced.[11]

The thalidomide story underlines something that toxicologists have known for a long time: species vary. Extrapolation from one species to another is a highly risky venture. Thalidomide is harmless to most animals. Insulin, on the other hand, can produce deformities in infant rabbits and mice, but not in humans.[12] And as another toxicologist has said: "If penicillin had been judged by its toxicity on guinea pigs it might never have been used on man."[13]

What we should learn from thalidomide, then, is not that animal testing is necessary, but that it is unreliable; not that we need to poison more animals, but that we need to find alternative methods of testing, and until then we should make do without new nonessential drugs.

When experiments can be brought under the heading "medical" we are inclined to think that any suffering they involve must be justifiable because the research is contributing to the alleviation of suffering. But the general label "medical research" can be used to cover research which is not directed toward the reduction of suffering, but is motivated by a general goalless curiosity that may be acceptable as part of a basic search for knowledge when it involves no suffering, but should not be tolerated if it causes pain. Very often this research has been going on for decades and much of it, in the long run, turns out to have been quite pointless. . . .

How can these things happen? How can a man who is not a sadist spend his working day heating an unanesthetized dog to death, or driving a monkey into a lifelong depression, and then remove his white coat, wash his hands, and go home to dinner with his wife and children? How can taxpayers allow their money to be used to support experiments of this kind? And how can students go through a turbulent era of protest against injustice, discrimination, and oppression of all kinds, no matter how far from home, while ignoring the cruelties that are being carried out on their own campuses?

The answers to these questions stem from the unquestioned acceptance of speciesism. We tolerate cruelties inflicted on members of other species that would outrage us if performed on members of our own species. Speciesism allows researchers to regard the animals they experiment on as items of equipment, laboratory tools rather than living, suffering creatures. Sometimes they even refer to the animals in this way. Robert White of the Cleveland Metropolitan General Hospital, who has performed numerous experiments involving the transplanting of heads of monkeys, and the keeping alive of monkey brains in fluid, outside the body, has said in an interview that:

> Our main purpose here is to offer a living laboratory tool: a monkey "model" in which and by which we can design new operative techniques for the brain.

And the reporter who conducted the interview and observed White's experiments found his experience

> a rare and chilling glimpse into the cold, clinical world of the scientist, where the life of an animal has no meaning beyond the immediate purpose of experimentation.[14]

This "scientific" attitude to animals was exhibited to a large audience in December 1974 when the American public television network brought together Harvard philosopher Robert Nozick and three scientists whose work involves animals. The program was a follow-up to Fred Wiseman's controversial film *Primate,* which had taken viewers inside the Yerkes Primate Center, a research center in Atlanta, Georgia. Nozick asked the scientists whether the fact that an experiment will kill hundreds of animals is ever regarded, by scientists, as a reason for not performing it. One of the scientists answered: "Not that I know of." Nozick pressed his question: "Don't the animals count at all?" Dr. A. Perachio, of the Yerkes Center, replied: "Why should they?" while Dr. D. Baltimore, of the Massachusetts Institute of Technology, added that he did not think that

experimenting on animals raised a moral issue at all.[15]

As well as the general attitude of speciesism which researchers share with other citizens there are some special factors operating to make possible the experiments I have described. Foremost among these is the immense respect that we still have for scientists. Although the advent of nuclear weapons and environmental pollution have made us realize that science and technology need to be controlled to some extent, we still tend to be in awe of anyone who wears a white coat and has a PhD. In a well known series of experiments Stanley Milgram, a Harvard psychologist, has demonstrated that ordinary people will obey the directions of a white-coated research worker to administer what appears to be (but in fact is not) electric shock to a human subject as "punishment" for failing to answer questions correctly; and they will continue to do this even when the human subject cries out and pretends to be in great pain.[16] If this can happen when the participant believes he is inflicting pain on a human, how much easier is it for a student to push aside his initial qualms when his professor instructs him to perform experiments on animals? What Alice Heim has rightly called the "indoctrination" of the student is a gradual process, beginning with the dissection of frogs in school biology classes. When the budding medical student, or psychology student, or veterinarian, reaches the university and finds that to complete the course of studies on which he has set his heart he must experiment on living animals, it is difficult for him to refuse to do so, especially since he knows that what he is being asked to do is standard practice in the field.

Individual students will often admit feeling uneasy about what they are asked to do, but public protests are very rare. An organized protest did occur in Britain recently, however, when students at the Welsh National School of Medicine in Cardiff complained publicly that a dog was unnecessarily injected with drugs more than 30 times to demonstrate a point during a lecture. The dog was then killed. One student said: "We learned nothing new. It could all have been looked up in textbooks. A film could be made so that only one dog dies and all this unnecessary suffering is stopped."[17] The student's comment was true; but such things happen routinely in every medical school. Why are protests so rare?

The pressure to conform does not let up when the student receives his degree. If he goes on to a graduate degree in fields in which experiments on animals are usual, he will be encouraged to devise his own experiments and write them up for his PhD dissertation. . . . Naturally, if this is how students are educated they will tend to continue in the same manner when they become professors, and they will, in turn, train their own students in the same manner.

It is not always easy for people outside the universities to understand the rationale for the research carried out under university auspices. Originally, perhaps, scholars and researchers just set out to solve the most important problems and did not allow themselves to be influenced by other considerations. Perhaps some are still motivated by these concerns. Too often, though, academic research gets bogged down in petty and insignificant details because the big questions have been studied already, and have either been solved or proven too difficult. So the researcher turns away from the well-ploughed fertile fields in search of virgin territory where whatever he learns will be new, although the connection with a major problem may be more remote. . . .

To return to the question of when an experiment might be justifiable. It will not do to say: "Never!" In extreme circumstances, absolutist answers always break down. Torturing a human being is almost always wrong, but it is not absolutely wrong. If torture were the only way in which we could discover the location of a nuclear time bomb hidden in a New York City basement, then torture would be justifiable. Similarly, if a single experiment could cure a major disease, that experiment would be justifiable. But in actual life the benefits are always much, much more remote, and more often than not they are nonexistent. So how do we decide when an experiment is justifiable?

We have seen that the experimenter reveals a bias in favor of his own species whenever he carries out an experiment on a nonhuman for a purpose that he would not think justified him in using a human being, even a retarded human being. This principle gives us a guide toward an answer to our question. Since a speciesist bias, like a racist bias, is unjustifiable, an experiment cannot be justifiable unless the experiment is so important that the use of a retarded human being would also be justifiable.

This is not an absolutist principle. I do not believe that it could *never* be justifiable to experiment on a retarded human. If it really were possible to save many lives by an experiment that would take just one life, and there were *no other way* those lives could be saved, it might be right to do the experiment. But this would be an extremely rare case. Not one tenth of one percent of the experiments now being performed on animals would fall into this category. Certainly none of the experiments described [here] could pass this test. . . .

NOTES

1 *Air Force Times,* 28 November 1973; *New York Times,* 14 November 1973.
2 From a paper by R. Maclellan, B. Boecher, and others in M. Goldman and L. Bustad, eds., *Biomedical Implications of Radio-Strontium Exposure,* Atomic Energy Commission Symposium, Series #25, CONF-710201 (April 1972). The source for the starting date of these experiments is *Laboratory Animal Care,* 20 (1) p. 61 (1970).
3 K. Woodward, S. Michaelson, T. Noonan, and J. Howland; *International Journal of Radiation Biology,* 12 (3) p. 265 (1967).
4 A. Tegeris, F. Earl, H. Smalley, and J. Curtis, *Archives of Environmental Health,* 13, p. 776 (1966).
5 Personal communication to the author, 8 October 1974.
6 Hearings before the Subcommittee on Livestock and Feed Grains of the Committee on Agriculture (US House of Representatives, 1966), p. 63.
7 *Christian Science Monitor,* 18 July 1973.
8 *Sunday Mirror* (London), 24 February 1974, p. 10.
9 M.N. Gleason et al., eds., *Clinical Toxicology of Commercial Products* (Baltimore: Williams and Wilkins, 1969).
10 S.F. Paget, ed., *Methods in Toxicology* (Blackwell Scientific Publications, 1970), p. 4.
11 Ibid., pp. 134-139.
12 Ibid., p. 132.
13 G.F. Somers, *Quantitative Method in Human Pharmacology and Therapeutics* (Elmsford, New York: Pergamon Press, 1959); quoted by Richard Ryder, *Victims of Science,* p. 153.
14 *Scope* (Durban, South Africa), 30 March 1973.
15 "The Price of Knowledge," broadcast in New York, 12 December 1974, WNET/13; transcript supplied courtesy WNET/13 and Henry Spira.
16 S. Milgram, *Obedience to Authority* (New York: Harper & Row, 1974). Incidentally, these experiments were widely criticized on ethical grounds because they involved human beings without their consent. It is indeed questionable whether Milgram should have deceived participants in his experiments as he did; but when we compare what was done to them with what is commonly done to nonhuman animals, we can appreciate the double standard with which critics of the experiment operate.
17 *South Wales Echo,* 21 January 1974.

NO

Office of Technology Assessment

ALTERNATIVES TO ANIMAL USE IN RESEARCH, TESTING, AND EDUCATION

THE ETHICAL QUESTIONS

... How, if at all, should animals be used in research, testing, and education? Before this can be answered, a preliminary question must be asked (3, 4, 23, 26): What moral standing does an animal have? Is it the kind of being to which humans could possibly have moral duties and obligations? Taking one side or another on the question need not include any particular moral judgment. Whatever its resolution, the separable moral issue remains: What constraints, if any, regulate humans' use of animals? These constraints might be weaker if animals lack moral standing, but not necessarily absent altogether.

Moral Standing

Modern moral theory operates under a "law conception" of ethics (1). It judges particular human actions as right (lawful) or wrong (unlawful) as they comply with or violate some universal principle of conduct. In this, it departs from the classical theory of the virtues, which makes individual character the unit of evaluation and does not attempt to reduce ethics to a system of rules. Under the law conception, moral standing also goes to persons, but it is not conferred by an individual, institution, or community. From this point of view, an individual counts as a person because of some inherent characteristic. This is the chief reason why it is within the moral domain to speak of the natural duties and the natural rights of a person. A legal system can, of course, recognize natural duties and rights.

For obvious reasons, no one has ever argued that animals can have moral duties (21). That would require that they freely choose to act among alternatives they judge to be right or wrong—a skill as demanding as full-blown linguistic competence would be. Nevertheless, it is possible to take the view that animals have moral standing but do not have rights.

There are two broad theoretical approaches to the subject of rights. The first, sometimes called the *will theory,* would discourage efforts to attribute rights to animals. In its classical form, as given by Emmanuel Kant, it would define a right as a capacity to obligate others to a duty. Possession of a right carries with it an authorization to use coercion to enforce the correlative duty (14). This, in turn, implies that the right-holder's capacity is a power of discre-

From, "Alternatives to Animal Use in Research, Testing and Education," Office of Technology Assessment, US Congress, February 1986, Washington, DC.

tion, either to enforce or waive the right. A right is therefore something that a right-holder may choose to exercise or not. The choice itself will be an act of will.

H.L.A. Hart, a leading contemporary defender of the will theory, treats a right as a choice that gives the right-holder authority to control the actions of someone else. The possessor of a moral right has a moral justification for limiting the freedom of another, not because the action the right-holder is entitled to require has some moral quality, but simply because in the circumstances a certain distribution of human freedom will be maintained if the right-holder has the choice to determine how that other shall act (13).

The will theory helps to avoid confusion between claims of right, and other, separable requirements to promote or secure some valued state of affairs (e.g., to assist someone in need). Since animals could not be said to have waived or exercised the rights they had, all references to animal rights could simply be translated into talk of human duties.

Those who would assign rights to animals have embraced the alternative *interest theory* of what it means to have a right. A right, in their view, is a claim to the performance of a duty by someone else, but the right-holder need not be in a position or possess the competence to make this claim by an act of will. It is enough that the right-holder has interests that can be represented (by others) in a normative forum (6). These interests will include things that are intrinsically good and things in which the right-holder "takes an interest," selfish or not (21). To have a right, then, will be simply to have interests that can be affected by someone else.

The interest theory surfaces in Peter Singer's *Animal Liberation,* among the first

contemporary theoretical statements of the case for animals. In that work, Singer uses the term "right" to describe any claim that individuals may make to have their interests equally considered with those of others. It implies, therefore, nothing more than a capacity for suffering, which both humans and animals possess (24).

The modest measure of animal awareness that such a test demands has been one source of its appeal. It has not, however, been free of controversy. Some have objected that animals cannot have interests because interests require beliefs and animals cannot have beliefs in the strict sense (10, 18). This criticism suggests that pain-avoidance is not an "interest" because it is not a "belief," a distinction that seems more semantical than useful. Nevertheless, a more serious charge remains. As stated, the interest theory shows only that having interests is a necessary condition for having rights, not that it is sufficient. Singer himself has since abandoned the attempt to show sufficiency and, accordingly, recanted his earlier references to the language of rights (25):

> I could easily have dispensed with it altogether. I think that the only right I ever attribute to animals is the "right" to equal consideration of interests, and anything that is expressed by talking of such a right could equally be expressed by the assertion that animals' interests ought to be given equal consideration with the interests of humans.

Singer effectively acknowledges Hart's charge that the notion of a right has lost its distinctive function in this context because it no longer refers to the discretionary control that one individual has over the conduct of another.

There is one very general consideration that appears to weigh against the will theory, if not entirely in favor of the interest theory. It underlies a form of argument so ubiquitous in the animal-rights literature that it deserves a name. The *consistency argument* is exemplified in the following passage from an essay on vegetarianism by Tom Regan. Rejecting rationality, freedom of choice, and self-consciousness as conditions for having a right to life, Regan adds (22):

> It is reasonably clear that not all human beings satisfy them. The severely mentally feeble, for example, fail to satisfy them. Accordingly, *if* we want to insist that they have a right to life, then we cannot also maintain that they have it because they satisfy one or another of these conditions. Thus, *if* we want to insist that they have an equal right to life, despite their failure to satisfy these conditions, we cannot consistently maintain that animals, because they fail to satisfy these conditions, therefore lack this right.
>
> Another possible ground is that of sentience, by which I understand the capacity to experience pleasure and pain. But this view, too, must encounter a familiar difficulty—namely, that it could not justify restricting the right *only* to human beings.

In short, given that some human beings (infants, mental defectives, and senile adults) lack such capacity as well, Regan points to the inconsistency of holding both that this capacity is a condition of having a right *and* that *all* humans and *only* humans have moral rights. Any less burdensome test, however, will presumably admit animals as possible right-holders (16, 24). (For an opposing perspective, see refs. 8 and 10).

This reasoning appears to overlook a significant difference between an incompetent human being and an animal. In most cases, human beings have the capacity for rationality, freedom of choice, and self-consciousness, whereas in all cases animals do not. If most humans have these characteristics, it might be appropriate (or at least convenient) to treat humans as a homogenous group, even though some members lack these characteristics. If all animals lack certain characteristics, it may be similarly appropriate to treat them as a group, regardless of whether some humans also lack these characteristics.

Furthermore, if rights do not imply *present* possession of the qualifying condition (as suggested by the way that people treat those who are mentally incapacitated only for a time), then babies who have yet to mature and people who have become incapacitated after a period of competence will still have rights. The animal, as far as can be ascertained, has never met and will never meet this qualification. The rare human being whose deficiency is complete over a lifespan is nevertheless differently situated from the animal. The condition is a *disability*—the loss of some skill the person would normally be expected to have. The animal's condition is not disabling, even though it lacks the same skill. The very fact that the human has been deprived of an ability implies that the person has been harmed; a human's failure to acquire an ability means that person is in need of help. The condition of the animal does not call for either inference. This difference, to be sure, makes no mention of rights. Yet it creates a special duty to meet the human need that would not extend to animals. Because the animal without a will has not lost what it was biologically programmed to possess, it "needs" a will only as a human might "need" to fly. In neither case does the condition give rise to a moral demand for assistance.

Ironically, the consistency argument contains a basic inconsistency. On the one hand, the argument asserts that humans are not superior to animals; animals should therefore be treated like humans. On the other hand, the very nature of the moral argument is promotion of morally superior behavior: Humans should refuse to exploit other species, even though the other species exploit each other.

The consistency argument nevertheless succeeds to the extent that it shows that the *general* reason for moral concern in the cases discussed cannot be limited to humans. Other things being equal, the fact that a condition is harmful or threatens harm to an individual—human or animal— creates a moral reason to intervene. That reason need not take the form of a duty owed to the victim, with a correlative right that this would entail. It need not always be a duty of any sort. The highest approval is often reserved for the good deed that, like the Good Samaritan's, goes beyond what duty strictly requires.

There is a spectrum of possible positions, beginning at one end with a strict prohibition against the cruel infliction of suffering, moving to a still powerful requirement to lend help when the individual alone is in a position to provide it for someone in great need, and then to the milder requirements of charity and generosity when the individual can provide them without great personal sacrifice (even if others can do the same), and finally, at the other extreme, to the highly praised but not binding act of genuine self-sacrifice that distinguishes the moral saint. The moral vernacular covers this spectrum with a single term. The act in question is called the "humane" thing to do, and sometimes failure to perform it is labeled inhumane. . . .

Humane treatment is the most commonly cited standard in federal legislation concerning animals. Its wide range of application due to its lack of precision, however, leads to a temptation to dismiss it as a pious but essentially vacuous sentiment. A theory of moral constraints is needed to determine whether this or some other standard is sufficiently precise to serve as a guide for legislation regulating the use of animals.

Moral Constraints

A rule that allows an individual to do whatever that person wished would not be a moral rule. Morality by its very nature operates as a check on the tendency to go wherever desire leads. The constraints it imposes can be applied prospectively, contemporaneously, or retrospectively. Prospective analysis looks ahead to the possible consequences, while retrospective analysis may restrict the results it is permissible to promote (19). Before the action is taken, it can be said that the action that morally ought to be performed is the one with the best consequences. An individual succeeds in this objective to the extent that an action produces as much benefit and as little harm as possible. During the course of the action, conditions concerning the intention of the individual and the consent of the recipient may have to be met before a moral license to pursue the best consequences is granted. The fact that a lie will produce more benefit than the truth will not necessarily make it the right thing to do.

Moral theories divide according to the weight they give to one or the other kind of constraint. In its purest form, the prospective approach holds that an action or policy is right if it has better consequences, for everyone affected by it, than any available alternative. The language here is carefully drawn. "Better" does not mean "morally better." A good consequence is simply an outcome that someone finds desirable. If an action gives pleasure to someone, the enjoyment is a good thing; if it causes pain, the person's suffering

263

would be a bad thing. It is not necessary to ask whether the pleasure or pain is morally fitting.

Intuition will ideally play no part in determining an outcome. One consequence will count as better than another if, after assigning positive numerical values to its good elements and negative values to its bad ones, the sum of positive values exceeds that of negative values (2).

Better for whom? The utilitarian principle, still the most influential formulation of the forward-looking approach, holds that actions and policies are to be evaluated by their effects, for good or ill, on everyone, not just the individual alone or some select group of individuals. Between an individual's own good and the good of others, "utilitarianism requires him to be as strictly impartial as a disinterested and benevolent spectator" (2, 17). The interests of each affected individual are to count equally. Any two experiences that are alike except that they occur in different individuals are to be given the same value. Among utilitarians, enjoyment is a good and suffering an evil, and so every animal with the capacity for such experiences will also count as one individual. Sentience suffices for possessing this value, even if it does not confer rights. "The question," as Bentham once put it, "is not, Can they reason? nor Can they talk?, but Can they suffer?" (2).

Because it extends the scope of moral concern to animals without committing itself to a vulnerable theory of animal rights, utilitarianism has become the theory of choice among those who would press for more constraints on humans' treatment of animals. Singer derives the credo that all animals are equal from the utilitarian conception of equality (24). If the principle of utility requires that suffering be minimized, and if some kinds of suffering are found in animals as well as humans, then to count human suffering while ignoring animal suffering would violate the canon of equality. It would make a simple difference of location—in one species rather than another—the basis for a distinction in value. Like racism, such "speciesism" enshrines an arbitrary preference for interests simply because of their location in some set of individuals (24). ((For arguments that speciesism is not immoral, see refs. 5, 9, 27, 28.)

As a general moral principle, utilitarianism is subject to several objections, the most serious being that its standard of equality is much too weak to satisfy the demands of justice (11, 19, 20). Since it only requires that individuals with interests be given the same consideration, but in its summation of interests allows the claims of any one individual to be overridden by the sheer weight of numbers on the other side, it seems to sanction a tyranny of the majority that permits violations of individual rights. This may not, however, undermine the utilitarian case for animals if animals have doubtful standing as rightholders.

Some commentators have suggested that there may be an acceptable double standard in morals, consisting of a nonutilitarian principle for agents with standing as persons and a utilitarian rule for handling individuals with interests but not rights (7, 19). The use of different rules for different kinds of individuals is already well established. Rules that would be objectionably paternalistic if applied to adults are admissible if restricted to children. The dangers are that inconsistent standards might hold for the same individual or that differences between the two classes of individuals might be arbitrary.

The suggestion that the adult-child and human-animal distinctions are comparably rational and justifiable (7) is superficial for two reasons. First, it does not seem to be arbitrary to distinguish between the adult and the child, because human society understands that children may be intellectually and experientially unable to make wise choices. Thus, society can choose for children that which society believes is in their best interests. The problem with the human-animal distinction is that an animal may in fact be able to make and communicate a decision that expresses the animal's self-interest: It wants no part of any scientific procedure that results in pain or distress. Even if the animal could not make or communicate a decision, it may be arbitrary to distinguish between such animals and humans who are similar in their inability to make such decisions (the profoundly mentally handicapped), allowing society to use the former but not the latter as research subjects.

The second difference between the adult-child and human-animal distinctions relates to the *purpose* for distinguishing between two groups. The first distinction is permissible because it allows society to *protect* the interests of the child, while the purpose of the human-animal distinction is to allow society to *ignore,* or at least *diminish,* the interests of the animal.

The device of a double standard is often used to explain the sharp differences in the constraints governing the treatment of animals and humans as experimental subjects. For animals the standard is humane treatment, which forbids unnecessary suffering but otherwise allows experiments that harm and even kill the animal. That same rule, proposed for human subjects, is generally considered unethical. There are many experiments in which reliable results can only be obtained by doing to a human what is now done to an animal. Nevertheless, without the subject's informed consent—indeed, sometimes even with it—such experiments are absolutely impermissible, no matter how beneficial the consequence might be. They would violate the rights of the human subject.

The proscription against unnecessary suffering is best understood as a corollary of the principle of utlity. Since suffering is a bad consequence, there is an initial utilitarian onus against behavior that would produce it. Such treatment calls for justification. To meet this burden, a bare appeal to some offsetting good consequence will not be sufficient. The principle of utility, as formulated, is comparative. It requires that an action or policy have better consequences than any available alternative. Among the alternatives will be uses that do not involve animal suffering. If one of them has consequences at least as good as or better than the one proposed, the suffering will be unnecessary. Other things being equal, then, it should prove harder to establish necessity than the contrary, since the former must rule out all the alternatives while the latter need find only one.

Necessity is a relation between a means (an action or policy) and an end (its objective). *Restricted necessity* takes the end as given-that is, not subject to evaluation—and asks only whether the course of action suggested is an indispensable means to that end. For example, in an LD_{50} test for toxicity that uses 40 rats as subjects, if no alternative procedure using fewer or no rats could get the same results with the same reliability, that test would be necessary in the restricted sense. In *unrestricted* necessity, the end is open to assessment on utilitarian grounds:

• How likely is the objective to be met, in comparison with other possible goals? If the LD_{50} test yields unreliable results, its necessity in the unrestricted sense would be open to challenge.

• Assuming that the objective will be met, how beneficial will it be? Suppose, for instance, that an LD_{50} test were to be run on a new cosmetic not significantly different from those already on the market. The test may be considered unnecessary because the objective is unnecessary.

Unrestricted necessity is more difficult to prove, because it always includes restricted necessity and more. Thus, a stringent standard of necessity, one that lets fewer procedures through, would require that a procedure be necessary in the unrestricted sense. In addition, since necessity is more difficult to establish than the possibility of substitution, the burden of proving both the existence of necessity and the absence of alternatives could be placed on those who would use the procedure. A more lenient test could invert these priorities by presuming that the procedure is necessary and that alternatives are lacking unless shown otherwise. This approach would not expect the user to show beforehand that no other alternative was available; it is generally followed when a research proposal is reviewed by a scientist's peers or an institutional animal care and use committee (12).

Nonutilitarian positions on the use of animals have one feature in common: Although virtually none ignores consequences, they unite in denying that a course of action can be justified wholly by appeal to the value of its consequences (20). This leaves room for substantial variation, with the differences traceable to the considerations they would add in order to complete a moral assessment.

Ironically, both extremes in the animal treatment debate are nonutilitarian. The hard line supporting unlimited exploitation of animals builds from the premise that animals lack moral standing. On some theories of value, moreover, enjoyment does not count as a good thing in itself, nor is suffering per se an evil. Kant, for example, thought that the only unconditional good was a will whose choices are undermined by desire for enjoyment or fear of punishment (14). Not having a will, animals could not have this value. Morally, they were indistinguishable from inanimate tools—mere means to be used for the purposes of beings who do have a will. Like Aquinas, however, Kant did acknowledge an *indirect duty* of kindness, given that "tender feelings toward dumb animals develop humane feelings toward mankind" (15).

The indirect duty theory stumbles in the attempt to explain why there should be any empirical connection at all between people's feelings for animals and their feelings for other humans. Some similarity must be seen in the objects of the two sentiments if one is to influence the other; yet the theory says that there is no such likeness in reality. Thus either a person's motive is proof by itself that humans have a direct moral interest in animals, in which case the theory is mistaken; or the theory is correct and the individual has misunderstood it, in which case the person will be free, once educated in the theory, to abuse animals without fear that this will tempt abuse of human beings. Kant cannot have it both ways: He cannot require individuals to act on a belief that his own theory alleges to be false (16). . . .

SUMMARY AND CONCLUSIONS

The present debate over animal use in research, testing, and education is marked by a cacophony of voices. A critical survey of the religious and philosophical backgrounds to the debate yields some hope that, if the competing voices were muted by reflection, they would begin to coalesce as variations around a single theme. That theme would be the standard of humane treatment, extended to animals as well as to humans.

Much has been made of the historical contrast between Western and Oriental religious views on animals. The biblical and theological texts in the Judeo-Christian tradition do not give us a principle of unconditional respect for animals. Humans alone are accorded inherent value as being created in the image of God, and this gives them a license to use animals for their own purposes. Not, however, to abuse them. Cruelty and callous indifference to the needs of animals find no scriptural support, and virtually all religious thinkers condemn them. If God is a good shepherd, treating humans kindly without being bound to, humans can be as much to the animals in their care. The Christian position thus amounts to a synthesis of two elements in tension. On the one hand, animals are inferior in worth to humans, as the body of a person is inferior to the soul. On the other hand, they are not so inferior that their own welfare cannot stand in the way of unbridled use of them.

Modern religious and philosophical patterns of thought are branches of the same ancestral trunk. It should not be surprising, then, that the philosophical tradition exhibits the same tension on the subject of animals. Humans have standing as persons—that is, as individuals who can assume duties and enjoy rights. To join them, animals must at least be capable of possessing rights. But they cannot assume duties and do not have the power of discretion that gives rights a distinctive role in morals. Consistency suggests rights should be ascribed to animals once rights are given to infants and mentally handicapped humans who also lack discretion. Yet it would be inconsistent to assert that humans are not superior to animals while suggesting that humans should refuse to exploit other species, even though other species exploit each other.

Even if animals are not moral persons, however, it does not follow that they are mere things, morally indistinguishable from machines. They are sufficiently like humans in one morally relevant respect—their capacity for suffering in basic forms—to generate a moral claim on humans. It would be inconsistent to hold that, other things being equal, human suffering ought to be relieved, but animal suffering ought not.

Because it extends the scope of moral concern to animals without committing itself to a vulnerable theory of animal rights, utilitarianism has become the theory of choice among those who would press for more constraints on humans' treatment of animals. If the principle of utility requires that suffering be minimized, and if some kinds of suffering are found in animals as well as humans, then to count human suffering while ignoring animal suffering would violate the canon of equality. It would make a simple difference of location—in one species rather than another—the basis for a distinction in value. Like racism, such "speciesism" enshrines an arbitrary preference for interests simply because of their location in some set of individuals.

The rule that suffering ought to be relieved, in humans or animals, is the principle of humane treatment. It covers a large and heterogeneous range of situations; the most germane, for the debate over animal use, are those in which someone inflicts suffering on someone else. The humane treatment principle establishes a presumption against doing this, but that presumption can be overcome—always in the case of animals, and sometimes even in the case of a human—by showing that the harm done is necessary. Necessity here is not bare utility, but necessity overall. The harm must not only be a means to a good end, it must be the only means. A broader definition of necessity might also require that the harm be a means to an end whose value is considered in light of the degree of harm necessary to achieve that end. In addition, necessity always implies a comparison with available alternatives.

Animal use in research, testing, and education creates a conflict of interests between the liberty that humans have to use animals for human ends (knowledge, health, safety) and the need that animals have to be free of suffering. There is no reason why either one of these broad interests should always prevail over the other. The fulcrum on which they are balanced is the necessity standard itself. That is, when the suffering inflicted on animals is not necessary to satisfy a desirable human objective, the animal interest will prevail. And when the suffering is unavoidable, the human interest will be controlling. Animals are morally entitled to be treated humanely; whether they are entitled to more than that is unclear.

REFERENCES

1. Ancombe, G.E.M., "Modern Moral Philosophy," *Philosophy* 33:1-19, 1958.
2. Bentham, J., *Introduction to the Principles of Morals and Legislation* (New York: Columbia University Press, 1945).
3. Caplan, A.L., "Beastly Conduct: Ethical Issues in Animal Experimentation," *Ann. N.Y. Acad. Sci.* 406:159-169, 1983.
4. Caplan, A.L., "Animal Husbandry and Moral Duty," presentation at Second CFN Symposium, *The Ethics of Animal Experimentation,* Stockholm, Sweden, Aug. 12-14, 1985.
5. Cigman, R., "Death, Misfortune, and Species Inequality," *Phil. Public Affairs* 10:47-64, 1981.
6. Feinberg, J., "The Rights of Animals and Unborn Generations," *Rights, Justice, and the Bounds of Liberty,* J. Feinberg (ed.) (Princeton, NJ: Princeton University Press, 1980).
7. Flemming, A.H., "Ethical Considerations," contract report prepared for the Office of Technology Assessment, U.S. Congress, 1984.
8. Fox, M.A., *The Case for Animal Experimentation: An Evolutionary and Ethical Perspective* (Berkeley, CA: University of California Press, 1985).
9. Francis, L.P., and Norman, R., "Some Animals Are More Equal Than Others," *Philosophy* 53:507-527, 1978.
10. Frey, R.G., *Interests and Rights: The Case Against Animals* (Oxford, England: Clarendon Press, 1980).
11. Gewirth, A., *Reason and Morality* (Chicago: University of Chicago Press, 1978).
12. Halvorsyn, H.O., "Ethics of Animal Research: Philosophy and Practice," *Am. Soc., Microbiol. News* 51(8):375-377, 1985.
13. Hart, H.L.A., "Are There Any Natural Rights?" *Rights,* D. Lyons (ed.) (Belmont, CA: Wadsworth, 1980).
14. Kant, E., *Foundations of Metaphysics of Morals,* tr. L.W. Beck (Indianapolis, IN: Bobbs-Merrill, 1969).
15. Kant, E., *Lectures on Ethics,* tr. L. Infield (New York: Harper and Row, 1941).
16. Midgeley, M. *Animals and Why They Matter* (Athens, GA: University of Georgia Press, 1983).
17. Mill, J.S., *Utilitariansm, Liberty, Representative Government* (New York: Dutton, 1910).
18. McCloskey, H.J., "Rights," *Phil. Quart.* 15:113-127, 1965.
19. Nozick, R., *Anarchy, State, and Utopia* (New York: Basic Books, 1974).
20. Rawls, J., *A Theory of Justice* (Cambridge, MA: Harvard University Press, 1971).
21. Regan, T., *The Case for Animal Rights* (Berkeley, CA: University of California Press, 1983).
22. Regan, T., "The Moral Basis of Vegetarianism," *All That Dwell Within,* T. Regan (ed.) (Berkeley, CA: University of California Press, 1982).
23. Rowan, A.N., *Of Mice, Models & Men: A Critical Evaluation of Animal Research* (Albany, NY: State University of New York Press, 1984).
24. Singer, P., *Animal Liberation* (New York: Avon Books, 1975).
25. Singer, P., "The Parable of the Fox and the Unliberated Animals," *Ethics* 88:122, 1978.
26. Tannenbaum, J., and Rowan, A.N., "Rethinking the Morality of Animal Research," *Hastings Center Report* 15(5):32-43, 1985.
27. Watson, R.A., "Self-Consciousness and the Rights of Nonhuman Animals and Nature," *Environ. Ethics* 1:99-129, 1979.
28. Williams, M., "Rights, Interest, and Moral Equality," *Environ. Ethics* 2:149-161, 1980.

POSTSCRIPT

SHOULD ANIMAL EXPERIMENTATION BE STOPPED?

In May 1984 members of the Animal Liberation Front broke into the Experimental Head Injury Laboratory of the University of Pennsylvania and stole videotape records of experiments on baboons. The resulting publicity led to a National Institutes of Health (NIH) investigation and the withdrawal of federal funding from the head trauma unit. Similar incidents have occurred elsewhere.

The NIH has issued new policies requiring institutions that receive federal grants to establish Animal Care and Use Committees, and legislative proposals have been introduced that would apply the federal rules to all institutions. On the other hand, a California Congressman introduced a bill that would make it a federal crime to vandalize an animal research facility. Although the future of particular bills is unclear, it is certain that political efforts to ban or limit animal research will continue, despite protests from the research community that such restrictions will disrupt research and drive up costs.

For views of the animal liberation movement, see Peter Singer, *Practical Ethics* (Cambridge, 1979); Tom Regan and Peter Singer, editors, *Animal Rights and Human Obligations* (Prentice-Hall, 1976); and Richard Knowles Morris and Michael W. Fox, editors, *On the Fifth Day: Animal Rights and Human Ethics* (Acropolis, 1978). Opposing views are found in R.G. Frey, *Interests and Rights: The Case Against Animals* (Clarendon, 1980); and Joseph Margolis, "Animals Have No Rights and Are Not the Equal of Humans," *Philosophic Exchange* 1 (Summer 1974), and *The Case for Animal Experimentation* by Michael Allan Fox (University of California Press, 1986). Also see *Ethics and Animals,* edited by Harlan B. Miller and William H. Williams (Humana, 1983), and *Man and Mouse: Animals in Medical Research* (Oxford University Press, 1984).

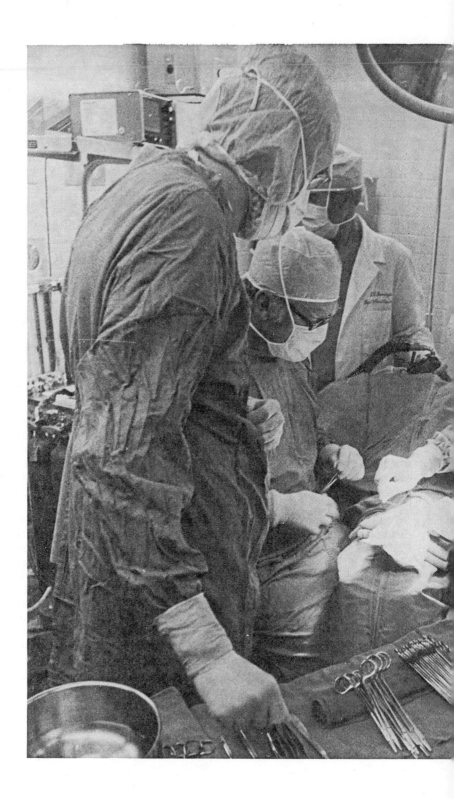

PART V
PUBLIC POLICY
AND BIOETHICS

As is often the case, public policy in the field of bioethics has had to struggle to respond to events and technical advances. Decisions in this field can no longer be the sole province of individual doctors or patients. Rapid progress in the development of artificial organs and organ transplant technology has occurred in recent years. Genetic engineering techniques have opened new possibilities for the treatment of disease, though some would say that they have created new dangers as well. In the face of these advances, an epidemic of AIDS threatens to consume scarce resources. Financial and medical resources remain extremely limited and the demand is great. How should these life-saving techniques be allocated? How can the costs of medical care in general be contained without sacrificing quality care? This section deals with issues that have moved from the technical arena to the forefront of the battle to define social values.

Should Organ Donation Be a Voluntary System?

Do We Need the Artificial Heart?

Should Doctors Cut Costs at the Bedside?

Should Insurance Companies Be Allowed to Screen for Antibodies to the AIDS Virus?

Is Genetic Engineering a Threat to Future Generations?

ISSUE 16

SHOULD ORGAN PROCUREMENT BE BASED ON VOLUNTARISM?

YES: Alfred M. Sadler, Jr., and Blair L. Sadler, from "A Community of Givers, Not Takers," *Hastings Center Report* 14, October 1984

NO: Arthur L. Caplan, "Organ Procurement: It's Not in the Cards," *Hastings Center Report* 14, October 1984

ISSUE SUMMARY

YES: Physician Alfred M. Sadler, Jr., and attorney Blair L. Sadler maintain that the system of encouraged voluntarism in procuring organs for transplantation increases the supply of organs without infringing on the rights of individuals and families.
NO: Philosopher Arthur L. Caplan argues that current laws should be overridden in favor of a system of required request, in which physicians would have to ask the families of newly-dead persons if they will permit the retrieval of organs.

Not so long ago organ transplants were the stuff of science fiction. Although the first successful cornea transplant took place in 1905, the first kidney transplant (between identical twins) did not take place until 1954. The first liver transplant was performed in 1966, and the first heart transplant in 1967. Today—with the aid of better surgical techniques, better tissue-matching capabilities, and most important, new drugs that suppress the body's natural tendency to reject a transplanted organ—kidneys, hearts, pancreases, livers, lungs, spleens, and bone marrow can all be transplanted. And people are living longer with the transplanted organs than ever before. At Stanford University, for example, about eighty percent of the people who receive heart transplants now live two years or longer, while a decade or so ago only twenty percent survived as long as a year.

In the 1960s and 1970s the question was: Are these admittedly experimental operations too risky? Today the question is: Where are we going to get all the transplantable organs to fill the ever-expanding demand? A person can donate one of the body's two kidneys to a relative (assuming there is a tissue match) without endangering his or her own health, but the other organs must come from cadavers. Many people, of course, have no suitable live kidney donor in their families, and nationwide about ten thousand people are waiting for cadaver kidneys. Some cardiologists estimate that the lives of as many as fifty thousand to 100 thousand people could be saved each year if heart transplants were more readily available.

If medical technology has created the demand, it has also created a means to obtain the supply. For in the same period in which organ transplantation moved from experiment to therapy, medical technology also perfected techniques of maintaining heart and respiratory function in people whose brains had stopped functioning. In many states the definition of death has been changed from one that describes the cessation of heart and lung function as legal death, to one that includes the cessation of all functions of the entire brain, often called a "brain death" criterion. In effect, dead bodies can be made to breathe, blood to circulate, hearts to beat. And from these dead bodies can come organs to serve the living. About twenty thousand people die each year from accidents or from other causes, and they are potential organ donors—that is, they are young enough, healthy enough (except of course for the fatal injury) that their organs are suitable for transplantation.

The Uniform Anatomical Gift Act, adopted in 1968, was intended to eliminate unnecessary formalities and to make available human organs for transplantation while protecting the rights and interests of the families of the deceased. It stressed the need for informed consent before any organs or tissue were removed from a dead body. But voluntary donations, either from people who have signed organ donor cards or from families who have been approached by transplant teams when a relative has died, have not kept pace with the need. Last year only about two thousand to twenty-five hundred of the twenty thousand potential donors actually provided organs. The main reason, it appears, is not that families are reluctant to donate (although that does occur) but that physicians and other medical personnel are reluctant to ask a grieving family.

The selections that follow examine the question of whether the voluntary system is still valid. Alfred M. Sadler, Jr., a physician, and Blair L. Sadler, an attorney, say that it is. They believe that public support for transplantation remains high because the principles of giving rather than taking are honored. Arthur L. Caplan, a philosopher, argues that there would be a greater supply of organs if families were required to be asked to donate the organs of their dead relatives. In this scheme they could still refuse. But, he says, "We should not allow our concern for the rights and values of the individual to blind us to the policy options that can accommodate both individual autonomy and community good."

YES

Alfred M. Sadler, Jr.
and Blair L. Sadler

A COMMUNITY OF GIVERS, NOT TAKERS

In the late 1960s, when we became involved in the questions surrounding the procurement of organs for the newly developing technology of transplantation, we and others espoused the principles of informed consent and encouraged voluntarism. The Uniform Anatomical Gift Act, drafted in 1968 by the National Conference of Commissioners on Uniform State Laws and adopted in every state and the District of Columbia by 1971, embodied those principles.[1] Despite the expansion of transplantation programs and challenges to those principles, we believe that there is no reason to discard them now. The law is doing well what it was intended to do: providing a clear mechanism for individuals and next-of-kin to consent to organ and tissue donation for humanitarian purposes. It was designed to strike a socially acceptable balance that facilitates organ donation and procurement without infringing upon other deeply held values and rights.[2]

THE TAKING OF PITUITARY GLANDS

The importance of balancing competing interests and values is not merely of theoretical interest and is underscored by the following case study. In 1963, the National Pituitary Agency, under the auspices of the National Institutes of Health (NIH), established a program to obtain cadaver pituitary glands for extraction of pituitary hormones, particularly human growth hormone. This nationwide effort enabled clinical research to be performed on human subjects who had hypopituitary dwarfism. During that period 70,000 pituitary glands were obtained annually. Because the yield of pituitary hormone from each gland was very small, the National Pituitary Agency estimated the need at up to 7,000,000 pituitary glands annually.

Two incidents in the mid-1960s highlighted the necessity to reassess the ethical and legal implications of organ removal. In Los Angeles, headlines in the *Los Angeles Times* revealed that a technician in the County Coroner's

Reprinted by permission from the *Hastings Center Report,* 14, October 1984. Copyright © 1984 by the Hastings Center.

Office was accused of removing pituitary glands from cadavers during autopsy without having obtained consent. In Hennepin County, Minnesota, the coroner's authority to remove human parts for other purposes was also questioned. This information surfaced in emotionally charged newspaper articles that sharply criticized a Federal government agency's role in supporting the taking of human cadaver material without consent. This unauthorized taking, even for humanitarian purposes, was described with alarm and even horror and threatened to undermine if not destroy the enterprise. The NIH moved quickly to ensure that human cadaver material was obtained with consent only and commissioned an intensive study of the subject.

LEGAL HISTORY AND PRECEDENTS

In 1967, there was considerable variation in the law relating to dead bodies. American statutes, derived from English common law, gave next-of-kin the authority and obligation to dispose of the remains of the deceased in a timely and respectful manner. As such, kin were given possession of the body for the purposes of burial. The body was considered incapable of being owned in the commercial sense and thus could not be bought or sold. This principle was expressed in the doctrine that there were no "property rights" in the dead body. The body was not part of a deceased's estate; thus a person could not direct the disposition of his own remains.

That doctine had been challenged in the 1950s when Grace Metalious, a well-known author, wished to donate her body to one of two medical schools and asked that no funeral services be held. Her next-of-kin objected and the matter was contested after her death. In reviewing the common law tradition, the court recognized traditional next-of-kin rights, but noted that an individual ought to have a say in his own burial and that these wishes should override next-of-kin concerns. The term "quasi-property rights" was used to identify the rights of individuals to direct the disposition of their remains.[3]

To further complicate matters, every state had adopted other laws that affected, and in some cases impinged upon, the traditional next-of-kin rights for burial. All states have autopsy laws concerning the need to determine the cause of death. Next-of-kin have authority to grant autopsy permission, and in about one-half of the states statutes allow an individual to authorize an autopsy on his or her remains.

Medical examiner or coroner's statutes define the interests of states to determine the cause of death in certain cases such as those involving crime, violence, or communicable disease. In these instances, the autopsy authority of a state overrides the objections of individuals or next-of-kin. Finally, unclaimed-body statutes specify that bodies not claimed by anyone in a defined time period can be turned over to medical schools for medical science. Does the medical examiner's authority to perform an autopsy in order to determine the causes of death include authority to remove other tissues for medical purposes? Strictly speaking, no, but the practice had apparently been going on unobserved for years in some parts of the country.[4]

CONSENT UNDER THE UNIFORM ANATOMICAL GIFT ACT

After the successful transplantation of corneas in the 1950s, states began to enact donation statutes that allowed individuals to make testamentary gifts of all or parts of their bodies for medical, scientific, or therapeutic purposes. By 1965, forty-four states had adopted some type of donation law. Four others permitted the donation of eyes only and three states had no donation statute. Each law was different: some required that a donation be made as part of a will; others said nothing about next-of-kin; some required three witnesses; still others, none. To redress this disparity, the National Conference of Commissioners on Uniform State Laws (CUSL) drafted a model law called the Uniform Anatomical Gift Act. This model was designed to foster national organ donation and tissue-matching programs. It was recognized that as transplantation became more successful, a nationwide pool for tissue typing and organ matching would be required.

A special committee of the CUSL, chaired by E. Blythe Stason, former dean of the University of Michigan Law School, worked for two years to develop a suitable law. The Uniform Anatomical Gift Act (UAGA) was completed on July 30, 1968, and was approved by the American Bar Association on August 7. A national meeting, called by the National Research Council in September, brought together representatives of the medical schools and major scientific organizations involved in this field.[5] Articles were published in law reviews and medical journals; the Commissioners, three from each state, took the model law back to the state legislatures for consideration. Forty-four state legislatures met in 1969 and forty-one adopted the law. By 1971, just three years after completion, all fifty states and the District of Columbia had adopted the model with no major modifications.[6] In the ninety-year history of the CUSL, no uniform act has ever done so well.

The Act authorizes persons eighteen years or older to donate all or part of their body for medical purposes to take effect after death. It also gives next-of-kin authority to donate if an individual before death has not given any contrary directions. A clear order of priority of next-of-kin is established. The Act specifies who can receive donations and the mechanisms by which donations can be made, including a simple card to be carried on the patient's person. Provisions are made to streamline the next-of-kin consent mechanism by authorizing a simple written statement or recorded telephone message. The act specifies that its provisions are subject to state laws governing autopsies.

Why did the law pass so quickly? First, the principles of informed consent and voluntary donation were protected. If one is opposed to organ removal, one simply does not give consent. In 1968, a Gallup Poll showed that 90 percent of Americans would be willing to donate if asked. Second, public interest in transplantation was widespread. Just as the law neared completion, Dr. Christiaan Barnard performed the first heart transplant. Many of these issues became front-page news when the model law emerged.

Comprehensive organizational efforts followed. After the act was adopted, a meeting of concerned organ donation groups was convened and a uniform donor card developed.[7] At no time was it expected that the donor card would provide all or even a large percentage of cadaver organs because many people do not bother to fill out the card. It was recognized that next-of-kin consent would remain a major part of the donation process, but the donor card could serve a very important educational function among family members. As people discuss organ donation and one family member fills out a donor card, the wishes of that person become known and shared.

ALTERNATIVES TO CONSENT

What are alternatives to consent and encouraged voluntarism? In 1968, Jesse Dukeminier and David Sanders proposed that "routine salvaging of cadaver organs" was preferable to consent.[8] Arthur Caplan has now resurrected the Dukeminier and Sanders approach.[9] They proposed that cadaver organs be removed routinely unless an objection is entered before removal (presumed consent). The burden of action would be on the person who did not want his or her organs removed to enter an objection. Under this system, a person could object during life to the taking of his or her organs after death. The next-of-kin could also object to the use of the deceased's organs before removal if the deceased did not specifically authorize donation. These writers would shift the burden from the surgeon to obtain consent to the individual or the next-of-kin to object. In so doing, they believe that more cadaver material would become available.

We believed that the "routine salvaging" argument was dubious in 1968 and we believe it is dubious now. Next-of-kin will have an opportunity to object only if a duty is placed on the physician or hospital to notify them that a family member has died or is facing imminent death. In the absence of such notice, important constitutional problems (discussed below) might invalidate the system. Adequate notice is fundamental to the protection of constitutional rights. Without a notice requirement, the next-of-kin could forcefully argue that because they were not aware of their relative's death they could not exercise their authority to object.

To obviate the notice problem, a central registry for recording objections was proposed. Practically, a registry is fraught with major problems. The first and most important concerns the temporary nature of next-of-kin relationships. Through marriage, divorce, and death, family relationships change. Each change requires a fresh entry for the registry. Second, under this system modifying the scope of the gift is cumbersome: each time an individual wishes to change the gift, he or she must report back to the registry. Third, the creation and maintenance of such a registry will be costly. Finally, a registry forces physicians to go through an additional mechanism, which may not be up-to-date, rather than rely on a donor card or deal directly with the family.

One solution to the notice problem is to place a legal duty upon the physician or hospital to give notice to the next-of-kin so that they can object. This eliminates constitutional problems relating to freedom of religion and due process. However, the obligation of the physician or hospital to give notice to the family (that a kidney or other organ will be taken for transplant purposes unless they object) is little different from the obligation under consent statutes to request permission. We conclude that if a physician is required by law to give adequate notice that an organ will be taken, the gains for transplantation over the consent approach are illusory.

A more extreme approach authorizes compulsory removal of cadaver organs as needed for medical purposes. A compulsory removal law could be drawn narrowly and be limited to therapy such as transplantation, which is directly life-saving. There is no doubt that a compulsory removal statute would yield more organs than either of the other systems.[10]

However, it would do so at the expense of the legally protected interests previously discussed. This is important in terms of: (a) its effect on public attitudes toward medical therapeutic innovation in general and transplantation in particular; (b) its likelihood of enactment by state legislatures; and (c) its possible conflict with constitutional principles. (In the last case, the statute would be invalid.) Individuals challenging a compulsory statute could reasonably raise at least two issues of constitutional dimension: freedom of religion and due process. A detailed analysis of these issues has been presented elsewhere and will not be repeated here.[11]

THE PHILOSOPHICAL BASIS FOR CONSENT

Philosophical and humanistic principles strongly support a system based on consent. Put simply, we believe most people would prefer a community of givers rather than takers. In 1970, Paul Ramsey articulated a preference for the voluntary donation of organs over the "routine salvage" approach and concluded: "A society will be a better human community in which giving and receiving is the rule, not taking for the sake of good to come." He asserted that "the civilizing task of mankind is the fostering, the achievement, or the shoring up of consensual community" and that in "answering the need for gifts by encouraging real givers," the consent approach "meets the measure of authentic community among men. . . . The moral sequels that might flow from education and action in line with the proposed Gift Acts may be of far more importance than prolonging lives routinely. The moral history of mankind is of more importance than its medical advancement, unless the latter can be joined with the former in a community of affirmative consent."[12]

Hans Jonas, also writing at this time, stressed the need for public confidence in physicians relating to respect for life and warned: "The patient must be absolutely sure that his doctor does not become his executioner, and that no definition (of death) ever authorizes him to become one." He continues, "His right to this certainty is absolute, and so is his right to his own body with all its organs. Absolute respect for these rights violates no one else's rights, for no one has a right to another's body." Jonas further distinguishes "between the moral or emotional appeal of a cause that elicits volunteering and a right that demands compliance, for example . . . between the moral claim of a common good and society's right to that good and to the means of its realization. A moral claim cannot be met without consent; a right can do without it." Finally, Jonas reminds us that making any such choice between the "rights" of the individual and the "interests" of society requires "a careful clarification of what the needs, interests, and rights of society are, for society—as distinct from any plurality of individuals—is an abstract and as such is subject to our definition."[13]

Sir Harold Himsworth wrote in the *Daedalus* volume in which Jonas's article appeared "that the public at large must be kept involved and informed about the cost and other factors related to medical advancements." He continues that "without favorable public opinion and support, medical research and therapeutic intervention would be curtailed." He states the primary duty of the physician is to "act always to increase trust." We doubt that trust can be fostered by taking organs for transplantation.

After careful analysis, William May concluded in a similar vein: "While the procedure of routine salvaging may, in the short run, furnish more organs for transplants, in the long run, its systemic effect on the institutions of medical care would seem to be depressing and corrosive of that trust upon which acts of healing depend."[14]. . .

Any comprehensive review of the implications of alternative legal systems requires an understanding of the scientific and organizational barriers to transplantation. As was true fifteen years ago, the major barriers are: the scientific problems of donor/recipient matching and organ preservation, the educational needs of informing the public and key medical personnel, the logistical constraints of procuring and transporting organs throughout the country twenty-four hours a day and the extraordinary cost of transplantation programs.

Equally important in the long term is the recognition that transplantation represents at best a halfway technology. It will never be a substitute for curing or preventing the underlying diseases that currently lead to transplantation. The case study of pituitary gland procurement is applicable here. Scientific advances have allowed the synthesis and production of human growth hormone via genetic engineering and thus the need for cadaver pituitary procurement programs is disappearing.

In conclusion, laws based on voluntary donation and consent have accomplished their major objective. The rights of individuals and families are clear and simplified mechanisms of consent are in place under the Uniform Anatomical Gift Act. Equally important, considerable public support for transplantation continues to exist because the principles of giving rather than taking are maintained.

In the absence of convincing evidence that presumed consent legislation makes considerably more organs available for transplantation and in light of the substantial nonlegal barriers listed above, we believe it is unwise to consider dismantling the present consent system.

REFERENCES

1. A.M. Sadler, Jr., B.L. Sadler, E.B. Stason, and D.L. Stickel, "Transplantation: A Case for Consent," *New England Journal of Medicine* 280 (1969), 862-67.

2. A.M. Sadler, Jr., B.L. Sadler and E.B. Stason, "Uniform Anatomical Gift Act: A Model for Reform," *Journal of the American Medical Association,* 206 (1968), 2501-06.

3. *Holland v. Metalious,* 105 N.H. 290, 198 A. 2nd 654 (1964).

4. A.M. Sadler, Jr. and B.L. Sadler, "Transplantation and the Law: The Need for Organized Sensitivity," *Georgetown Law Journal* 57 (1968), 5-54.

5. R.E. Stevenson,, W.J. Burdette, M. Head, J.E. Murray, A.M. Sadler, Jr., and B.L. Sadler, "A Report to the Committee on Tissue Transplantation of the National Academy of Sciences—National Research Council from the Ad Hoc Committee on Medical-Legal Problems" (1968).

6. A.M. Stadler, Jr., B.L. Sadler and E.B. Stason, "Transplantation and the Law: Progress Toward Uniformity," *New England Journal of Medicine* 282 (1970), 717-23.

7. A.M. Sadler, Jr., B.L. Sadler and G.E. Schreiner, "A Uniform Card for Organ and Tissue Donation," *Modern Medicine* 37 (1969), 20-23.

8. D. Sanders and J. Dukeminier, Jr., "Medical Advance and Legal Lag: Hemodialysis and Kidney Transplantation," *UCLA Law Review* 15 (1968), 357-413; J. Dukeminier and D. Sanders, "Organ Transplantation: Proposal for Routine Salvaging of Cadaver Organs," *New England Journal of Medicine* 279 (1968), 413-19.

9. A.L. Caplan, "Organ Transplants: The Costs of Success," *Hastings Center Report* 13 (December 1983), 23-32.

10. Note, "Compulsory Removal of Cadaver Organs," *Columbia Law Review,* 69 (1969), 693-705.

11. B.L. Sadler and A.M. Sadler, Jr. "Providing Cadaver Organs: Three Legal Alternatives," *Hastings Center Studies,* 1 (1973), 13-26.

12. Paul Ramsey, *The Patient as a Person* (New Haven: Yale University Press), 1970, p. 210.

13. Hans Jonas, "Philosophical Reflections on Experimenting with Human Subjects," *Daedalus* 98 (1969), 221.

14. William May, "Attitudes Toward the Newly Dead," *Hastings Center Studies* 1 (1973), 6.

NO

Arthur L. Caplan

ORGAN PROCUREMENT: IT'S NOT IN THE CARDS

Not so long ago the distinguished Senator from Vermont, George Aiken, proposed a novel solution to the problem of ending the Vietnam War. He wryly observed that the fastest way to stop that conflict was simply to declare ourselves the winners and go home.

Defenders of the philosophy of voluntarism in the procurement of cadaver organs for transplantation seem to have taken to heart Aiken's ironic proposal for resolving an apparently intractable problem. Alfred and Blair Sadler declare that they are unable to see "any significant developments in transplantation [that] would justify discarding the principles of informed consent and encouraged voluntarism embodied in the Uniform Anatomical Gift Act." They are not looking carefully enough. The facts about both the supply of and the demand for cadaver organs do not support their decision to solve the crisis in organ procurement by declaring the system a success. Our society's decision in the late 1960s to rely on a public policy of voluntarism as the primary means for assuring an adequate supply of organs for transplantation is no longer tenable. Perhaps such a system was appropriate when organ transplantation was in its infancy, but this is no longer the case.

The Centers for Disease Control estimates that about 20,000 persons die each year under circumstances that would make them suitable for cadaver organ donation. This number should provide a maximum possible pool of 40,000 kidneys for transplant. Yet in 1982 only 3,691 cadaver kidney transplants were performed. The best estimates are that less than 15 percent of potential donors are utilized under the present policy.

Recent studies estimate that between 6,000 and 10,000 persons on hemodialysis are waiting for kidney transplants.[1] Some believe the number of possible recipients in the United States would be as high as 22,500 per year if transplant surgeons were not forced by the severe inadequacy of the present supply of cadaver kidneys to be so conservative in formulating criteria for eligibility for renal transplantation. Similar statistics exist concerning the shortfall of

Reprinted by permission from the *Hastings Center Report*, 14, October 1984. Copyright © 1984 by the Hastings Center.

tissues for corneal transplants, hearts, lungs and, as the media remind us every day, livers. And unless something is done to modify the present reliance on a voluntary system, the shortage in cadaver organs will continue to worsen. Rapid progress in the development of surgical techniques, tissue matching, and immunosuppressive drugs will lead to incessant demands for more cadaver organs in the years ahead.

Transplantation may be, as the Sadlers observe, a "halfway" solution to the problem of organ failure. But for those suffering from renal failure, kidney transplants afford a better quality of life than dialysis, and they are far cheaper. Medicare's End-Stage Renal Disease Program has passed the $2 billion mark in reimbursing the costs of more than 70,000 dialysis patients. How can anyone possibly conclude that the present approach to procurement is adequate, acceptable, or working well?

Nor is it at all evident that donor cards have played a significant role in helping to produce even the small degree of procurement success that has been attained in the United States. Less than 15 percent of the population carry donor cards.[2] Transplant coordinators estimate that less than 3 percent of donors have cards in their possession at the time of death. Where data are available on the number of drivers designated as donors in states where organ donation boxes are provided on licenses the compliance rate is not impressive.[3]

THREE POSSIBLE ALTERNATIVES

What then are the possible policy alternatives to the present system of voluntarism and donor cards? And more important, which of these alternatives is most consistent with the values of individual choice, altruism, and freedom?

One possible public policy alternative is to allow the creation of a market in cadaver organs. There are two variants of this approach. The "strong market approach" would allow individuals or, after death, their next of kin to auction organs for sale to the highest bidder. The "weak market approach," on the other hand, would discourage direct compensation of donors by recipients but would allow for the creation of various tax incentives or in-kind reimbursements (those who donate could guarantee their loved ones or friends priority for future transplants) to encourage donation.

A second approach—that of "presumed consent"—would grant medical personnel the authority to remove organs from cadavers for transplantation whenever usable organs were available at the time of death. Again, there are two variants. In "strong presumed consent" the state would grant physicians complete authority to remove usable tissues regardless of the wishes of the deceased or family members. In "weak presumed consent" the law would presume that organ procurement can be undertaken in the absence of some form of objection from the deceased or family members. Weak consent places the burden of opting out of organ donation on those who have objections to this procedure rather than, as is the case under the present system of voluntarism, upon those who wish to opt for organ donation.

A third approach, which has not been widely discussed in the current debate about organ procurement policies, is what I have termed "required request."[4] In the strong version, every citizen would be asked to indicate his or her willingness to participate in organ donation, perhaps by means of a mandatory check-off on applications for a driver's license, a social security card, or on tax returns.

In the weak version, current legislation pertaining to the definition of death might be modified to state that at the time of death is declared a person who has no connection to the process of determining death would be required to ask family members about the possibility of organ donation.

WHAT THE PUBLIC THINKS

There has been a good deal of public debate about the moral acceptability of the strong market approach to procuring cadaver organs. Near unanimity of public opinion has emerged about the unacceptability of an open market in cadaver organs. At least one state, Virginia, banned the sale of organs for transplantation. Other states are considering such bans, as is the United States Congress. Transplant surgeons have repeatedly stated their adamant opposition to market solutions. The moral revulsion that has characterized discussions in the popular press and in professional journals about the spectacle of the desperately ill furiously bidding against one another for a kidney or a liver has, at least for the present, rendered both versions of this policy academic.

Similarly, little public enthusiasm has emerged for a system of strong presumed consent. In a recent survey the Battelle National Heart Transplantation Study found that less than 8 percent of those interviewed felt that "doctors should have the power to remove organs from people who died recently but have not signed an organ donor card without consulting the next-of-kin."[5]

Public opinion aside, the Sadlers argue that any form of presumed consent would have a corrosive effect on the trust that exists between the medical community and the public. They also note that presumed consent would not necessarily lead to an increase in the supply of cadaver organs for transplant. But in those European nations that have adopted versions of presumed consent we lack evidence to determine whether these concerns are justified.

THE EUROPEAN EXPERIENCE

Various European nations, including Austria, Denmark, Poland, Switzerland, and France, have legislation mandating a policy of strong presumed consent. Other nations such as Finland, Greece, Italy, Norway, Spain, and Sweden have adopted versions of weak presumed consent.[6] However, as the Sadlers correctly observe, the available empirical data does not show that these countries have dramatically increased their supply of cadaver organs.

The Swedes, for example, transplant nearly as many patients suffering from kidney failure as they maintain on hemodialysis.[7] This compares quite favorably with the one-to-nine ratio that prevails in the United States. However, statistics on the rates of organ procurement in Sweden and other European countries are not readily available. Indeed, all these countries still have waiting lists for those needing kidney transplants.

In June 1984 I visited France to discuss organ procurement with a number of transplant surgeons and nurses.[8] Organ transplantation in France has been confined almost exclusively to corneas and kidneys. French physicians and government officials estimated that approximately 800 kidney transplants were performed in

1982. This suggests a rate that is only slightly higher than the rate of kidney transplantation in the United States. There are indeed waiting lists for those on hemodialysis who hope for a transplant.

Why should this be so, given that France has a policy of strong presumed consent? French physicians offer two explanations. First, though the law has resulted in an increase in the number of cadaver organs available for transplant, this increase is not reflected in the overall rates because the additional organs have been utilized to decrease the numbers of live donors. Whereas live donors had provided about a third of the kidneys available for transplant in France in the late 1970s, today live donors make up less than 10 percent of the donor pool. (Live donors constitute nearly a third of the donor pool in the United States, Britain, and other nations with public policies of voluntarism based upon donor cards.)

Second, French physicians note that, despite a public policy allowing strong presumed consent, doctors are not willing to remove organs from cadavers without the consent of family members. Strong presumed consent exists only on paper in France. In practice French physicians find it psychologically intolerable to remove tissues from a body without obtaining the permission of next-of-kin.

In the view of both physicians and nurses, however, the French public strongly supports organ transplantation. The physicians I spoke with reported consent rates of between 90 and 95 percent when permission was sought to remove solid organs. In practice French physicians believe strongly in allowing family members to retain the right to object to organ removal. But few family members actually do object, indicating that a public policy of weak presumed consent is compatible with the moral values of both health professionals and the public in France.

Even if French physicians are only willing to participate in a system whose governing philosophy is one of weak presumed consent, why, given the low rate of refusal, are a larger number of organs not available for transplant? The answer is illuminating for its policy implications for the United States.

France, unlike the United States, does not have a cadre of highly trained personnel to handle the process of organ procurement. Health professionals, usually nurses, must bear the burdens of inquiring about objections to organ removal, locating a suitable recipient, and arranging the removal of organs. French hospital administrators, physicians, and nurses all reported that this process was both time-consuming and costly. Given the growing concern of France over the rising costs of health care there is a reluctance to devote scarce medical resources to organ procurement. French transplant surgeons also noted that, at present, there were severe limits both in terms of personnel and hospital space on the number of transplants of all types that can now be performed. One surgeon noted that "if we had your resources and facilities for transplantation we would be much more aggressive in pursuing organ donors." Limits on the availability of transplant services in France seem to dampen the ardor with which organ procurement is undertaken.

Moreover, the French, like their American counterparts, find it psychologically difficult to approach grieving family members about the prospect of organ procurement even if only to ascertain whether the family objects to what is usually described in the consent process as a routine, customary, and legally sanctioned practice. Busy emergency room personnel are loathe to take the time necessary to fully discuss the subject of transplantation with distraught family members. In sum, despite the existence on paper of a strong version of presumed consent, health care professionals in France are only willing to operate within the boundaries of weak presumed consent. And while this approach has helped to increase the supply of available cadaver kidneys to the point where few live donations are utilized, economic, organizational, and psychological factors limit the willingness of French medical personnel to ask about objections to removing kidneys and other solid organs for transplantation.

The French experience with strong presumed consent legislation holds important lessons for those, such as myself, who believe that our system of organ procurement must be changed. The French physicians' unwillingness to act upon the authority granted them by the state to remove organs regardless of the wishes of family members parallels the unwillingness of American physicians to remove organs solely on the basis of the legal authority granted by donor cards. As organ procurement specialists know all too well, donor cards are almost never viewed by hospital administrators and physicians as adequate authorization for allowing organ retrieval. The permission of family members is always sought prior to organ removal whether or not a donor card or other legal document can be found.

On the other hand, the practical experience obtained by the French with a version of weak presumed consent does not support the sorts of concerns raised by the Sadlers about presumed consent. French physicians are impressed with the fact that objections have been raised by less than 10 percent of the families who have been given the opportunity to refuse consent. The French press has not reported any dissatisfaction on the part of the public with presumed consent. And French physicians were uniformly relieved to be able to decrease their earlier dependence on live donors. A policy of weak presumed consent appears to have produced a significant amount of social good while allowing for family choice and autonomy in an atmosphere of mutual respect.

The organizational, financial, and psychological factors at work in the French system of organ procurement are also present in the United States. Unlike the French, we have a large number of highly trained and proficient specialists available in the field of organ procurement, but constant pressures to reduce costs in combination with an increasingly litigious atmosphere in medicine make it unlikely that the modest reforms of the present voluntary system proposed by the Sadlers and others[9] will lead to significant improvement in the supply of cadaver organs.

THE PRIMACY OF THE FAMILY

One key factor emerges from both the French and the American experience: the major obstacle to organ procurement is the failure to ask family members about organ donation. French physicians are entitled by law to take tissues without asking anyone but are unwilling to do so. American physicians are entitled by the Uniform Anatomical Gift Act to take tissues from those who sign donor cards but they are unwilling to do so. Whether or not one believes that the wishes of the family should supersede either the wishes of the public, as in France, or the wishes of the individual, as in the United States, in fact both countries always treat the family as the final authority insofar as the disposition of the dead is concerned.

The respect accorded family members' wishes in these two large and medically sophisticated nations would seem to dictate the kind of public policy change that has the greatest chance of alleviating the shortage in cadaver donors. The French experience indicates that the only practical policy options are those that recognize and respect the role of family members in participating in decisions about cadaver donation. The weak version of required request acknowledges the role of family members, while at the same time ensuring that an optimal environment exists for eliciting organ donations.

Physicians, nurses, or other hospital personnel should be required to inquire whether available family members will give their consent to organ donation. This could be accomplished by modifying the current legal process for declaring death in all states to include a provision requiring that a request concerning organ donation be made to available family members by a party not connected with the determination of death. When family members are not available, organs would be removed only if a donor card or other legal document were present. Or, hospital accreditation requirements could be revised to include a provision mandating that at death the families of potential donors be approached about their willingness to consent.

LINKING REQUEST AND CONSENT

A public policy of weak required request could be merged with a further change in our current procurement policy. We could modify the consent process from the present system of opting in to one of opting out along the lines of the weak presumed consent approach used in Scandinavia and, de facto, in France. But weak required request need not be linked to any version of presumed consent. If, as the Sadlers apparently believe, there is something coercive about family members being asked to opt out of donations rather than being asked to opt in, our society might wish to see what the effects are of merely modifying the present emphasis on voluntarism to include required request.

In considering the alternatives of presumed consent or required request, four combinations of request and consent are possible:

Request	Consent
Optional	Opt in
Required	Opt out

The current system of donor cards is, in practice, an optional-opt-in approach. While sound moral arguments can be mounted in favor of the strongest alternative approach—a required-opt-out system—I believe that public and professional consensus could be achieved for a required-opt-in policy.

The Sadlers note that many philosophers, theologians, and social theorists have emphasized the importance of encouraging altruism on the part of every individual within a society. But, as those involved in blood donation in this country learned through years of hard-won efforts to improve the frequency with which blood is given, altruism is not sufficient to assure adequate supplies of necessary medical resources. People must be asked to act if their altruistic motivations are to make a significant difference in helping those in need.

285

16. SHOULD ORGAN DONATION BE A VOLUNTARY SYSTEM?

Cadaver organ donation is, whether we like it or not, a family matter. Families should be given every opportunity to act upon their desire to transform the tragedy of death into the gift of life. But they must be asked. If our society were to institute a policy of weak required request, those who are, according to the public opinion polls, willing to give would have a maximum opportunity to do so. We should not allow our concern for the rights and values of the individual to blind us to policy options that can accommodate both individual autonomy and community good.

REFERENCES

1. G. Kolata, "Organ Shortage Clouds New Transplant Era," *Science* 221 (July 1, 1983); 32-33.

2. R.W. Evans, "Organ Scarcity and Issues of Distribution: An Overview," paper presented at a conference; "The Future of Technology in a New Payment Environment," American Enterprise Institute, Washington, D.C., January 24, 1984.

3. T.D. Overcast, R.W. Evans, et al., "Problems in the Identification of Potential Organ Donors," JAMA (March 23-30, 1984), 1559-62.

4. See A.L. Caplan, "Public Policy and Organ Transplantation," Testimony to New York State Assembly Health Committee, April 26, 1984, and, "Morality Dissected: A Plea for Reform of Current Policies With Respect to Autopsy," *Human Pathology*, forthcoming, December, 1984.

5. Evans, op. cit.

6. A.J. Matas and F.J. Veith, "Presumed Consent for Organ Retrieval," *Theoretical Medicine* 5 (1984), 155-66.

7. P. Safar, Hearings on Organ Transplants before the Subcommittee on Science and Technology, U.S. House of Representatives, April 23, 1983, Washington, D.C., pp. 653-59.

8. I would like to thank Claire Ambroselli at INSERM and the personnel at Hopital Necker and Hotel Dieu for providing information.

9. J.M. Prottas, "Obtaining Replacements: The Organizational Framework of Organ Procurement," Hearings on Organ Transplants before the Subcommittee on Investigations and Oversight of the Committee on Science and Technology, U.S. House of Representatives, April 1983, pp. 714-51.

POSTSCRIPT

SHOULD ORGAN PROCUREMENT
BE BASED ON VOLUNTARISM?

Since 1985, when New York became the first state to enact a "required request" law, over a dozen other states have followed suit. In New York, the number of donations has doubled, and in Oregon, donations have risen at least 50 percent.

Highly publicized cases of newborns needing heart or liver transplants have focused attention on the distribution of these scarce resources. Baby Jesse, a California newborn, was at first denied admission to the list for heart transplants at Loma Linda University Medical Center because his parents were young and unmarried. As a result of the publicity, officials reconsidered and Baby Jesse received a transplant ahead of other infants in the nation. The lack of available donors for newborn organ transplants has led to proposals to use the organs of anencephalic infants (those born without a brain and doomed to die). See "Case Studies: The Anencaphalic Newborn as Organ Donor," commentaries by Michael R. Harrison and Gilbert Meilaender, *Hastings Center Report* 16 (April 1986).

Several state task forces have examined the questions of a fair distribution of organs. In May 1986 the Department of Health and Human Services' Task Force on Organ Transplantation recommended that "routine inquiry/required request" legislation be enacted in all states, and that a national organ-sharing network be established.

Two classic articles on the question of organ retrieval are Willard Gaylin, "Harvesting the Dead," *Harpers* (September 1974) and William May, "Attitudes Toward the Newly Dead," *Hastings Center Studies* (No. 1 for 1973). Also see James F. Childress "Who Shall Live When Not All Can Live?" *Soundings* (Winter 1970); and Nicholas Rescher, "The Allocation of Exotic Medical Lifesaving Therapy," *Ethics* (April 1969). A good summary of the current status of organ shortages is John K. Iglehart, "Transplantation: The Problem of Limited Resources," *New England Journal of Medicine* (July 14, 1983). The problem of coercing a potential donor is discussed in "Mrs. X and the Bone Marrow Transplant," *Hastings Center Report* (June 1983). Also see Renee C. Fox and Judith P. Swazey, *The Courage to Fail: A Social View of Organ Transplants and Dialysis,* Second edition (Chicago, 1979).

ISSUE 17

DO WE NEED THE ARTIFICIAL HEART?

YES: The Working Group on Mechanical Circulatory Support of the National Heart, Lung, and Blood Institute, from *Artificial Heart and Assist Devices: Directions, Needs, Costs, Societal and Ethical Issues* (Washington, D.C., May 1985)

NO: Thomas A. Preston, from "Who Benefits from the Artificial Heart?" *Hastings Center Report,* February 1985

ISSUE SUMMARY

YES: The Working Group on Mechanical Circulatory Support of the NHLBI concludes that effective, fully implantable, long-term, mechanical circulatory support systems—that is, artificial hearts—could provide a significant increase in life span, with acceptable quality of life, for 17,000 to 35,000 patients a year.
NO: Cardiologist Thomas A. Preston opposes further development of the artificial heart without stringent regulation, because claims for its therapeutic benefits are unwarranted and the costs to society for the limited gains it might provide are too high.

On December 2, 1982, Dr. Barney B. Clark, a 61-year-old Seattle dentist, was operated on at the University of Utah Medical Center. After removing Dr. Clark's diseased heart, Dr. William DeVries implanted a Jarvik-7 artificial heart, connected to a bulky mechanical pump and power source, in Dr. Clark's chest. For the next 112 days the world followed Dr. Clark's decline and ultimate death.

The highly publicized events in Utah were not the first attempts to implant an artificial heart in a human being. Three other attempts had been made in the United States—one in 1969, and two in 1981—by other surgeons; these, however, were intended as temporary implants while donor hearts for transplantation were located. The Jarvik-7 was designed as a permanent installation.

As Dr. Robert K. Jarvik, the inventor of the device, pointed out in a 1981 article, "The concept of replacing the function of the heart with a mechanical device is far from new." He traced the idea to the nineteenth century; various devices were tested in animals starting in the 1950s. In the 1960s the most promising device appeared to be a nuclear-powered one. However, a panel convened in 1972 by the National Heart and Lung Institute recommended against further development of that idea. Even though the recipient himself might derive much benefit from the device, a person walking around with a capsule containing 53 grams of Plutonium 238 in his chest posed too great a risk to others, the panel said in its September 1973 report. One radiation expert told the panel, "My main worry about a Plutonium 238-powered heart pump is that one day on a trans-Pacific flight, economy class, I will be seated between two of them." The panel, however, encouraged development of a battery-powered device.

Although an estimated $218 million of federal money was spent on the development of the artificial heart, the device that was implanted in Dr. Clark and in the succeeding patients is the product of a private company, Symbion, headed by Dr. Jarvik. Furthermore, Dr. DeVries, the only physician approved by the Federal Food and Drug Administration to perform permanent implants of the Jarvik-7, which is still considered an experimental device, moved his program from the academic nonprofit setting at the University of Utah to the privately owned Humana Hospital—Audubon in Louisville, Kentucky.

The questions surrounding the future of the artificial heart are diverse. First, does the device provide sufficient benefit to the recipient to warrant its use? Second, should the decision about whether to continue development of the artificial heart be left to private enterprise? Third, should the money be spent on other forms of health care, either to prevent heart disease or to provide other therapies?

A second panel convened by the National Heart, Lung, and Blood Institute (renamed since the 1970s) believes that the fully implantable total artificial heart should be included in its mission, along with other mechanical forms of circulatory assistance such as left-ventricular-assist devices. It concludes that "the promise for benefit from mechanical circulatory support systems to significant numbers in society makes the effort of development and incorporation into the health care system worthwhile." Dr. Thomas A. Preston disagrees, calling the artificial heart "crude." He doubts that within the next two decades we can achieve a device that can predictably add two years of life without serious complications. Moreover, he warns against placing drama above reason in setting priorities in health care expenditures.

YES

ARTIFICIAL HEART
AND ASSIST DEVICES:

SOCIETAL AND ETHICAL ISSUES

Introduction of an expensive new medical technology poses problems of public acceptance, economic impact, equitable access, and equitable distribution of cost. It is far easier to increase than to decrease the use of a technology after it is in place. It is not enough to justify the introduction of the artificial heart by asserting that it will save lives. The burdens its introduction will impose on other lives must also be considered.

Experience with medical procedures indicates that dissemination proceeds in the manner of a ratchet; once a medical technology has reached a certain level of use, the public may come to expect and even demand it as a right. This observation can be true even if the expectations are developed while the procedure is in an investigational stage and if subsequent information on the benefits, risks, and costs would justify abandonment.

Societal Acceptance

General public response to the initial implantations of artificial hearts probably has been, and will continue to be, more positive than is justified by either the state of the technology or the benefit derived by the recipients through extended lives of a reasonable quality. This situation is often observed in the first phase of clinical investigation. While the media may be perceived as taking the lead in unwarranted heralding of "technological breakthroughs," the public and even the research teams involved are usually willing accomplices. All share the hope that medical technology will provide another, effective tool in preventing or postponing death. All share as well, albeit with varying focus, the desire to "celebrate" and to express regard for the pioneers, both patient and physician-researcher.

The long-range problem will be to supply the general public, whose support is essential to the success of any policy established, with a realistic picture of the advantages and disadvantages of the device. The media are basi-

From, *Artificial Heart and Assist Devices: Directions, Needs, Costs, Societal and Ethical Issues,* by the Working Group on Mechanical Circulatory Support of the National Heart, Lung and Blood Institute, Washington, DC, May 1985.

cally oriented toward reporting unique events. Thus, as the postoperative period advances, bulletins on the condition of the patient are less and less likely to be reported except when there is a dramatic change. Also, even in the investigational phase, an increasing number of implantations will cause the procedure to lose its uniqueness, although early deaths might still be considered newsworthy. The general public would thus be left to make a possibly false inference either that "no news is good news," or that the mortality rate is excessive. Either misapprehension could lead to premature demands for action, to expand or to terminate the program.

Dramatic therapeutic innovations such as the artificial heart have a tendency to be turned into media events. Efforts must be made to balance the public's interest and the patient-subject's right to choose his or her self-presentation. To the extent that damage to the latter can be anticipated or cannot be avoided, the prospective subject must be made aware of what to expect so that this consideration may enter into his or her "risk-benefit calculation" in deciding whether to consent. No patient should be excluded from selection on the basis of unwillingness to make public personal or private information, and the patient should be informed that this choice is available.

A further problem is that all communications to the media, and ultimately to the public, may not be disinterested. Public relations must not distort the truth about the benefits and burdens the recipients do and will experience. Honest exposure of these experiences is necessary for the informed consent of future patients and the "informed consent" of society to admit yet another expensive technical device. Future patients and society at large are entitled to the knowledge that will allow judicious

choices. In general, the introduction of the artificial heart into medical use should not depend on the public perception that another medical miracle has been performed, but on informed awareness of the real benefits and limitations of the new device.

Even with an adequate perspective on the benefits accruing to the individual, society may begin to realize that this innovation could bring disadvantages. We are concerned that the extraordinary capabilities of technological medicine may have some adverse effects. Concentration on the technical may attenuate the more humane aspects of health care. Also, technical solutions have a tendency to creep from the area of appropriate applications to others less appropriate.

An emotional and ethical issue of importance to society as a whole is the ability to sustain a biological life with negative value to the patient. We must face the possiblity that individuals who accept the artificial heart with clear awareness of its implications may later choose to discontinue its use. Since this choice will amount to a deliberate decision no longer to live, society should consider its response. Will this act be seen as refusal of an "extraordinary" means of life support or as suicide? Strong traditions still decry suicide; even the refusal of life-sustaining measures by competent persons meets resistance on many sides. There should be a clearer social consensus than now exists about the moral implications of the unwillingness of a bearer of an artificial heart to continue to accept it.

Economic Impact
Regardless of the mechanisms ultimately chosen to pay for the artificial heart as "standard" therapy, it is certain that one way or another—through insurance premiums, fees, or higher taxes—the costs will

be paid by people. It thus becomes unnecessary to ask if people want to spend their money in this way.

There is no precise answer to the question of how much people are willing to spend to "save a life." Decisions made in the "medical marketplace" are of little help because (a) neither physicians nor patients have precise or accurate information about the effects of most medical procedures; (b) most patients pay only a fraction of the full costs; (c) many people who influence the decisions of the marketplace—investigators who are developing procedures, physicians who are applying them, and companies that produce equipment and medications—have biases and conflicts of interest; and (d) societal expectations and ethical norms may have overriding influence.

The key question in such circumstances would be whether society's values dictate that the artificial heart must be made available even if it restricts access to other goods and services. Perhaps spending resources on the artificial heart will displace no other expenditures on health. If so, the health of the public in general will not be adversely affected by introduction of the device, but there will be displacements in other segments of the economy. In the private sector, people will be denied freedom to spend that money on housing, entertainment, food, or other goods, programs, and services. In the public sector, the necessary increases in spending for Medicare, Medicaid, and/or entitlements could cause a decrease in spending for other items in federal and state budgets such as schools, social programs, roads, and weapons. The question would then be whether people prefer the availability of the artificial heart more than they want the other goods and services.

In order to assess the impact of the ar-

tificial heart on the health of the population, it is useful to apply the principle of equal marginal returns. Efficient allocation of medical resources must satisfy three criteria. First, no procedure should be used if the benefits are not worth the costs. Second, there must be no other procedures for the same condition that are as effective and less expensive, or as expensive and more effective. Third, the cost-effectiveness of the procedure in question should be equal to or greater than that of all possible procedures to which the resources could be allocated.

It has not been customary to apply these principles in the American system of medical care. In fact, it is difficult to translate these principles into practice.

The Working Group identified three main categories of procedures that could be affected by the existence of an artificial heart: (a) procedures for treating patients with end-stage heart disease with refractory pump failure; (b) procedures for preventing and treating heart disease in general; and (c) procedures for improving health in general.

Within the set of procedures now used to manage patients having end-stage heart disease, none known to be more efficient would be displaced by the artificial heart. Furthermore, we do not see new technologies on the horizon (five to fifteen years) that might make the artificial heart obsolete as a treatment for end-stage cardiovascular disease.

In the second and third categories, more effective and efficient ways undoubtedly exist to reduce the morbidity and mortality of cardiovascular disease and to improve health in general. Cigarette smoking provides an example. A smoker's decision to stop smoking, or a youth's decision not to start, is likely to have an impact on that person's prospects for dying of cardiovascular disease many times greater than the ultimate availability of the artificial heart. To the extent that individuals can be helped to combat their tobacco addiction, the incidence of cardiovascular disease should drop; the need for the artificial heart should decrease; and the total cost of cardiovascular disease should decrease. The case could be made that priority be given to antismoking education and treatment for tobacco addiction. It should be noted that improved preventive measures might make availability of the artificial heart even more attractive, because a lower incidence of end-stage heart disease would result in a lower total societal cost associated with its use.

If the artificial heart were to displace more efficient procedures, the approximate impact can be estimated as a function of the difference in cost-effectiveness of the displaced procedures and the number of artificial hearts that are implanted. To return to the smoking example, if prevention of smoking is more efficient than the artificial heart in reducing cardiovascular morbidity and mortality, then support of the artificial heart rather than antismoking programs would result in larger numbers of people developing heart disease. Thus, the years of life salvaged would be smaller and accomplished at a greater cost.

Given the available information, quantitative conclusions cannot be drawn regarding the cost-effectiveness of the artificial heart or its impact on the quality of care in the United States. Such conclusions would require a more formal analysis of other activities that might be more efficient and exploration of mechanisms for allocating resources according to their efficiency. The Working Group suspects that such an exercise would reveal the existence of more efficient activities and would indicate

that a reallocation of health resources, involving not only the artificial heart, could improve the health of our population. Even so, the probability that the artificial heart will be a useful tool for managing terminal cardiovascular disease in patients who have not been helped by other preventive or treatment approaches is judged to be high enough to warrant proceeding with its development.

Equitable Access

In 1973, the Artificial Heart Assessment Panel of the NHLBI recommended:

> (5) In the event artificial heart resources are in scarce supply, decisions as to the selection of candidates . . . should be made by physicians and medical institutions on the basis of medical criteria. If the pool of patients with equal medical needs exceeds supply, procedures should be devised for some form of random selection. Social worth criteria should not be used, and every effort should be exerted to minimize the possibility that social worth may implicitly be taken into account.
> (6) Particularly in view of the substantial commitment of public funds for the development of the artificial heart, implantation should be broadly available, and availability should not be limited only to those able to pay.

The Working Group affirms the general principles articulated by the Panel in 1973. However, the second major point—that implantation should be broadly available and should not be limited only to those able to pay—must be qualified. It is the judgment of the Working Group that cost and cost-effectiveness are legitimate considerations in such reimbursement and entitlement issues.

The President's Commission for the Study of Ethical Problems in Medicine and in Biomedical and Behavioral Research concluded: "Society has an ethical obligation to ensure equitable access to an adequate level of health care without the imposition of excessive burden." According to the Commission, "equitable access" refers to achieving an adequate level of care and not to equality in the sense that everyone receives an equal share of the health care dollar or is provided with the same level of care. Equitable access must also be free of excessive burdens for the individuals seeking care: burdens in expenditure of significant resources, inconvenience, time, etc. At the same time, the Commission indicated that equity requires that the individual's needs should not be met at the expense of more important needs of society as a whole. "Adequate" was defined as that level of care that will enable individuals to achieve sufficient welfare, opportunity, information and evidence of interpersonal concern to facilitate a reasonably full and satisfying life.

Given the high visibility of the artificial heart, it is likely that more patients will seek help than can be served by available resources. The capacity of institutions to provide such technically demanding service will always be limited. Similar situations accompanied the advent of chronic hemodialysis and renal and cardiac transplantation. Concerned that selection based on socially valued criteria would introduce discrimination into the availability of a lifesaving therapy, ethicists suggested equitable systems of rationing. Many favored a lottery that would be blind to all personal and social characteristics. In effect, the natural lottery of randomly distributed illness and compatibility of donor and recipient tissue, together with massive public funding for care of renal disease, has created a relatively fair distribution of these therapies without reliance on strictly controlled, artificial lotteries. The potential off-the-shelf availability of artificial hearts and the likelihood that medical indications will be restrictive will act to counter the prospect that demand will exceed supply, as is currently the case with organ transplants. However, should excess demand occur, the primary criteria should be medical and only beyond that should other selection methods be considered.

Equitable Distribution of Cost

Even without availability of artificial hearts, our mechanisms for sharing health care costs across society are being stressed by the growing number and cost of available therapies. The Medicare trust fund has been in hazardous condition, and the individual's cost of supplementing this coverage has been increasing steadily; various limitations have been placed on payments and services available under Medicaid; and the concept of co-insurance, which involves supplemental payments for services actually used, is being introduced into group health insurance. Each of these developments has undoubtedly eliminated some individuals' access to adequate care. An attempt to impose a new technology costing $2.5-5 billion annually on this structure might cause it serious damage and significantly impair its ability to meet society's basic needs.

On the other hand, if the artificial heart is disseminated as an uncovered, discretionary therapy, its probable cost of $150,000 or more would restrict its use to wealthy patients. The older segment of our population, the primary beneficiary, is unlikely to let pass unprotested a policy of distribution solely according to individual means. Perhaps a benefit of the artificial heart will be to stimulate public discussion of the limits on society's responsibility for the health care of its members and whether some lifesaving therapies can reasonably be considered luxuries rather than components of adequate care.

CONCLUSIONS

Technical progress to date presents evidence that effective and safe mechanical circulatory support systems, reliable for time periods of several years, are feasible. Some such devices are approaching a stage of development where their use may provide clinical benefits to certain patients. The Working Group projects that such devices, with currently envisioned technology and preliminary but reasonable assumptions about clinical success and complications, will provide an extended lifetime of acceptable quality.

Although clinical testing has begun with a tethered, pneumatically actuated, total artificial heart system, great advantage will accrue from totally implantable systems. Systems that do not permit substantial levels of ambulation and relatively normal activity are importantly suboptimal. Electrically energized systems lend themselves to full implantation and presumably to relatively normal activity. Fully implantable ventricular assist systems, in which an auxiliary pump takes over the function of the diseased ventricle, may be beneficial for some patients; for other patients, bilateral functional replacement or a total artificial heart will be necessary. Therefore, the mission of the NHLBI program should include the fully implantable total artificial heart.

The Working Group has reviewed previous assessments of need and carried out an independent survey. The group concludes that effective, fully implantable, long-term, mechanical circulatory support systems could provide a significant increase in life span, with an acceptable quality of life, for 17,000 to 35,000 patients below age 70 annually. Such estimates are highly sensitive to the precise criteria of patient suitability, the effectiveness, safety and long-term reliability of the device, and its availability.

Much of society will accept mechanical circulatory support systems. Indeed, currently the expectations of many are probably unrealistically optimistic.

Research, development, and clinical investigation of MCSSs are appropriate uses of public as well as other funds. Approval of an institutional review board and the FDA are sufficient to permit clinical trials. Funding of clinical research by NIH/NHLBI would provide an opportunity for necessary close surveillance that might otherwise be lacking. Such an approach has a number of advantages, not the least of which is the opportunity to provide a thoughtful model for the continuing evaluation that should precede investigational and the potential more general clinical use.

Mechanical circulatory support systems will add another high-cost technology to medical treatment. The Working Group's preliminary assessment is that the total cost of the device, its implantation, and its maintenance for a projected average of 4½ years of survival will be approximately $150,000 (in 1983 dollars). These costs and the level of cost-effectiveness are not outside the range reimbursed for such therapies as heart transplantation, renal dialysis, and bone marrow transplants. However, addition of another high-cost medical technology increases the need to evaluate its cost-effectiveness and to address questions of how it will be paid for and what might be displaced.

If effectiveness and cost-effectiveness of the device are demonstrated in specific clinical circumstances, use will still have to be restricted to patients in whom these conditions are favorable. These decisions may often be difficult ones in which the emotional judgments of some may not coincide with a dispassionate analysis of facts. As for most technologies, there will be a tendency for usage to expand and include new clinical circumstances without validating data.

There is likely to be considerable public pressure for such systems to be made available, initially for identified individuals and ultimately as a public entitlement. It must be recognized that the widespread use of high-cost treatment may displace other uses to which such funds might be put. The Working Group believes that cost-effectiveness is an appropriate and legitimate element in making reimbursement and entitlement decisions, even for procedures that might be lifesaving. Society must come to terms with this necessity in its expectations and promises, in its mores and ethics.

The ethical issues related to the artificial heart are not unique, but rather are the universal issues related to medical practices. With regard to individual patients, there are particular sensitivities during the investigative phase to informed consent, to patient selection, and to privacy.

Ethical problems for society are primarily related to distributive justice. Access to medical care is an important consideration, but this is not an entitlement to every form of medical care, independent of cost-effectiveness.

The Working Group has noted the entry of for-profit entities and recognized the advantages as well as the potential disadvantages. Although the private sector is a source of funds, it is unlikely to assume the total cost of the research, development, and validation of fully implanted, long-term devices that are deemed necessary. The legitimate corporate desire for profitability should not jeopardize availability of an optimal device, benefit to the patient, the public interest, or the timely disclosure of data through scientific channels.

The advent of mechanical circulatory support is now being realized. The existence of this therapy will pose very serious problems to society from the standpoint of cost, distributive justice, and patient selection. These problems are not unique to this development but highlight the need to direct attention to the issues often associated with increasingly complicated medical care. Indeed, such issues exist for some current practices that may not be "high technology." The promise for benefit from mechanical circulatory support systems to significant numbers in society makes the effort of development and incorporation into the health care system worthwhile.

RECOMMENDATIONS

1. Research on mechanical circulatory support systems (MCSSs) should continue.

2. The targeted program of fully implantable long-term ventricular assist devices should be continued as planned.

3. The fully implantable, long-term, total artificial heart should become a part of the targeted program and should be actively pursued.

4. The sequence of bench and animal validation of MCSSs, and progression to clinical investigation only when satisfactory reliability has been demonstrated should be maintained.

5. Clinical application of MCSSs should at this time be considered investigational and therefore should be maintained under close surveillance.

6. During clinical investigation, use of such devices should be limited to experimental programs studying technological and clinical effectiveness, physiological

and psychological responses, quality of life, safety, and cost. The national program should assure that such factors as cost-effectiveness, psychological and societal impact, and ethical issues are also studied.

7. NHLBI should participate in clinical research costs during the investigative phase of MCSSs.

8. Except as a part of NHLBI research protocols, public funds should not be available for clinical use of MCSSs until their effectiveness and reasonable cost-effectiveness are demonstrated.

9. Even when MCSSs are clinically available, their use should be restricted to expert groups, with the experience and training and with the institutional resources and commitments that are necessary ingredients for successful programs.

10. Cost-effectiveness should be an essential ingredient in decisions on appropriate medical care and on its reimbursement, whether by third-party payers or government. Even lifesaving technologies should be accepted for public funding only if they fall within the accepted cost-effectiveness boundary.

11. Cost-effectiveness must be applied generally in the field of medicine and not only to highly visible technologies.

12. Even when the effectiveness and cost-effectiveness of MCSSs are demonstrated in specific circumstances, usage must be restricted to circumstances in which these factors remain favorable.

13. Society should be presented with a balanced view of MCSSs, so that it can anticipate the problems and failures that will be encountered, as well as the hoped-for successes.

14. The complexity of patient suitability criteria for MCSSs must be recognized.

15. In spite of public interest, the privacy of the patient and family must be respected. Institutions involved have a responsibility to help patients and families in this respect. Participation in media relations should not become a precondition for participation in clinical investigative use of MCSSs.

16. Research results should be presented through national scientific meetings and peer-reviewed journals, following traditional patterns.

NO
Thomas A. Preston

WHO BENEFITS FROM
THE ARTIFICIAL HEART?

The debate over the artificial heart is not just a matter of one physician treating one patient. Nor is it a matter of two, or seven, or a hundred patients dealing in isolation with one medical team.

When Dr. William DeVries replaced first Barney Clark's and then William Schroeder's failing hearts with artificial ones, he initiated a sequence of events that will affect all patients. In time, the artificial heart program will have an indirect but certain influence on levels and types of Medicare expenditures, medical research, mechanisms and limits of insurance, the federal health care budget, and more. How all this works out will determine who gets what and how much medical care, how we apportion our expenditures between medical and nonmedical services, and whether individuals perceive the distribution of services as just.

The central issue is whether our utilization of the artificial heart shall be directed by a small group of medical investigators and their entrepreneurial backers, or by representatives of the society that has developed the technology and will have to live with its consequences. It is a classic conflict between the economic independence of individuals, and the determination of the public good in an increasingly interdependent society.

Tradition, inertia, the peculiarities of medical financing, and the absence of an effective mechanism for public direction of medical policies combine to favor the independent course of Dr. DeVries, his medical team, and Humana, Inc. Time and a rising insistence for public accountability are working against them. In my opinion, resolution of the many political and ethical issues surrounding the artificial heart will not be possible until we come to grips with the central issue of who shall make policy.

THE CLAIM OF THERAPEUTIC BENEFIT

Virtually every statement by the Humana team and its representatives revolves around two arguments: we desperately need a technology by which we can save the lives of the thousands who die from heart disease, our number one killer; and, the present model of the artificial heart can achieve this goal. The first assertion—that we need more effective therapy for patients with end-stage heart disease—is indisputable. But physicians and the public usually assume that what *can* be done through modern technology *must* be done.

What is missing is a hard look at whether the new technology is likely to be of net benefit to all of us, and is a better choice than other options. There is almost never a mechanism to do this kind of assessment.

In answering criticism while Barney Clark was still alive, Dr. Chase Peterson defended the artificial heart as a "legitimate idea," and added, "If this country somehow ever got the notion that an idea is dangerous, we would be in the intellectual Dark Ages." Dr. DeVries used the same metaphor a few weeks after the implantation of Mr. Schroeder. But the issue has nothing to do with an *idea* as such, or the freedom to pursue one. The distinction is between the freedom of investigators to ask questions and seek solutions, and the right of society to impose restrictions on the implementation of technology. We might decide that the artificial heart is a good idea, but one that we do not want to implement.

The second assertion—that the present model of the artificial heart is of therapeutic value—edges the advocates onto shakier ethical ground by making dubious claims of clinical success. Virtually the first statement Dr. DeVries made after the first implant was that Barney Clark would have been dead within hours had he not received the artificial heart. Other physicians might argue that life actually was shortened by the procedure. By predicting Barney Clark's imminent demise, the team precluded the most serious objection to the implantation of the artificial heart.

But is the claim correct? Before his operation Barney Clark suffered life-threatening arrhythmias because of drugs he was given, but he had had the same complication, even more sustained and for the same reason, on several occasions during the previous year and a half. And William

Schroeder underwent an uncomplicated elective removal of his gall bladder just eight days before swapping hearts. Such an operation is never performed on a patient "hours" from death.

The only patient who can be said to be within hours of death is one who has in fact died already and been resuscitated. Even then, as volumes of medical evidence attest, one cannot be sure of when death might recur. We'll never know how long Clark or Schroeder would have lived without an artificial heart.

The team also has made general claims of therapeutic benefit for the artificial heart. DeVries, in explaining his move from Salt Lake City to Louisville, said, "I don't like to see people die while I wait for the red tape." The claim has locked the team into producing a patina of therapeutic success (or denial of setback) covering each clinical development. This framework foreclosed the far more legitimate option of proceeding strictly as a research project, with quiet approval of the medical community and relative indifference to the media. Instead, the team's primary goal is a substantiation of their claim; to be "vindicated," as Dr. DeVries put it. Good research needs no vindication.

The need to show benefit led to a publicity barrage. Barney Clark was set up as a media event, and then cancelled. Two video-taped interviews in which Clark had nothing positive to say were not released; finally, a short clip was culled from an extensive interview in which, encouraged by Dr. DeVries, Clark issued a semblance of a positive statement. The same thing with Schroeder. After "prolonging his life," the team was "astounded" by his fast recovery. Schroeder recovered "brilliantly"—how is this done?—from his stroke. This is not medical research. What a tangled web they weave, when first they practice to achieve.

The confusion between research and therapy runs afoul of national medical policy as established by the National Institutes of Health (NIH) and the Food and Drug Administration (FDA). For more than a decade, the NIH has favored the development of left ventricular assist devices (partial artificial hearts) rather than total artificial hearts. Moreover, NIH officials vigorously opposed FDA approval of Utah's request for permission to use the Jarvik-7 heart. The FDA did not approve the artificial heart as a device capable of achieving therapeutic benefit, but rather gave its users an *exemption* from the need to show therapeutic benefit, so that it might be used strictly on an experimental basis. In allowing claims of therapeutic benefit without demonstration of such, the FDA is exceeding its mandate from Congress and condoning a violation of its own rules.

As things now stand, the Humana team will slow down only if the clinical outcome of Mr. Schroeder and those who may follow him is poor enough to alarm the public, which has been primed to expect miraculous outcomes. This unwise and unscientific approach is a consequence of the team's unnecessary claim of therapeutic benefit. In the startup phase of any medical technology, and especially the artificial heart, adverse clinical results are expected, and the team may ironically abort its mission because of failure to achieve what seems unrealistic to most other investigators.

A CORPORATE MARKETING STRATEGY

The National Institutes of Health (NIH) have been the primary source of approximately $250 million of federal expenditures for development of the artificial heart over the last twenty years, including work done on the model now being used. But the Humana team and Symbion, Inc., the manufacturer of the artificial heart, have used the quirks of our legal system to become free of the public agencies that nurtured them. By shifting patent rights from the University of Utah to Symbion, Inc., Jarvik and his co-workers became free of any NIH control.

The surgical team became impatient with the Utah Institutional Review Board (IRB), which moved cautiously and insisted on a review after each case. Humana offered DeVries freedom, funding for his artificial heart patients, plus a tripling of salary, and he left for Louisville. The Humana IRB approved the team's application shortly after its arrival. There is now no assurance of an independent mechanism to protect the rights of patients, as the Utah IRB attempted to do.

Humana, Inc. answers to its stockholders, not to the community or to a university, as do nonprofit research centers. To be sure, universities also seek publicity, do not want to lose money, and have to answer to trustees; but there is in my view a fundamental difference between the broader goals of universities and enterprises whose existence depends on making a profit. Humana's interest in research is to create an "enhanced reputation," according to its chairman, David Jones. For this company with 1983 profits of $193 million, a few million dollars spent over a year or more to achieve this status should be an extremely good investment. But the artificial heart program as it now exists will fail as research because it is a corporate marketing strategy, not research.

Nevertheless, the Humana team holds that they can implant the artificial heart better than anyone else; therefore they should push on and find its value. They reiterate that we must first find out how well it works, or else we will never know and may lose a life-saving technology. Then, if it is of value, we can work out the social and economic problems attending it. DeVries, who thinks the debate is premature, said, "We have to find out if it works and then (debate) what it costs."

This argument is entirely within medical precedent, and that is what bothers most critics. A medical practice, once established, and especially if it is compensable through insurers and is popular with the public, is almost impossible to reduce or eliminate, so long as it is not patently of no value. Therefore, in our medical system in which rationing exists indirectly (a lot of medical services lack forceful advocates and so never become available), what physicians establish is what we get, with indifference to relative social or medical value.

Once the artificial heart is established as workable—and it need not be even demonstrably of real benefit for the public to clamor for it—and especially if channels of public funding are established, it will be on the slippery slope from which it cannot be withdrawn. Dr. DeVries expressed this to a *Washington Post* reporter with another metaphor: "I think the snowball's started and I don't think anybody can stop it now." But when everyone who might benefit from the artificial heart will want it, will Humana pay? The federal government will be asked to pay, and then it will be too late to say no. The only alternative would be to make the heart accessible only to those who can afford it, an ethically unacceptable policy in an egalitarian society.

ASSESSING TECHNOLOGIES

In thinking about whether we want the artificial heart we must consider first its technologic capabilities, and then our priorities for expending our resources. Dr. Robert Jarvik, in a 1981 *Scientific American* article, said "Neither the Jarvik-7 nor any of the several other total artificial hearts being developed is yet ready to permanently replace a human heart, even on a trial basis. . . ." I suspect that this statement, written before the decision to push ahead, is still correct.

The artificial pacemaker provides a good analogy of development during which there were repeated failures due to a number of causes, most of which were not anticipated by medical and engineering investigators. Packmakers are an order of magnitude simpler than artificial hearts, having only one moving part and requiring one-millionth the power to run. Furthermore, when a pacemaker stops suddenly, as they still do, the consequences are seldom serious and deaths are extremely rare.

Sudden failure of an artificial heart could result in death or irreversible brain damage within ten to fifteeen seconds. If and when we get to the point when artificial heart patients leave the protective environment of a hospital, we will undoubtedly encounter disasters due to unanticipated failures at times and places where patients cannot receive immediate emergency treatment. It will take a decade or more for investigators to learn what the problems are and how to deal with them, and artificial hearts will always run the risk of sudden failure. We must give serious thought to whether we want to promote this sort of existence.

SETTING PRIORITIES

Finally, we must decide whether the artificial heart is a high-priority item. The cost, if it is some day successful enough to be used for all who could benefit from it, would be great. By best estimates, approximately 50,000 persons a year are candidates for a reliable new heart. At an average cost of $125,000 apiece (half the cost for Barney Clark), the annual bill would be $6.25 billion by today's prices. The $2 billion a year now spent on end-stage kidney disease is seriously straining the Medicare budget, which is already threatened with cuts. By the most optimistic estimates the artificial heart will extend the life expectancy of the recipient by one to two years and of the total population by an average of a few days. Is the cost worth the limited gain?

If the goal is to save lives, that can be done more quickly, more broadly, and more surely by other means. Let us spend our resources instead on reducing our infant mortality rate, or treating hypertension in the inner cities, or taking care of the twenty-five million Americans who are without insurance or means of attaining adequate medical care. Let us work on prevention of heart disease, an approach that is preferable to a crude method of altering the lives of a few who already have the disease. Recent studies suggest that a reduction of fat in the average American's diet would prolong lives far in excess of what could be achieved with any high technology.

All medical expenses ultimately are paid for by the public through individual insurance, which is shared by the public-at-large, employers, or the government. The public already is paying for these experiments. Medicare and private insurance paid about $60,000 of Barney Clark's bill at Utah, and Humana has applied to a private insurance company for partial payment of Schroeder's expenses. We must decide whether we want to spend our money on what will be at best a troublesome stopgap device, or adequate nutrition for school children, or better schools, or more parks.

In the tug for our minds and our money, all too often we place drama above reason. It is easy to empathize with a Barney Clark, or a William Schroeder, media heroes. It's much harder to send our well-wishes to someone dying in anonymity who must base his hope not on a sensational technological breakthrough but on our love and support. When President Reagan telephoned Mr. Schroeder he chose not to call the tens of thousands of others who were dying at that moment, many for lack of care from us, and some for lack of adequate medical attention. Who will call these people and offer them the help they need?

What is happening now is not good medicine, is not good science, and is not in the public interest. The artificial heart team should proceed under the public purview of an impartial commission, such as could be formed under the aegis of the National Academy of Sciences. The FDA has jurisdiction over medical devices, and it alone can represent the public in this matter. I believe that the FDA should refuse allowance of further implants because they do not represent good science, and because the claims of therapeutic efficacy are unwarranted and exceed the terms of FDA approval.

The artificial heart is still crude. Whether within two decades we can achieve a device that can predictably add two years of life without serious complications is questionable. Meanwhile, the existence of the artificial heart, with its potential for benefit, forces decisions that are for the most part not medical, but ethical and political. The stakes are too high, and the consequences too great, to exclude the public from these decisions.

POSTSCRIPT

DO WE NEED THE ARTIFICIAL HEART?

After Dr. William DeVries moved to Humana, he implanted three more artificial hearts. One of the patients—William Schroeder—died in August of 1986 after surviving for 620 days. He had been severely incapacitated by a series of strokes that resulted from blood clots in the device. Dr. DeVries has the FDA's permission to do one more implant. Another artificial heart recipient in Sweden died of a massive stroke after several months on the device. He and Schroeder were the only patients to be well enough to leave the hospital for more than an outing.

In a series of controversial implantations, artificial hearts have been used on a temporary basis, as a "bridge to transplant." In one case, in March 1985, an Arizona surgeon used a device that had been designed for a calf and that had not been submitted to the FDA for approval. These implantations have been both praised as "heroic" and condemned as unjustified experimentation. Some of the recipients have done well when they received their heart transplants; some have died anyway. Another criticism has been that the use of temporary artificial hearts is unfair, because a recipient of a device under these circumstances moves to the head of the queue waiting for a donor heart, perhaps displacing another, sicker person.

For reflections on the Utah artificial heart program, see *After Barney Clark,* edited by Margery W. Shaw (University of Texas Press, 1984). Dr. Arnold S. Relman, editor of the *New England Journal of Medicine,* calls for federal support for further research on totally implantable artificial hearts and carefully controlled clinical trials on their temporary use (*NEJM,* March 6, 1986). Attorney George J. Annas, however, calls for a moratorium on both permanent and temporary artificial hearts ("No Cheers for Temporary Artificial Hearts," *Hastings Center Report,* October 1985).

ISSUE 18

SHOULD DOCTORS CUT COSTS AT THE BEDSIDE?

YES: Percy Brazil, from "Cost Effective Care Is Better Care," *Hastings Center Report,* 16:1, February 1986

NO: Allen R. Dyer, from "Patients, Not Costs, Come First," *Hastings Center Report,* 16:1, February 1986

ISSUE SUMMARY

YES: Physician Percy Brazil asserts that cost containment in medical care is a fact of life, and that the responsibility of the medical profession should be to ensure that the new system provides quality care, not to wage a rearguard battle for a system that is outdated.
NO: Psychiatrist Allen R. Dyer argues that the physician's primary responsibility is to the patient. To ask conscientious physicians to bear the responsibility for lowering the cost of medical care is to create a conflict of interest that threatens to alter the nature of the doctor-patient relationship.

Health care in America is big business. Only education employs more people, and only food and housing account for more consumer spending. In 1984 the share of the Gross National Product devoted to medical care was $387 billion, or 10.6 percent. The largest single health care customer is the federal government, which in 1984 paid about $112 billion for health care, in the form of Medicare payments to the elderly and disabled, Medicaid payments to the states for the care of poor people, and in a variety of other ways. As the health care system has grown to huge proportions, the pressure to cut costs has similarly increased.

Some of the measures to cut costs have involved federal reimbursement of hospital payments for Medicare patients; Diagnosis-Related Groups (or

DRGs), which are based on average length of stay for a particular condition rather than the actual costs incurred by a patient, are now in widespread use. Alternate forms of providing medical care—Health Maintenance Organizations, Physician Provider Organizations, group care, and the like—all face the problem of containing costs. In addition, new, for-profit hospital chains are competing with traditional, nonprofit providers.

On a societal level, this new and expanding market in health care creates questions of the just allocation of scarce resources. When not everything can be provided to everyone who might benefit, how will those resources be distributed? But the ethical questions also affect decision making by individual physicians and patients. While physicians and patients have always taken economics into account to some degree, and patients have not always been able to afford every kind of health care they want or need, now the situation has moved one step away from personal ability to pay. Can society afford to let patients make these decisions, when the total impact may be to increase costs? Physicians have traditionally stopped treatments when there was no benefit; they now have to consider stopping treatment when benefits are marginal. As Lester Thurow, an economist, put it in the *New England Journal of Medicine* ("Learning to Say 'No,' " Dec. 13, 1984, pp. 1569-75), "Where is the point at which marginal costs equal marginal benefits? And who is to make this ethical decision—the patient, the doctor, some third-party payer? And how do we as a society decide that we cannot afford a medical treatment that may marginally benefit someone?"

The following selections discuss one aspect of the broad subject of economics and ethics in health care. Percy Brazil asserts that doctors will become directly involved in cost-effective care (a term he prefers to "cost containment") in the hospital, at the bedside in the patient's home, at the bedside in the skilled nursing facility, and at his own bedside. He says that the challenge is to make these decisions as humanely as possible. Allen R. Dyer resists making cost-cutting decisions at the bedside. The physician, he believes, is primarily responsible to the patient, not to society. Waste and redundancy should be eliminated, but doctors should not become the agents of society in cutting costs at the expense of patient care.

YES
Percy Brazil

COST EFFECTIVE CARE
IS BETTER CARE

The moral imperative on which the new medical systems must be based is the delivery of quality health care. Doctors know this, society will demand it, and government and venture capital will have to come to terms with it.

The U.S. spends more on health care than any other country in the world, and will continue to do so. If this is so, then I submit that the arguments regarding the economics of health care should take place not under the rubric of cost containment, but more properly under that of cost effectiveness.

Today no one is arguing that we should spend less on health care than the $450 billion a year that we are now spending: in fact the forecasters anticipate that the figure will rise to $700 billion within the next five years. The criticism is that we have not been spending it wisely or well. The demand is that we now begin to do so.

Thus the issue is no longer whether doctors should be ethically or morally involved in cost effectiveness, for indeed hospitals and HMOs and IPAs and PPOs and government and capital and industry and labor and doctors themselves now require it. The responsibility of the medical profession should not be to wage a rearguard battle for a system that was, but rather to ensure that the product of the new systems is quality health care. Some contend that this cannot be done. They argue that we will end up with a two- or three-tier system of medical care, omitting to mention that we have always had that anyway. We should distinguish between luxury health care and quality health care. And while we obviously cannot afford the former we must insist on the latter.

Doctors will become directly involved in cost effectiveness at the bedside; at the bedside in the hospital, at the bedside in the patient's home, at the bedside in the skilled nursing facility, and at the doctor's own bedside.

IN THE HOSPITAL

Few doctors who have participated in utilization review work in their hospital would disagree with the proposition that probably around 25 percent of hospitalized patients do not require a hospital setting for the care of their illnesses. Not *their* patients perhaps, but patients in general. The providers of health care insurance, both private and public, have finally figured this out, and are increasingly looking to preadmission screening as a way of reducing unnecessary hospitalizations.

Physicians, for example, now have to decide in advance whether a patient with bronchitis truly requires hospitalization. The old clincher, "Put me in the

Reprinted by permission from the *Hastings Center Report,* 16:1, February 1986. Copyright © 1986 by the Hastings Center.

hospital, Doc, I've got insurance," will not be as compelling to either doctor or patient when hospitalization benefits can be retroactively denied by the insurance carrier. Surgeons will have to monitor the increasing list of surgical procedures that they used to assume required hospital admission, but that they must now perform on an ambulatory basis. They always could have been performed in an ambulatory surgery unit (ASU), but few existed and the surgeon wasn't required to think along those lines. And in truth as we now know these procedures can be performed effectively, safely, and well in an ASU setting.

Given an organism that sensitivity studies indicate will respond to a $60-a-day antibiotic or a $2-a-day antibiotic, physicians treating a urinary tract infection in a hospital setting are urged to use the latter. Protocols of management or flow sheets are being developed in hospitals for the management of G.I. bleeding or acute myocardial infarction, not as cookbook medicine, but as a guide not only to cost effectiveness but also to quality care. Orthopedic surgeons will be asked to consider in knee surgery procedures whether arthroscopic surgery is not preferable to open knee surgery, for the hospital DRG allowance is the same for both, while the length of stay for arthroscopy is significantly shorter. Such examples of cost effective considerations are not antiethical to quality care and actually may enhance it.

IN THE PATIENT'S HOME

A necessary consequence of the concern for the cost effectiveness in patient care is the development of an understanding of the issues by the patient. This will make the patient have a more responsible role in decision making. I suspect that this will not prove to be as much of a problem as many now assume. In my experience most patients would prefer not to have to go to the hospital; physicians often see patients who have avoided seeking medical care precisely because they are afraid they will wind up in the hospital. Clearly they would prefer to get well at home.

Under many HMO payment practices care will be provided for the sick patient at home with full backup of professional services. One New York HMO works with a capitation system for the primary care doctors. These physicians are paid a fixed amount of money per year to take care of a given patient. There is no additional payment to the doctor if the patient has to be admitted to the hospital and that primary care doctor continues to provide the care.

If the patient develops, for example, an acute low back problem for which the physician might have previously have admitted her to the hospital for seven or eight days of bed rest, hospital care, and perhaps pelvic traction, the HMO says to the doctor, "You take care of the patient at home, we'll have RNs come in every day, you make house calls as necessary, and we'll give you an extra $300 *for this illness,* if you'll take care of the patient at home." The HMO may save around $1500 for the management of this illness, the patient will be cared for at home, and the doctor will earn an extra $300. Obviously some homes will not be suitable for this and so it will not always apply, but cost effectiveness will clearly be part of the decision making by the attending doctor in such instances. Such patients were generally hospitalized in the past because that is how the system funded care. Change the funding and you change the practice. And in a humanistic and therefore medical sense the quality of health care improves.

THE SKILLED NURSING FACILTY

In this setting the physician is mostly dealing with chronic illnesses and usually has the patient on a variety of drugs and medications. As the daily use of these pharmaceuticals adds to the considerable cost of maintaining a patient in a skilled nursing facility (SNF) the physician will have to consider whether all the drugs are necessary or effective, and furthermore will be asked where possible to use a generic equivalent of proven efficacy.

I also suspect that the time is not far off when the doctor will be asked to decide, along with the patient and the family, whether the SNF is in fact the best place for that patient to receive care. At present, funding practices encourage the placement of the chronically ill in a nursing facility. A large part of this funding comes from the public sector. In my area, New York State will provide over $2000 per month to keep a patient in the SNF but absolutely nothing if the family takes care of the patient at home. Sooner or later it will be recognized that many families would prefer to take care of such patients in their own homes if they received, let's say, $700 or $800 a month for the care they provided. Again from a humanistic view of the patient and family, and ultimately of society, this would represent an improvement in the quality of health care delivery. When this comes to pass, as I believe it will, doctors will be required to make such cost effective and humane judgments.

AT THE DOCTOR'S BEDSIDE

For the past fifteen to twenty years, with the development of the hospital Emergency Room Service, doctors who are called on the telephone during the night have tended to ask their patients to go to the ER for care. This worked for two reasons. First, medical insurance often paid for the ER visit but did not pay for a house call by the doctor. Second, the tired doctor was relieved of getting out of bed in the middle of the night. With most of the HMO, IPA, PPO and payment plans, coverage will not be available unless the ER visit really represents an emergency. If it does not, the patient will have to bear the cost of the ER visit; moreover, some contracts in which the doctor is capitated require that the doctor will be liable for the cost of an unnecessary ER referral. In such cases the cost of the ER care will be paid by the HMO and deducted from the doctor's next monthly check from the HMO on his capitation allowance. Under such circumstances I strongly suspect that many physicians will think carefully about cost effectiveness at *their* own bedside. Affirmative disentitlement is the term now in vogue to describe the action of taking away from people certain things to which they have become accustomed. The new rules regarding ER referral will constitute a form of affirmative disentitlement for the doctor.

As necessity has been reported to be the mother of invention, and as reality often determines consciousness, doctors will unquestionably find themselves increasingly making cost effective decisions. The challenge will be to think, to educate, and to plan, so that our health care system, besides being the costliest, will also be more thoughtful, more humane, and the best in the world.

NO

Allen R. Dyer

PATIENTS, NOT COSTS, COME FIRST

Though containing medical costs has been a recurring theme for the past decade, only recently have we begun to speak directly about the possibility of rationing. Attention is now being directed to the role physicians should play at the patient's bedside. Consider the following cases:

• A physician who is caring for a young child with liver failure feels that a liver transplant, which costs $100,000, might save her life. Since her parents cannot afford that amount and their insurance will not cover the costs, should the physician even bring up the possibility of a liver transplant?

• An automobile crashes into a motorcyclist one block from a for-profit hospital. The unconsious motorcyclist is rushed to the emergency room where a neurosurgeon diagnoses an epidural hematoma that requires immediate surgery. But a hospital administrator is unable to determine whether the patient has health insurance and wants to transfer him to a public hospital on the opposite side of town. Should the physician agree to the request for a transfer?

• Dr. Brown is caring for Mr. White, a seventy-five-year-old man with terminal cancer. He is mentally alert, but depressed, and says he wants to die "with dignity." When he develops renal failure, Dr. Brown considers whether to offer renal dialysis, which Medicare will cover. She is aware that dialysis is costing the national treasury a great deal and will only temporarily benefit Mr. White. Should she provide every treatment that could benefit him? Or would she be justified in withholding a potentially beneficial but costly treatment for an elderly patient with a terminal illness?

• Mr. Smith, who has suffered two heart attacks, is in the emergency room with chest pain for the second time this month. Dr. Green is aware that Mr. Smith has become a "cardiac neurotic." With another trip to the hospital Dr. Green feels he can reassure Mr. Smith and probably avoid admitting him. Should he arrange for Mr. Smith to be admitted overnight so he can review his EKG and enzymes in the morning?

• The same Mr. Smith has been hospitalized for eighteen days with a third heart attack. This is the last day for which Medicaid will pay for this diagnosis under DRGs, but Dr. Green is not comfortable sending him home at this point. Mr. Smith has hinted at mild substernal pain. Should Dr. Green send the patient home? Or to a psychiatrist? Or keep him for further observation?

• A psychiatrist is asked to consult with a man who suffered a head injury a year ago in an industrial accident when a machine he was fixing fell on his head. His neurologist says there is nothing wrong with him physically, but he complains of headaches, says he feels humiliated, and has become depressed. The psychiatrist agrees to treat him for his depression, but Workman's Compensation says it will pay only for physical treatment. The patient's insurance company will not pay because his complaints resulted from an industrial accident. Should the psychiatrist offer him short-term treatment, rather than long-term therapy, which he feels might be more beneficial?

In each of these cases cost is factored into medical decision making in a way that potentially complicates the care the physician renders. In situations like these the physician has the opportunity to serve the common good of reducing health care costs by limiting the care an individual patient receives. Physicians are logical agents of rationing because they appear to have direct control over health care dollars.

ECONOMIC AND
SOCIAL DISTORTIONS

However, even at the bedside the options are limited by social and economic policies already in place, which can lead to ethically inconsistent decisions. For example, organ transplants and artificial organ implants, still relatively few in number, may be funded by research rather than insurance programs, or (as has often been the case with liver transplants) by community fund raising programs or public appeals. Renal dialysis, on the other hand, is generally available to all who may need it under Medicare/Medicaid funding in part because the issue of federal funding was politicized in the 1960s and there seemed to be no humane way of saying "no." The young child might get her liver transplant only if her parents know how to manage the system while Mr. White might receive renal dialysis because it would be difficult to deny it to him under the law although the benefit would be limited and temporary. Similarly, the neurosurgeon would probably render emergency care to the injured motorcyclist, but before long the town's ambulance drivers would start sorting out which hospitals will provide emergency care to their uninsured patients. In the case of Mr. Smith, although doctors have some discretion under Diagnosis Related Groups, that system provides direct incentive to limit costs to particular patients.

If physicians have limited choices at the bedside, they still wield considerable influence. In our haste to make sure health costs don't outstrip our ability to pay them, have we gone too far? Should the physician be society's agent in reducing health costs? Should rationing decisions be made by doctors at the bedside?

My answer is an emphatic "No." The physician's primary responsibility is to the patient. Since Hippocratic times a central tenet of the medical ethic has been the responsibility of the physician for the patient in a relationship of trust. To ask conscientious physicians to bear the responsibility for lowering the cost of medical care is to create a conflict of interest that threatens to alter the nature of the doctor-patient relationship and the nature of the medical profession itself.

DOCTORS AS "PROVIDERS"

Whereas doctors were once accountable solely to their patients in a private, confidential relationship, they are now often spoken of as "providers," and patients as "consumers" of a commodity, in which third-party payers may have a legitimate interest. There are increasing pressures for doctors to answer not only to the patient but also to "society" as payer for costs incurred.

The cost-consciousness movement of the past decade has rightly encouraged physicians to eliminate waste and redundancy in the expectation that costs can be brought into line without compromising the quality of care each patient receives. The possibility of rationing only becomes alarming when the possibility of compromising quality is introduced—either through limiting services (by focusing on populations rather than individuals, as HMOs and DRGs do) or by introducing new technologies that may not be available to all (such as organ transplants or artificial organs).

Unlike cost, quality allows no precise calculation. Competing values are at stake, which can only be resolved in particular cases by reference to ethical principles. Those principles may be subjected to explicit analysis or they may be left implicit.

THE UNACKNOWLEDGED TRAGIC CHOICE

Clearly, when the choices are agonizing, there are compelling psychological reasons for not reflecting explicitly on the underlying conflicts. In a book of the same name, Guido Calabresi and Philip P. Bobbitt speak of the decisions we now face as "tragic choices." They are tragic because, in Hegel's definition of tragedy, there is no clear-cut distinction between good and evil, but rather a conflict between competing goods or values.

In this case egalitarian ideals are ultimately incompatible with any belief in a capitalist sense of freedom. If the technology for replacing body parts exists, do we make this available to everyone? If we cannot afford to, do we deny it to those who can afford to purchase it on their own? If we decide to allocate health care on the basis of wealth, can we tolerate the social inequities that allow some to live while others similarly affected must die?

It is in the nature of tragic choices, Calabresi and Bobbitt point out, that a society tries to escape them or disguise what it is doing. Is the transformation of health care from a human service into a commodity an attempt to make the tragic choices more bearable? If so, we should seek to rescue ourselves from this slippery slope by explicitly reflecting on the ethical conflicts involved.

One way of attempting to escape tragic choices is to delegate to doctors the task of rationing health care at the bedside. This assumes a passive role for the patient, which is hardly acceptable in the 1980s. Another evasion is to attempt a strictly market approach to health care: people get what they choose. This is equally unacceptable because not all people have the foresight or the economic opportunity to protect themselves against potential medical catastrophes.

INVOLVING THE PATIENT

Ultimately there is no way of escaping the ethical dimensions of our tragic choices. A whole spectrum of decisions must be made daily not only by physicians, patients, and families at the bedside, but by all of us as we "choose" a lifestyle that promotes or does not promote a healthy existence: Do we smoke? Get adequate exercise? Attend to health risk factors? Choose a suitable kind of health insurance and health care? At another level our political choices reflect the kind of health care we expect and will receive.

The issue of cost is now an inescapable part of medical practice. As we look for a locus of decision-making where this issue can be dealt with—physician or patient/consumer or the marketplace or the political process—we should not overlook one traditionally very important location of medical decision-making, the doctor-patient relationship. Traditionally it has been the better part of discretion for the physician and patient not to discuss money

matters, but such discussions may now be appropriate.

In each of my examples, the issue of cost is primarily the patient's concern, not the physician's. However (except for the comatose motorcyclist patient) in each instance the physician may offer some counsel to the patient in what should be a joint decision-making process. For example, Dr. Green might involve Mr. Smith in an ongoing discussion about how his particular health care needs might best be met. Dr. Brown might find out whether Mr. White wants to undergo dialysis, with all its potential discomforts, and proceed accordingly. In the transplant case, the doctor could discuss with the parents whether some local funding organization might underwrite the cost of their child's transplant. Such discussions, carried out over time and in a humane and unpressured manner, are not only good economics; they are the essence of good medicine.

POSTSCRIPT

SHOULD DOCTORS CUT COSTS
AT THE BEDSIDE?

Industry, the primary payer of health care insurance in the United States, is trying to lower medical costs through a number of mechanisms: shifting some of the costs to employees, reducing hospital utilization by requiring second opinions and by limiting length of stay, and by limiting choice of provider. These cost-containment measures reduce the physician's discretion in recommending treatment, but they may also reduce unnecessary surgery and other forms of treatment. In June 1985, the US Supreme Court upheld a Massachusetts statute requiring that certain health care benefits be provided to residents who are insured under employee health care plans. At present, the level of benefits that must be provided varies from state to state.

Joseph A. Califano, Jr., a former secretary of Health, Education and Welfare (now Health and Human Services) advocates in *America's Health Care Revolution: Who Lives? Who Dies? Who Pays?* (New York: Random House, 1986) a sweeping program of change: altering American health habits, reducing by half the number of hospital beds, and curbing excessive fees and profits.

Norman G. Levinsky, "The Rationing of Medical Care," *New England Journal of Medicine* (Dec. 13, 1984) defends the thesis that "the doctor's master must be the patient." Norman Daniels, in "Why Saying No to Patients in the United States Is So Hard" (*New England Journal of Medicine,* May 22, 1986), compares rationing in the United States with the British system and finds that the absence of a rationale of social justice in the United States intensifies conflict and leads to erratic decision making.

For a comprehensive discussion of for-profit medicine, see Bradford H. Gray, editor, *For-Profit Enterprise in Health Care* (Institute of Medicine: Washington, D.C., 1986), especially "An Exchange on For-Profit Health Care," by Arnold S. Relman and Uwe Reinhardt, pp. 209-23.

ISSUE 19

SHOULD INSURANCE COMPANIES BE ALLOWED TO SCREEN FOR ANTIBODIES TO THE AIDS VIRUS?

YES: American Council of Life Insurance and the Health Insurance Association of America, from "White Paper: The Acquired Immonodeficiency Syndrome and HTLV-III Antibody Testing," Washington, D.C., February 1986

NO: Mark Scherzer, "The Public Interest in Maintaining Insurance Coverage for AIDS," from *Yale AIDS/Law Sourcebook* (Yale University Press, 1986)

ISSUE SUMMARY

YES: The health and life insurance industries believe that their obligation to use sound underwriting practices that assure fair premiums for all policyholders requires the use of screening tests for antibodies to HTLV-III, the virus that causes AIDS, in order to determine risk for the disease.
NO: Attorney Mark Scherzer argues that maintaining insurance coverage for AIDS serves important social goals and that the insurance industry has exaggerated its potential losses.

Throughout history epidemics of infectious diseases have created social and political havoc. The discovery of antibiotics and the development of vaccines in the 1940s led to a sense of security that infectious diseases were no longer a major threat. In 1981 that sense of security turned out to be false. In Los Angeles, then in New York and San Francisco, physicians reported to the Centers for Disease Control (CDC), the federal agency concerned with monitoring health problems in this country, a mysterious series of rare infections and cancer in previously healthy homosexual young men. As the cases increased, the name of Acquired Immonodeficiency Syndrome—AIDS—was given to this disease. Only a few years later it has become one of the most feared, most misunderstood, and most complex diseases to confront our society.

In addition to gay and bisexual men, groups at high risk for the disease are intravenous drug users, the sexual partners (men and women) of infected people, children born to infected mothers, and recent immigrants from

314

areas in the world (primarily Haiti and Central Africa) where AIDS cases have not been associated with known risk factors. These groups are already at risk for social and economic discrimination; AIDS has heightened their concern about being stigmatized and deprived of their civil rights and equal opportunities.

AIDS is caused by a retrovirus—variously called HTLV-III (human T cell lymphotropic virus Type III), LAV (lymphadenopathy-associated virus), or HIV (human immonodeficiency virus). The presence of the virus appears to be necessary for infection to occur, but other, unknown factors may determine which infected people develop symptoms of illness and which remain healthy. AIDS is the extreme, and ultimately fatal, end of a spectrum of infection, which includes many more cases of AIDS-related complex (ARC) or minor illnesses. AIDS cannot be transmitted by casual contact—that is, the kinds of contacts people ordinarily have in the workplace, public places, or at home. It can only be transmitted through intimate sexual contact and through blood, either through the sharing of contaminated needles and syringes in drug use or through contaminated blood transfusions. The development of tests to screen blood donations for antibodies to the virus—evidence that the person has been infected—has greatly reduced the risk of transmission through blood transfusions.

While no one objects to the use of the tests for screening blood, other possible uses have been controversial. For example, the military now screens all recruits and will refuse to accept anyone who has a positive test result. The Department of Defense justifies its policy on the grounds that all soldiers must be "walking blood banks"; a person who has been infected with HIV cannot safely donate blood. Critics say, however, that the military wants to eliminate homosexuals and drug users and to avoid the high health care costs associated with AIDS.

The use of screening tests by insurers poses another such dilemma. In the US, unlike nearly all industrialized democracies, there is no program of national health insurance or a national health service. Only the elderly and disabled (under Medicare) and the very poor (under Medicaid) have government-sponsored insurance; even these programs have been severely cut back in recent years. Most people obtain health insurance at their place of employment through private companies. These companies set premiums based on their assessment of risk. As the White Paper from the insurance industry explains in the following selection, they want to screen for antibodies to the AIDS virus as part of their underwriting process to assure fair premiums for all policyholders. Mark Scherzer asserts, however, that insurance is a regulated industry that serves important social ends. Decisions about the use of the antibody tests should consider more than actuarial figures.

YES

The American Council of Life Insurance

THE ACQUIRED IMMUNODEFICIENCY SYNDROME & HTLV-III ANTIBODY TESTING

AIDS (acquired immunodeficiency syndrome) poses major problems for insurers and policyholders, as well as for the whole of society. If recent trends in the spread of this national health threat continue, the insurance industry could be faced with billions of dollars in AIDS-related medical, disability and death claims in the next few years.

In addition, the ability of companies to determine an applicant's insurability is under legislative challenge; a number of states seek to restrict the AIDS-related medical information available to an insurer. If life and health insurance companies are prevented from using medical information that would enable them to identify applicants who are at high risk of contracting AIDS, low-risk policyholders will have to pay higher premiums to compensate for the inadequate premiums received from high-risk policyholders.

Insurance companies have an obligation to use sound underwriting practices that assure fair premiums for all policyholders. This paper will examine the AIDS problem in detail, including the role of insurance underwriting, testing as part of the underwriting process, types of tests and who uses them, and confidentiality. Through such an overview of the issue, both the American Council of Life Insurance and the Health Insurance Association of America hope to provide member companies with a basic understanding of this important issue.

THE SYNDROME

AIDS is caused by what is called HTLV-III—the AIDS virus—which attacks and severely damages the victim's immune system, allowing normally harmless organisms—various protozoa, bacteria, viruses and fungi—to cause pneumonia, cancer, meningitis and other life-threatening illnesses. These so-called opportunistic infections characterize AIDS, and serve as the principal means by which it is diagnosed. The time from infection to development of clinical

From, "White Paper: The Acquired Immunodeficiency Syndrome and HTLV-III Antibody Testing," by the American Council of Life Insurance and the Health Insurance Association of America, Washington, DC, February 1986. Reprinted by permission.

signs or symptoms of the condition can range from months to several years.(1) During this incubation period, people seemingly remain healthy.

The most common means of transmitting AIDS is intimate sexual contact. Any sexual partner of someone who is infected may become infected by the virus and may subsequently develop AIDS. Sexual encounters with multiple partners greatly increase the risk of becoming infected (3, 1), both for heterosexuals and homosexuals.(4) Approximately 73 percent of all AIDS patients in the U.S. are homosexual or bisexual men.(3) AIDS tends to be highly prevalent in metropolitan areas that have large gay communities.(4) About half of all AIDS cases have been reported in New York City and San Francisco.

Intravenous (IV) drug users are also at high risk of contracting AIDS, and constitute about 17 percent of all AIDS patients in the United States.(3) The virus is transmitted from one person to another by the use of contaminated needles. Seventy percent of IV drug users who contract AIDS are male (4); more than 94 percent of all AIDS patients in the U.S. are male.(5)

Hemophiliacs who required repeated infusions of clotting factor concentrates from 1980 to 1984 to control bleeding episodes are another group at high risk of having been infected.(6) Heat treating of these products since 1984 has reduced the risk of such transmission. AIDS antibody testing now being done by blood banks should virtually eliminate risk arising from future infusions of blood products. Nonetheless, in several studies, the majority of hemophilia A patients who received factor concentrates between 1980 and 1984 were found to have antibodies to the AIDS virus.(3) Many may contract AIDS in the future.

Others at high risk include newborns of infected mothers. In addition, those who received multiple blood transfusions in the last five years are at a slightly increased risk, owing to blood contaminated with the AIDS virus. Of the millions of people who have received blood transfusions, however, only about 300 cases of transfusion-associated AIDS have occurred.(3) Screening that now is being done by blood banks should virtually eliminate this risk in the future.

At present, there is no vaccine or cure for AIDS (7); there is no tested and proven antiviral drug (8) or other form of therapy. Those who develop the full syndrome face certain death, usually within 12 to 24 months. The median age at death is 35.(9)

According to the Centers for Disease Control (CDC), over 17,500 AIDS cases have been reported since 1981, half of which have resulted in death. In addition, the CDC has estimated that from 500,000 to 1,000,000 people in this country have been infected with the AIDS virus.(3) In January 1986, the CDC predicted there would be between 14,000 and 15,000 new cases this year. Although the annual rate of increase is slowing, the CDC still projects a doubling in the number of AIDS cases between fall 1986 and early 1988. Because the virus has a long incubation period, the rising curve of actual AIDS cases lags behind the rising curve of AIDS virus infection by about three years.

Studies cited by the CDC have shown that from 5 to 19 percent (10) of those in high-risk groups who tested positive on an ELISA test have developed AIDS within two to five years. In addition to the 5 to 19 percent of infected individuals who develop AIDS within two to five years, 25 percent (10) develop AIDS-related complex (ARC), which progresses to AIDS in some people. According to recent press ac-

317

counts, however, a number of researchers reportedly think that the percentage of infected individuals who will go on to develop AIDS is much greater than the range cited by the CDC.(11)

INSURANCE ASPECTS

Hospital expenses per AIDS patient have averaged $147,000, according to the CDC. In addition, ARC is likely to give rise to substantial medical expenses. Moreover, AIDS-related death-claims—given an average life insurance policy size of $46,360 in 1984—could total more than $5 billion within the next five years.

Existing life and health insurance contracts that provide coverage for loss of life, loss of income through disability, or medical expenses cover AIDS in the same manner as other illnesses, and will remain in full force (subject to the usual terms of such contracts). In addition, currently offered new contracts or additions to existing contracts that do not require individual evidence of insurability as a condition of coverage will routinely cover present or future AIDS victims.

For new individual coverage, however, and for some types of group coverage—groups of fewer than 10 people, late entrants—evidence of insurability is required. The need for such evidence of insurability, the right of an insurance company to require such evidence and the public interest in requiring such evidence are well-documented. The most fundamental principle of insurance—charging the same premium rate for individuals whose expected risk of loss is the same—requires that insurers and applicants have equal access to any knowledge that has a significant bearing on the assignment of an individual to an appropriate class of risk.

One tool that is useful in helping to determine the risk that a person poses is the AIDS antibody test. The test and its place in the underwriting process are discussed in the following sections.

The ELISA Test

Individuals who have been exposed to HTLV-III develop antibodies to the virus. An inexpensive test to detect the presence of such antibodies is the "ELISA" or "EIA."

Successive positive tests on a blood sample indicate that the person has probably been infected by HTLV-III.(10) If the person is still carrying the live virus, he or she may be capable of transmitting it to others.(11)

All blood banks and plasma centers initiated use of the ELISA test by April 1985. Such testing is expected to virtually eliminate future contamination problems and to restore public confidence in the nation's blood supply.

The ELISA test is but one in a series of tests used by insurers. It is very sensitive to the presence of HTLV-III antibodies, and thus will sometimes produce false positive results. By repeating the ELISA test, as is the practice, these false positives are largely eliminated. If both ELISA tests are positive, a positive result on a different type of test, the Western blot, gives a high degree of assurance that the positive is a true positive.(12) This testing protocol is based on procedures recommended by the American Red Cross in determining whether to notify a blood donor of a positive test result.

Recently, the CDC revised its case definition of AIDS, adding certain diseases that, if associated with a positive ELISA test, will now be acknowledged as being evidence of AIDS. Therefore, as the AIDS epidemic spreads, the ELISA test will be used increasingly by attending physicians to establish a probable cause for a patient's otherwise unexplained signs or symptoms.

At present, the ELISA test is better than most other blood tests that are used in clinical medicine. In light of the biological research currently being done, it will no doubt become still more reliable. Also possible is the development of better, independent confirmatory tests (13), and the Food and Drug Administration is presently evaluating a means of directly testing for the HTLV-III virus itself, rather than the antibody.

The Underwriting Process

In evaluating the AIDS risk, insurance underwriters use a similar approach to that used with other chronic health conditions. Coronary heart disease (CHD), for example, progresses in stages. It typically begins with those at high risk of developing the disease, such as cigarette smokers, hypertensives and obese individuals. All of these people pay higher premiums for their insurance, because of the higher risk they represent.

The next phase in the CHD progression involves signs that suggest the development of underlying heart disease. In this phase, the individual may experience anginal chest pains, and an insurer may require an electrocardiogram to identify abnormalities. Applicants judged to be in this phase of CHD are classified in an even higher risk group and are charged a significantly higher premium or, perhaps, declined for coverage.

As a group, people tend to progress from one stage of CHD to the next rather predictably. Although the progression of the illness varies for individuals, fairly accurate projections can be made for groups of individuals who have similar characteristics.

This, too, is the case with AIDS. Those who become infected with the AIDS virus manifest certain signs of infection. First, such people will develop antibodies to HTLV-III, and a test series will almost certainly be positive. Later, they may develop a certain type of lymph node enlargement, as well as other symptoms, including weight loss, night sweats, persistent fever, malaise and shortness of breath.

A mouth infection (oral thrush) may develop, suggesting that the individual's underlying immune system has been damaged. The number of cells that alert the body's immune system when invading organisms are present, so-called "T-helper cells," may decline, indicating further breakdown of the immune system. At this stage, patients are diagnosed as having AIDS-related complex, which may represent an advanced stage in the progression of the syndrome. Finally, the AIDS virus attacks and disables the body's immune system, leaving the patient vulnerable to the development of "opportunistic" infections—those that a healthy immune system would have been able to fight off. The patient then is diagnosed as having AIDS by the CDC case definition. Death usually occurs within one to two years.

The underwriting process recognizes that each phase of the natural progression of any chronic disease presents some inherent level of risk, and this risk increases as the disease advances. With AIDS, those who have been treated more than once for sexually transmitted disease, IV drug users and hemophiliacs are at increased risk of being infected by HTLV-III. Such individuals would be considered to present a still higher risk if they tested positive for antibodies to the AIDS virus. AIDS-related symptoms (e.g., unexplained weight loss) are a further indication that the syndrome has reached an advanced stage.

Insurance companies are generally not

faced with determining whether someone has full-scale AIDS. Because several years can elapse between the time an individual is infected with the AIDS virus and the time he or she manifests symptoms, the main underwriting challenge facing insurers is identifying people in earlier stages of the syndrome. At these stages, people are likely to want to buy insurance, when they already represent very high risks.

To accurately assess the level of risk posed by an applicant, an underwriter might ask AIDS-related questions, as well as request a physical examination and look for indications of treatment for sexually transmitted disease. In addition, the underwriter might look at unexplained signs and symptoms that suggest impaired immunity and might confirm that the insurance applied for is appropriate to the applicant's financial status. These kinds of steps have been elements of sound underwriting practices for many years.

In the case of AIDS, the underwriter might use an additional tool for determining insurability—AIDS antibody tests. The ELISA and Western blot tests permit reliable identification of applicants infected with the AIDS virus and, conversely, those *not* infected.

A growing number of states, however, seek to restrict an insurers' ability to underwrite for AIDS by denying companies the right to order and use AIDS antibody test results. Laws restricting such tests restrict an insurer's ability to treat *all* applicants and policyholders fairly. They also mark an unprecedented departure from insurers' traditional ability to underwrite with access to all pertinent medical information.

BLOOD BANKS
AND CONFIDENTIALITY

In addition to the AIDS antibody testing of people donating blood or plasma, individuals are being tested at alternate testing sites on an anonymous basis. AIDS antibody tests are now available through private physicians and most state and local health departments. Some of the people who test positive will be told that they are carrying the virus. Armed with that knowledge, they may apply for life and health insurance. There is evidence that high-risk people are often told to be sure they have adequate health insurance coverage.(14)

The insurance industry is not suggesting that blood banks, plasma centers or public testing facilities should be asked to divulge the results of the tests that they administer. If the centers do not treat such tests with appropriate confidentiality, people could be discouraged from donating blood or getting tested. Clearly, an adequate blood supply is vitally important to all citizens. Insurance companies will not seek to obtain from blood banks, plasma centers or alternative test sites the results of tests administered by them. However, they do need to be able to order their own AIDS-related blood tests.

The insurance industry has a long history of dealing with highly sensitive medical information such as chemical dependency, alcoholism or syphilis. If an insurer learns that an applicant has AIDS, the information is regarded as highly sensitive and confidential and is treated in strict accordance with both good common sense and legal safeguards. Antibody test results also are regarded as sensitive information that is protected in an equally secure fashion.

REFERENCES

1. "Annual AIDS cases could reach 30,000. Foresees 30,000 AIDS cases annually within next 10 years." *Family Prac. News,* July 1985.

2. "Frequent Transmission of HTLV-III Among Spouses of Patients with AIDS-Related Complex and AIDS," *Journal of the American Medical Association* (JAMA), March 15, 1985.

3. "Update: Acquired Immunodeficiency Syndrome—Limited States," *Morbidity and Mortality Weekly Report,* Centers for Disease Control. Vol. 35, No. 2, Jan. 17, 1986.

4. "The Incidence Rate of Acquired Immunodeficiency Syndrome in Selected Populations," Ann M. Hardy, DrPH, JAMA, Jan. 11, 1985, Vol. 253, No. 2, pp. 215-220.

5. World Health Organization Workshop: "Conclusions and Recommendations on Acquired Immunodeficiency Syndrome," "Leads from the MMWR," JAMA, June 21, 1985, Vol. 253, No. 23, pp. 3385-3391.

6. "Development and Early Natural History of HTLV-III Antibodies in Persons with Hemophilia," M. Elaine Eyster, M.D., JAMA, April 19, 1985, Vol. 253, No. 15, pp. 2219-2223.

7. "AIDS: The Emerging Ethical Dilemmas—Introduction," Arnold S. Relman. M.D., *Hastings Center Report,* A Special Supplement, August 1985, Vol. 15, No. 4.

8. "6 drugs have shown some success against HTLV-III," *Family Prac. News,* July 1985.

9. "CDC official calls for AIDS prevention plan," *American Medical News,* April 12, 1985.

10. "Important AIDS Information," Department of Health and Human Services, Food and Drug Administration (HFW-40).

11. "AIDS Potential Seen Worsening," *The Washington Post,* Jan. 10, 1986; 'AIDS in the Future: Experts Say Deaths Will Climb Sharply," *The New York Times,* Jan. 14, 1986.

12. "The Acquired Immunodeficiency Syndrome: An Update," Anthony S. Fauci, M.D., *Annals of Internal Medicine,* 1985, 102:800-813.

13. Results cited at July 31, 1985 NIH meeting in Bethesda, Maryland.

14. AIDS Antibody Testing at Alternative Test Sites—A program of the San Francisco Department of Public Health.

NO

Mark Scherzer

THE PUBLIC INTEREST
IN MAINTAINING INSURANCE
COVERAGE FOR AIDS

The AIDS epidemic has led to a broad politicization of business decisions made by life, health and disability insurers. There is a long history of government intervention in and regulation of the insurance business when public policy has been perceived to be in conflict with underwriting decisions made by insurance companies based on strict actuarial principles, or when industry business practices have appeared to present a threat to the public. But AIDS has produced a public debate focusing not just on underwriting but simultaneously on the insurance companies' fulfillment of their contractual obligations, on their obligations as holders and transmitters of information, on their rights to affect the course of medical diagnosis or treatment, and on their role in fostering or impeding social change. . . .

HOW INSURANCE OPERATES

. . . In discussing AIDS and insurance, the goals of the insurance companies to assume the least possible risk with the largest possible number of policyholders, and of the polity to give the broadest numbers of people the broadest insurance coverage possible, must always be kept in mind. The debate in its various forms is really a fight over how much risk the insurance companies will be required to assume. . . .

HOW INSURANCE COMPANIES ARE REGULATED

. . . There is no doubt that decisions regarding AIDS and insurance will be politically highly charged. AIDS primarily affects minorities (gay men, intravenous drug users) which are disfavored politically as the result of social, moral and religious bias. Equally important, the questions regarding insurance all relate to allocation of the cost of an expensive disease among different interests with varying degrees of power. How will insurance companies, individuals, state and local governments and providers of health care and other services divide the financial burden of dealing with AIDS?

Regulators will be called upon to deal with two types of risk minimalization by insurance companies. Those companies which issue insurance policies on the basis of characteristics of individual applicants will try to eliminate high-risk individuals from their roster of insureds. Those companies which issue policies to groups, in which individual characteristics are not made the subject of underwriting inquiry, will try to eliminate AIDS from among the risks covered. A variety of strategies may be employed, each of which calls for a different response.

MAY INSURERS REFUSE TO INSURE PEOPLE WITH AIDS?

People who have been diagnosed as having AIDS have, on average, a very short life expectancy—less than three years. They have also a high likelihood of incurring significant medical costs. The costs incurred vary widely geographically, but even in San Francisco, the region widely thought to have a model AIDS treatment program with a concentration on less expensive, out-of-hospital care, the average person with AIDS will incur $28,000.00 in medical care costs during the course of his or her illness.

An insurance company willing to offer life or health insurance to such a person would be unusual indeed. State regulators have generally recognized that requiring insurance companies to assume such risks could affect the companies' willingness to do business in their jurisdiction. Accordingly, they have almost uniformly permitted insurance companies to ask applicants for such insurance whether they have been told by their doctors that they have AIDS.

Regulation in this context generally takes the form of restricting the manner in which the questions may be asked. In New Jersey the state regulators have issued a bulletin providing guidelines to the insurance companies when formulating the application forms which the state must approve. Companies may ask whether applicants for insurance have been told by their doctors that they have AIDS, but may not ask whether applicants have had "any indication" that they have AIDS. The latter is deemed to be a subjective, and therefore unfair, question. In Maryland, on the other hand, insurance companies have been given somewhat greater latitude in asking subjective questions about exposure to AIDS of the applicant or the applicant's family. In no jurisdiction, however, are insurers required to offer individually underwritten insurance policies to people with AIDS.

MAY INSURERS REFUSE TO INSURE THOSE CARRYING ANTIBODIES TO THE HTLV-III VIRUS?

Although the HTLV-III virus has not been conclusively proved to cause AIDS, there is a wide consensus that it is a cause. Some of those who do not believe it is the cause of AIDS do believe that it may be at least a "marker" for AIDS. At the very least, most would agree with the scientist who concluded that it is not an "innocent passenger" through the body.

While chemical tests to determine the presence of the virus in the bloodstream are available, the strategy of insurance companies intent on reducing the risks of insuring those likely to develop AIDS has focused on use of different tests, which detect antibodies to the virus. These tests, initially designed to screen blood donated to blood banks, are far cheaper to perform than culturing of the virus would be, and they detect with varying degrees of accuracy whether exposure to the virus has led the subject to produce reactive chemicals in the bloodstream. The justification for use of the antibody test is actuarial—based on risk classifications derived from a number of longitudinal studies which suggest that a significant proportion of those who become "seropositive" will develop AIDS or ARC within a few years thereafter. The insurance industry claims that even less than perfectly accurate tests will produce a substantial benefit by screening out of those most likely to develop AIDS, at a minimal cost, and will thereby protect the economic soundness of the insurance system.

Risk classification is the process of grouping risks with similar characteristics together for the purpose of setting prices for insurance. Males in various age bands, for example, constitute different risk groups for insurance purposes. By law in many jurisdictions, insurance companies cannot subsidize one risk group with the profits made from another risk group. Each risk group must bear the costs of its benefits from the premiums it pays.

The American Academy of Actuaries has articulated the underlying rationale for risk classification as one of (1) maintaining the viability of the insurance system by protecting the system's financial soundness, (2) charging a fair price for the risk involved, and (3) encouraging widespread availability of coverage by permitting "economic incentives" to operate. One assumption underlying the risk classification system is that if an insurance company experiences unusually high claims because it has not properly screened out risks, it will have to raise its prices to cover the cost of benefits paid on those risks. Consumers who can do so (the lower-risk consumers) will move their business to a different insurer which charges lower premiums, thus leading to a spiral of "adverse selection." Those with HTLV-III antibodies, the Academy argues, are such extraordinary mortality risks that, if not screened out, they threaten precisely this result. The insurance company which should by normal statistical expectation pay 6 death claims in a five-year period for every 1,000 35-year-old males insured, would, if it insured 1,000 35-year-old seropositive males, instead have to pay up to 176 claims. The increased costs, passed on to the remaining policyholders, would, it argues, lead to a spiral of adverse selection.

The assumptions underlying the industry's argument, based though they are on principles of fairness, require further examination. Even if it is correct that the insurance market is fluid enough and open enough to permit large scale movement of consumers among insurance companies in response to price, it is not necessarily correct that the occasion will arise for consumers to make that shift. Suppose no insurers could determine who had the antibodies. Presumably every insurer would experience increases in health, disability and death claims related to AIDS, and the increased costs resulting from such claims would have to be collected from policyholders. If all insurers were legally prohibited from obtaining such information, no company would be at a competitive advantage, and the adverse selection spiral could not begin. The risk would be spread randomly.

Further, the figures on which the Academy relies in order to demonstrate the uninsurability of seropositive applicants are pessimistic and potentially skewed. It relies on a series of three-year cohort studies to assume that 8 percent to 34 percent of seropositive people will develop AIDS in a five-year period, and that the probable AIDS death rate among 35-year-olds would be in excess of 500 percent of normal death rates. It ignores other studies which show conversion from seropositivity to AIDS at a rate closer to 1 percent per year. It does not take into account that the cohorts were drawn from clinics treating sexually transmitted diseases, hence focusing on populations which may be at disproportionate risk for AIDS. (Sexually transmitted diseases may be significant "co-factors" in determining which seropositive people will develop AIDS). The Academy appears to support the insurance industry position that all seropositive applicants should be declined for insurance even if they are not 35-year-old men. Even under the assumptions made by the Academy, 50-year-old seropositive men may be insurable, yet it is doubtful that *any* seropositive people will be offered insurance in the current environment.

Finally, recent research suggests that some seropositive people may have antibodies which are effective at dealing with the HTLV-III virus. Although the chemical differences between these antibodies and the ineffective antibodies in people with AIDS has not been determined, some seropositive people may be *less* at risk than seronegative people who have yet to be exposed. They will be denied insurance anyway. The Academy broadly assumes that seropositivity itself is the risk factor.

None of these criticisms are intended to show that seropositivity may not be validly considered a risk by the insurance industry. They are offered, rather, to show that the cost of prohibiting use of the antibody test and consideration of the risk may well have been exaggerated. Prohibiting use of the antibody test would be unlikely to put

any insurers at severe competitive disadvantage or risk of insolvency. While it may well result in some increase in the cost of insurance to men in the age groups from which most AIDS cases are drawn, and may thereby drive some people out of the insurance market, the countervailing public benefits of prohibiting the use of the test must be considered.

Decisions to override actuarial differences and to mandate insurance for those at greater risk are, of course, not unprecedented. Numerous jurisdictions prohibit race and national origin discrimination in insurance. Some prohibit denial of insurance to people exposed to the carcinogenic drug, DES. Others prohibit denial of insurance to people carrying sickle cell anemia traits. Important social ends may be served by such intervention in the underwriting process.

With respect to the HTLV-III antibody tests, there is the obvious social utility of the same sort as results from prohibiting race discrimination, in keeping insurance available to a minority group—in this case gay men—who would be disproportionately affected by the use of the test. If, as a group, gay men cannot obtain mortgage life insurance, or key person business insurance, they may become excluded from significant areas of public and private endeavor, and the minority's insurance disabilities may become social disabilities and sources of social friction.

There is further social utility in providing the maximum possible health care benefits. Health insurance allows for a higher quality of health care. Aside from the moral imperative of assuring decent health care without impoverishing people, there is the social benefit of limiting economic loss from lost work time. The cost of lost productivity associated with AIDS has been estimated to be $4.1 billion to date. Limiting that loss, and limiting the other costs to society of other diseases which might affect gay men, should be an important goal.

Moreover, if the polity wishes to encourage people to take the antibody test for public health or epidemiological purposes, it must remove disincentives, such as potential deprivation of insurance, which may inhibit people from taking the test. Again, important social goals would be served by assuring those taking the test that they would not suffer potential uninsurability as a result. . . .

CONCLUSION

The AIDS epidemic has led to a broad debate about the role of private insurance in the nation's health care and welfare systems. It has highlighted many potential problems in the operation of our insurance industry, from the industry's role in gathering and exchanging information to its direct intervention in the provision of health care. Even as its role in providing health insurance has diminished (because of the shift to employer self-insurance) it has shown its pervasive influence in focusing the debate over AIDS on the screening methods it wishes to use. It has even been implicated in the delays of development of treatments for AIDS, since the unavailability of liability insurance for drug and vaccine trials has been cited as one major factor in the small number of experimental programs available.

The debate must continuously be shifted from the vantage point of the insurance companies to that of the public. The industry's desire to assess risk through tests and other means must continuously be balanced against the public interest in maximizing insurance coverage at the least social cost. The legitimate concerns of the industry can be met, but should only be met while securing people at risk for AIDS from the additional risk of being without insurance to deal with the disease.

POSTSCRIPT

SHOULD INSURANCE COMPANIES BE ALLOWED TO SCREEN FOR ANTIBODIES TO THE AIDS VIRUS?

Several states are considering whether to ban or to allow insurance companies to screen for antibodies to HIV. California, Florida, Maine, Wisconsin, and the District of Columbia have limited the use of the blood test to determine an individual's eligibility for insurance. New Mexico, however, allows insurance companies to test and exclude AIDS coverage if a person develops AIDS six months prior to or after the policy is issued. In the District of Columbia, at least three insurance companies decided to stop writing policies after a city council passed an ordinance stating that insurers cannot deny coverage to applicants who test positive.

One alternative is a special insurance pool available to AIDS or other high-risk patients: eight states (Minnesota, Indiana, Wisconsin, Florida, North Dakota, Montana, Nebraska, and Connecticut) now have such pools, and many other states are considering them. Given the high costs of premiums, federal support may be necessary to make this idea workable.

See Gerald Oppenheimer and Robert Padgug, "AIDS: The Risk to Insurers, the Threat to Equity," *Hastings Center Report*, October 1986, for an analysis of the crisis. For an ethical framework to evaluate a wide range of uses of the screening tests, see Ronald Bayer, Carol Levine, and Susan Wolf, "HIV Antibody Screening: An Ethical Framework to Evaluate Proposed Programs," *Journal of the American Medical Association* (in press). The National Institute of Medicine's *Mobilizing Against AIDS: The Unfinished Story of a Virus* (Harvard University Press, 1986) is a good account of the scientific and policy aspects of the disease.

ISSUE 20

IS GENETIC ENGINEERING A THREAT TO FUTURE GENERATIONS?

YES: Hans Jonas, from "Ethics and Biogenetic Art," *Social Research,* Vol. 52, No. 3, 1985

NO: President's Commission for the Study of Ethical Problems in Medicine and Biomedical and Behavioral Research, from *Splicing Life: The Social and Ethical Issues of Genetic Engineering with Human Beings* (Washington, D.C.: Government Printing Office, 1982)

ISSUE SUMMARY

YES: Philosopher Hans Jonas believes that expanding the uses of genetic engineering from bacteria to humans would open a Pandora's box of evils. We should not tamper with the inviolability of the human image.
NO: The President's Commission concludes that genetic engineering is not intrinsically wrong for human use and sees no fundamental danger to world safety or human values in any current or planned forms of the technology.

In 1953, James Watson and Francis Crick made one of the major scientific discoveries of our time: The structure of deoxyribonucleic acid (DNA), the basic building block of all living things, is a double helix. In a masterpiece of understatement, they wrote in a letter to *Nature:* "It has not escaped our notice that the specific pairing we have postulated suggests a possible copying mechanism for the genetic material." What they recognized, and what has become a reality in the past decade, is that pieces of DNA can be broken and relinked in different combinations (the technique of recombinant DNA or "gene splicing"). A new life form can be created by inserting the DNA of one species into the DNA of another. The new molecule then forms a genetic replica of itself and continues to reproduce. This process occurs in nature but now scientists can direct it to achieve particular goals.

Much of the potential application of genetic engineering lies in industry and agriculture—the creation of bacteria that will consume oil spills at sea, for example, or bacteria that will fix nitrogen and thereby increase crop harvests. The possibilities in the medical field are enormous as well: Products that are now scarce and expensive—such as hormones, enzymes, and vaccines—can be produced in large quantities. Cancer diagnosis and treatment can be improved by the use of targeted monoclonal antibodies, which will attack only the malignant cells. In the future genetic defects might be detected earlier, and some genetic disorders, such as Tay-Sachs disease, a fatal disorder, might be treated by replacing or altering the defective gene.

When recombinant DNA techniques first became possible in the early 1970s, most concern centered around their safety. Scientists themselves called a moratorium on DNA experiments until they felt sure that the creation of new life forms (mainly bacteria) would not pose any hazards either to themselves or to the public should a laboratory product escape into the environment. The general public became alarmed and a debate about how to regulate the technology raged for several years. Now, however, concern about safety has largely (although not entirely) disappeared; working with DNA appears to be no more hazardous than with any other material. Today the issue is: In what direction will this impressive technology move, and who will control it? Will it be used for good or evil?

The social and ethical issues of genetic engineering were not on the original agenda of the President's Commission for the Study of Ethical Problems in Medicine and Biomedical and Behavioral Research when Congress established it in 1978. However, the general secretaries of three Jewish, Catholic, and Protestant church associations urged the Commission, in a July 1980 letter, to explore the questions raised by the creation of new life forms. "Control of such life forms by any individual or group poses a potential threat to all of humanity," they warned. "Those who would play God will be tempted as never before."

In the selections that follow, Hans Jonas warns against moving from acceptable objectives, such as repairing genetic damage, to creating novel forms of life. Experiments on the unborn, he claims, are unethical, since there is a grave risk that something might go wrong. Moreover, biogenetic errors are irreversible and are not confined to the particular organism under experimentation. The results of germ-line therapy may not be known for generations. It is better, he says, to leave Pandora's box unopened.

Against this apocalyptic view of genetic engineering, the President's Commission concluded that no such sweeping plans to alter human nature have been proposed (or could be implemented at present) and that the benefits to medical therapy and diagnosis outweigh the risks. However, mindful of the deeply felt objections of many people, it stressed that great powers entail great responsibility.

YES

Hans Jonas

ETHICS AND BIOGENETIC ART

In a former article, [I] dwelt at some length on the tendency of the fruits of technological invention to acquire a force of their own and, as it were, make themselves independent of their makers. "Once developed by doing in the small, they have a way of enforcing their employment in the large and ever larger and making that employment an incessant need of life." In ascribing to the creations of technology a "life of their own," I was speaking figuratively, and exaggerating somewhat. Strictly speaking, what I said referred not to the creations themselves, the concrete objects produced, but to the process of their creation and utilization, an abstract system function that acts through man. As long as the creations of technology—tools in the broadest sense— are inanimate objects, as has always been the case hitherto, it is still "man" who has to activate them, who can turn them on and off at will, and who also chooses to bring about their further development, that is, technological progress, by means of new invention, even though this choice or will is, de facto, largely deprived of its options and pushed—by the aforementioned compulsions of current use—in the single direction of going ahead. "Man" in this context means such abstract notions as "society," "the economy," "politics," "nation-state," etc., yet the *archè kinëseos*, the prime cause of movement, is still to be found in "man" and, ultimately, in actual individuals. Thus, however true it may be that the collective-technological "sorcerer's apprentice" that we are can no longer get rid of the spirits he has summoned, nevertheless it would still be theoretically possible for the old master to enter at any time and command, "In the closet/broom! broom!/As you were,"[1] and there they would stand motionless.

But not even the old sorcerer can call this anymore if the creations of technology are no longer brooms but new living creatures. Such creatures, as Aristotle said long ago, contain within themselves the origin and principle of their movement, and this movement includes not merely their continued functioning—their living behaviour—but also their propagation and, through the chain of reproduction, even their possible further development into new forms. In such creations—now true creatures, with which he has qualitatively surpassed his previous creativity in the inanimate domain—homo faber forgoes being the sole causal agency. The work of his hands takes on a life of its own and independent force, no longer figuratively but literally. On this threshold of the new art, the potential fountainhead of extended evolutions, it is fitting that man should pause a moment for fundemental reflection.

What we are talking about is the planned creation of new forms of life by direct intervention in the molecularly encoded, hereditary blueprint of given species. This is not the same as the breeding of domestic animals and plants from wild ancestor forms, which, as a mixture of art and luck, has been practiced worldwide since the dawn of agriculture. That breeding operates via the phenotypes and relies on the intrinsic whims of the germ substance as they happen to manifest themselves in this or that somatic property. The natural variability of reproduction is used to obtain the desired characteristics from the original genotype by selection of the phenotypes over the generations, that is, to increase these characteristics by summation of the small, spontaneous deviations in the preferred direction. This is artificially steered and accelerated evolution, in which deliberate stock selection takes the place of the statistically slow-working selection mechanics of nature and enables forms to come to existence which nature would not permit, since they thrive only under cultivation (like American maize, which would soon die out in the wild). Nevertheless, it is still nature which supplies the selection material: what is evolving under the hand of man is the variety itself through its own mutants, which the breeder selects; and the genetic connection with the wild form, the ability to be crossed back with the latter, is usually not broken. Man, in other words, is manipulating what the existing range of species makes available to him with the distribution of its mutant store and its further mutations.

What is known as recombinant DNA technology is a very different matter. Barely a decade old, it has already made the transition, with its first handful of successes, from research to market production and promises to do the same with the further breakthroughs we may confidently expect in the future. These successes, each of which represents a new, self-propagating life-form—and one which has been "manufactured," not "bred"—can even be patented now in America. What is happening is that at a single stroke, with a single step, a whole posterity of altered organisms, enriched by a new characteristic, is being introduced onto the stage of life by "splicing in" alien genetic material into the chromosome package of a reproductive cell. We might call this process genetic surgery or gene manipulation or even nucleus re-building, all of which phrases express the element of mechanical skill, the handling from without of the innermost, the piecemeal reshuffling of the whole. At any rate, the process circumvents the soma and goes quite literally straight to the "core"—the cell nucleus which contains in its molecular alphabet the causative "information" for the cell's life performance and the constitution of its progeny. The altering of one letter, the interchanging of one word (= gene), the addition of a new one modifies the text and initiates a new hereditary sequence. Just this DNA rearrangement at the key point of life can now be contrived with the aid of microtechnology, and a newly introduced "word" can be one taken from the hereditary text of a completely different organism. We are dealing, then, with applied nuclear biology. Like applied nuclear physics, this too leads to unknown, unpredictable territory, where undreamed-of treasures beckon and dangers lurk which in their own way could fall little short of those of applied nuclear physics.

Let us take a look at what has already happened, but more to the point at what may happen—at the possibilities to which these beginnings, relatively innocent as yet, are pointing. Even at this early stage the tempo of progress to date has surpassed expectations, and the boldest of our up-and-coming biologists are pressing on with this new line of research, so that it is not too early to give advance consideration to what has never before been considered.

A reality at present (passing over the work being done on viruses) is the genetic remodelling of bacteria. Animal or human genes responsible for the production of particular hormones are transplanted into the bacteria and impart the same capability to the host organism, as a hereditary property. As bacteria reproduce rapidly, large, self-regenerating cultures are soon obtained, and the substance that is valuable for medicinal purposes can be harvested continuously from them. As a result, the badly needed insulin, the human growth hormone, the blood-clotting agent, the rare interferon for immunity are more plentifully, constantly and cheaply available than they would be by obtaining them from natural organic sources or by synthesis. The danger of such new microbes escaping into the outside world, with unforeseeable ecological consequences, was much discussed initially but seems not to exist in this case as the or-

ganisms concerned would soon perish in an exposed environment.

This comforting thought does not apply in the case of those neomicrobes— yet to be created—which are intended to perform their biochemical function in that very environment and must therefore be equipped to survive in it. The enticing objectives of research include the bacterium that will do for cereal varieties what nature already does for leguminosae by bacteria symbiotic with their roots: namely, supply them with the nitrogen (from the air) for which otherwise they would need chemical fertilizers. Or, still more freely spread through the environment, bacteria which break down crude oil and could be used to master the giant marine oil slicks caused by tanker accidents. It is unpredictable whether such imagined servants of man might not emancipate themselves from the narrow confines of their tasks, strike out on their own environmental and mutational careers, and drastically disturb an ecological equilibrium unprepared for them. Is it permissible to play such games of chance with the environment? The first, more modest instance of this class of disseminated neomicrobes to be ready for testing in the field is the bacillus causing ice crystals to form on the potato plant: the genetic lowering of its temperature threshold is to delay the seasonal onset of frost damage, with obvious advantages for agriculture. An American judge, acting on a protest by conservationists, has just granted an interim injunction against the first field tests, which of course is no more than a deferment. At all events, we are here entering an area where we should tread only with great caution; a quite new kind of responsibility rests here not only on the users but already on the biological inventors.

To return once more to the hormone bacteria, which (if indeed remaining captive) are ecologically unexceptionable, since only their inert product finds its way into the outside world, there is no disputing their medicinal value for compensating innate or acquired deficiencies. Not everything which can be done in this field is of the same level of importance as insulin, which quite literally keeps diabetics alive, and some of the less vital possibilities have also their dubious sides in the jostle of not-always-wise human wishes. The growth hormone can prevent stunted growth in children who have the corresponding genetic defect, and though this is not exactly life-saving it is certainly highly desirable. But the same hormone could also be used frivolously to treat what is not a deficiency at all but, for example, simply familial or ethnic shortness of stature in comparison to the dominant majority, or primitive parental vanity—"Tall is beautiful!"—combined with every conceivable kind of racial, class, and status prejudice. (We may think of a famous Prussian king's craze for the tallest soldiers, or of their modern match, the tallest basketball players.) If it comes down to a plain question of money, follies of this sort will be virtually impossible to prevent, and any organic damage would only become evident later. I leave it to each reader's imagination to picture to himself the uses that bacterial mass production of sex hormones of both genders might open up, such as prolonging the sexual and reproductive capacities into higher ages, for which no doubt male demand would be especially keen. Imagine it, and ask yourself whether it is good and wise, with respect to the individual or the group, to meddle for ephemeral-hedonistic reasons with the ways of nature, who here has set her own times by the long trial of evolution. It is by our essentially new capabilities that we find ourselves confronted with such fundamentally new questions (which I do not even attempt to answer here).

Now it may be said in answer to all this that every drug, even the most beneficial, whether subject to prescription or not, can be abused, and that the responsibility lies not with the discoverers and manufacturers but with the consumers and with the doctors in their capacity as middlemen. The question of apportioning responsibility is one which I shall leave open here—probably it extends in various ways to all participants in this social syndrome; my intention has simply been to show that the development of biogenetic techniques has led us into what, from the ethical point of view, is unexplored country, posing questions which have never been posed before and for which previous ethical theory has left us unprepared.

But the most important of these questions did not yet arise in discussing—as we have done so far—the present state of the art that busies itself with the very roots of life: the question as to whether or not such arbitrary recreation is fair to the direct objects of those techniques. It did not arise because, toward microbes, we feel ourselves absolved from asking it. But what can be done with unicellular organisms can also be done with multicellular ones—and, in principle, even using the same technique, for every multicellular organism begins as a unicellular one, and the all-important germ cell with its chromosome nucleus is no different from a microbe for the purposes of recombinant DNA technology. Thus, in theory, the door which leads to the higher animals and eventually to man is already open. Let us now take the theoretical step through this door—in advance of eventual practice, but perhaps only a little way in advance—and conclude our journey with an ethical preview of what we sorcerer's apprentices might encounter there, but which to encounter or not is still for us to decide.

Reasons of time compel me to go straight to the subject of man, although even considering animals close enough to us in size and evolutionary level the mere thought of "chimaeras" composed of hereditary material from different species may produce an involuntary shudder. There may still be room for debate here, as reverence for the natural order has become largely alien to the Western mind. But in the case of man the absolute makes its voice heard and, beyond any cost-benefit computations, brings into play ultimate moral, existential, even metaphysical aspects—even, with the category of the sacred, any surviving sentiments of a religion which, for the West, once began with that sentence from the sixth day of Creation which reads: "And God created man in his own image, in the image of God created he him, man and woman created he them." But let us hear Goethe on the subject of how human art even here can improve on the work of the creator and surpass the ways of its coming-to-be:

WAGNER
A man is being made.

MEPHISTOPHELES
A man? And what affectionate pair
Have you sealed up in that smoke-ridden den?

WAGNER
Heaven forbid! Old-fashioned reproduction
We here regard as mere frivolity.
The tender dot from which existence sprang,

And that fair power which burst forth from within
And took and gave, resolved to show itself,
To claim things close, then alien, for its own,
Is now from all its dignity cast down;
Though animals may still delight therein,
Man must henceforth, with all his many gifts,
Stem from a purer, higher origin.

The mysteries of nature, once admired,
We venture forth on here with understanding,
And what was once by nature organized
Is here and now by us being crystallized.

All great resolves seem rash at their beginning,
Yet in the future we will laugh at chance
And such a brain, made to excel at thought,
In time to come shall also make a thinker

HOMUNCULUS
Well father! How are things? It was no joke.
Come, take me tenderly into your arms!
But, not too tightly, or the glass will break.
That is the nature of the world's affairs.
The cosmos scarce contains what's natural,
What's made by art demands a closer space.[2]

From this wondrous text which says so much I shall select the line which says virtually everything there is to say on my concluding topic: "Yet in the future we will laugh at chance." Chance: that is the productive source of species evolution. Chance: that is the guarantee, in every case of sexual generation that every individual is born unique, none exactly like another. Chance surprises us with what is ever new and has never been. Yet surprises can be both pleasant and unpleasant. And if we replace chance by art, doing away with surprises as such, we conceivably could avoid the unpleasant ones, while securing the gifts of what would be pleasant ones at will. Yes, we could even become masters of the further evolution of our own species!

There are two contrasting ways of eliminating chance in the creation of the homunculus: recombinant DNA technology on human germ cells; and replication of model individuals by "cloning" body cells. Both methods fashion the future being from the chromosome base. One modifies the accidentally given by gene manipulation which improves it and may even be freely inventive. The other fixes (or, to use Goethe's word), "crystallizes") proven instances of genetic good fortune, or what are held to be such and would otherwise be swallowed up again by the flux of chance in the lottery of sexual reproduction—fixes it for as many faithful, asexual replications as are desired.

Let us take the second procedure first. Successful experiments have already been carried out here on several animals still remote from us—but in principle the method can be extended to the higher mammals and to man. It is based on the fact that under suitable conditions even the double (diploid) set of chromosomes in a body cell can be induced to act in the same way as the chromosome set of the fertilized egg cell composed of two halves each of different sexual origin; that is to say, it can be induced to "sprout" and bring forth the complete body for which it contains the full genetic "instructions." As these are exclusively and wholly those of the donor body, what is now formed—by circumventing the adventure of combining two haploid germ cells as happens in sexual generation—is a genetic duplicate of the sole parent organism, as if it were an identical twin of that organism. The required original cell can easily be obtained from a suitable tissue of the donor and be preserved in a nutrient culture or a cold-storage drawer, even beyond his death, and the rest takes place in vitro and eventually in a host uterus.[3]

What is the point? Well, we may deplore the rarity of geniuses in the population as a whole, and the "once only" of each ending with their death, and we may on behalf of humanity wish for more of one or other kind of specimens—poets, thinkers, researchers, leaders, top athletes, beauty queens, saints and heroes. And the wish can be fulfilled by cloning—according to taste—series or single replicas of Mozart and Einstein, Lenin and Hitler, Mother Theresa and Albert Schweitzer. Nor will there be any shortage of volunteers prompted by vanity or the desire for an immortality substitute, and backed by the necessary hard cash; nor of music-loving childless couples preferring an undiluted cutting from Rubinstein to a genetically anonymous adopted child. In the present state of science, all this is no longer a joke, but simply a question of technological progress.

I have already discussed, in a previous treatise,[4] the folly of this dream, the childishness of thinking that "the more the better" is a valid principle here, that more than the one Mozart would even be desirable, not to mention the question (with the Nazi experience behind us) of who is going to decide what it is desirable to select in the first place. The random nature of the sexual process is both the irreplaceable blessing and the inescapable burden of our lot, and its incalculability still deserves more confidence than our passing fancies. But, most of all, I have tried to show the crime that would be committed against the fruits of the technique, the actual progeny of the cloning. Let me sum up, very briefly.

To know oneself as a mere copy of a

335

being which has already revealed itself in a previous life must stifle the authenticity of being oneself and the freedom of first discovering oneself—surprising oneself and the world with what is within one. The same illicit knowledge stifles the open-minded approach of others to the new and yet not-so-new arrival. A basic right to ignorance, which is indispensable for existential freedom, is here being infringed by anticipation. The whole thing is frivolous in its motives and morally objectionable in its consequences, and this prior to the consideration of numbers and population-wide impact, relevant in the case of other biological adventures. Even a single sample would be a crime.

This whole enterprise would lack the excuse of a pressing emergency, of some ill crying out to be remedied; rather, it would be the work of arrogance, curiosity and caprice. Adding to this the experience that every skill, once acquired, has hitherto proved irresistible, and that it is then too late for the moral "No," we may for once counsel science not to pursue this line of exploration any further. The cause of neither truth nor the good is served thereby.

Less frivolous, and correspondingly more difficult from the philosophical point of view, is the opposite, "creative" path: modifying the hereditary substance by gene-splicing. In this instance one can adduce ills that can be remedied by the technique, hence legitimate, at least non-frivolous, grounds for developing the art. The greater in this case is the danger of error, abuse, even recklessness, because here man is making himself master of the hereditary model itself, not merely of the way in which it is transmitted. Let us, finally, also take a brief look at this approaching possibility.

Like so much in technology, it sets out with very acceptable objectives. Ask a diabetic, who is being supplied with insulin by the bacteria I mentioned earlier, whether it would not have been better to perform the gene transfer on him rather than on the bacteria, replacing his defective gene with a healthy one at the outset of his existence, and he would certainly answer yes. In fact his seems the ideal solution.[5] In order to extend to the entire future organism, including the gonads and hence to the progeny also, it would have to be done directly after fertilization (parental history first suggesting the gene defect). It might also be possible for somatic, more local genetic corrections to be performed later on the embryo for the benefit of the individual alone.

But let's keep to the radical and optimal solution-heritable modification literally *ab ovo*. As our hypothetical example is concerned with removing a damage, we are not yet dealing really with novel creation but rather with repair; and certainly it is a captivating and apparently blameless concept to aim at genetic rather than somatic therapy, elimination of causes rather than treatment of symptoms, a once-for-all, hereditary remedy rather than an ever-repeated one. Yet, in a comprehensive balance, misgivings weigh heavily on the other side of the scale:

1. Experiments on the unborn are in themselves unethical. And, in the very nature of things, any intervention in the delicate control mechanism of a nascent life is an experiment, and one involving a grave risk that something might go wrong, resulting in a deformity.

2. If a mechanical construction turns out wrong, we scrap it. Are we supposed to do the same with a biological reconstruction that turns out wrong? Our whole

attitude to human misfortune and those afflicted by it would take a new, antihumane direction.

3. Mechanical errors are reversible. Biogenetic errors are irreversible.

4. Mechanical errors are confined to the object actually involved. Biogenetic errors spread out from that object, as indeed it is hoped that the successes will also.

5. In somatic surgery, there is a known interrelationship between the transplanted organ and the rest of the organism. In genetic surgery, the way in which the transplanted gene will interact with other members of the chromosome whole is unknown and unpredictable, and may not become apparent for generations.

6. By applying the technique as such to man, we would be opening the Pandora's box of melioristic, stochastic, inventive or simply perversely inquisitive adventuring, leaving behind the conservative spirit of genetic repairs and embarking on the path of creative arrogance. We are not entitled to do this and not equipped to do it—not equipped with the wisdom, the judgment or the self-discipline. No ancient awe still protects us disenchanters of the world from the enchantment of reckless and impious deed. It would be better, then, to leave the box unopened.

There is no time to consider all the possibilities that might be thought up here or have indeed been thought up in the playful imaginings of biologists. They do not even stop short of the interchange of genetic material between animals and man—a concept which calls to mind such ancient, forgotten terms as "sacrilege" and "abomination." As in the case of cloning, numbers do not matter here. The very first trial creation of a "chimaera" with a human admixture would commit the abomination, and scarcely less so the first case of purely intrahuman repatterning. And so research, which can only find out what is possible by first doing it, is here already venturing into forbidden territory.

Is there any prospect of keeping Pandor's box closed? Is there, in other words, any prospect of avoiding the transition from bacterial to human genetic surgery—the threshold where the *principiis obsta* could still find a footing? I don't think so. Medicine, anxious to help, will not be deprived of the opportunity to carry out what, in the short term, are legitimate "repairs," and at that point the lid will have been opened. It would probably be wiser to resist even the charitable temptation for once, in this instance, but the pressure of human suffering makes this unlikely. Beyond this, already risky, twilight zone between what is still permissible and what is forbidden there beckon Pandora's further gifts—gifts which we are driven to accept not by any want but simply by the Promethean urge. We today, emancipated as we are, are less well armed than all our forebears against the temptations of that urge, including Wagner's temptations of the homunculus; and yet now we, more than all our forebears, would need what we proudly left behind to protect us against the demons of our own skills. Our world, so completely stripped of its taboos, must voluntarily establish new ones to match the new types of power it possesses. We must understand that we have ventured very far, and must relearn to understand that there is such a thing as "too far." It begins where the integrity of the human image is concerned, which we should regard as inviolable. Only as bunglers could we try our hand on it, and not even as masters should we trespass there. We must rediscover fear and trembling and, even without God, awe of what is holy. There is work enough to be done this side of the boundary we should be setting ourselves.

The human condition constantly cries out for improvement. Let us try to help. Let us try to prevent, to alleviate, and to heal. But let us not try to play creators at the roots of our being, at the primal seat of its mystery.

NOTES

1. From Goethe's poem Der Zauberlehrling ("The Sorcerer's Apprentice").

2. Faust II, Act 2, Scene "Laboratory."

3. This is as yet a theoretical fantasy where animals above the amphibians are concerned. (The first successes were with frogs.) Practicality depends on the ability to "reawaken" the gene portions rendered dormant in an adult, specialized body cell, thereby restoring to it the "totipotency" of the predifferentiated, embryonic stage. The latest scientific view, after an expansive earlier euphoria, seems to deem this "forever" impossible to do with mammalian cells. (One purported cloning of a mouse is now dismissed as untrue.) But biologists did, in public speech and print, play thought games of the sort that underlie my present discourse; and they might do so again (and then more than that!), should the current verdict of "not feasible" prove to be temporary.

4. "Biological Engineering—A Preview" (1974), in H. Jonas, *Philosophical Essays* (Chicago, 1980), pp. 153-163.

5. Here again, presently prevailing opinions among geneticists doubt the technical feasibility of any targeted insertion, substitution, translocation, etc. of individual genes in the enormous complexity of human chromosomes, and we are told not to fear what will be impossible anyway. But we have heard the verdict of "impossible" not so long ago, and from eminent scientists, about splitting the atom; and the bacterial beginnings of gene engineering ("splicing") are plainly there. Experimental probing surely will go on from there, and the increasing offer of redundant human embryos from *in vitro* fertilization invites its extension to this material too.

NO

President's Commission for the Study of Ethical Problems in Research

SPLICING LIFE

CONCERNS ABOUT "PLAYING GOD"

... Hardly a popular article has been written about the social and ethical implications of genetic engineering that does not suggest a link between "God-like powers" and the ability to manipulate the basic material of life. Indeed, a popular book about gene splicing is entitled *Who Should Play God?*, and in their June 1980 letter to the President, three religious leaders sounded a tocsin against the lack of a governmental policy concerning "[t]hose who would play God" through genetic engineering.

Religious Viewpoints
The Commission asked the General Secretaries of the three religious organizations to elaborate on any uniquely theological considerations underlying their concern about gene splicing in humans. ...

In the view of the theologians, contemporary developments in molecular biology raise issues of responsibility rather than being matters to be prohibited because they usurp powers that human beings should not possess. The Biblical religions teach that human beings are, in some sense, co-creators with the Supreme Creator. Thus, as interpreted for the Commission by their representatives, these major religious faiths respect and encourage the enhancement of knowledge about nature as well as responsible use of that knowledge. Endorsement of genetic engineering, which is praised for its potential to improve the human estate, is linked with the recognition that the misuse of human freedom creates evil and that human knowledge and power can result in harm.

From *Splicing Life,* President's Commission for the Study of Ethical Problems in Medicine and Biomedical and Behavioral Research, 1983.

While religious leaders present theological bases for their concerns, essentially the same concerns have been raised—sometimes in slightly different words—by many thoughtful secular observers of contemporary science and technology. Concerns over unintended effects, over the morality of genetic manipulation in all its forms, and over the social and political consequences of new technologies are shared by religious and secular commentators. The examination of the various specific concerns need not be limited, therefore, to the religious format in which some of the issues have been raised.

Fully Understanding the Machinery of Life

Although it does not have a specific religious meaning, the objection to scientists "playing God" is assumed to be self-explanatory. On closer examination, however, it appears to the Commission that it conveys several rather different ideas, some describing the power of gene splicing itself and some relating merely to its consequences.

At its heart, the term represents a reaction to the realization that human beings are on the threshold of understanding how the fundamental machinery of life works. A full understanding of what are now great mysteries, and the powers inherent in that understanding, would be so awesome as to justify the description "God-like." In this view, playing God is not actually an objection to the research but an expression of a sense of awe—and concern.

Since the Enlightenment, Western societies have exalted the search for greater knowledge, while recognizing its awesome implications. Some scientific discoveries reverberate with particular force because they not only open new avenues of research but also challenge people's entire understanding of the world and their place in it. Current discoveries in gene splicing—like the new knowledge associated with Copernicus and Darwin—further dethrone human beings as the unique center of the universe. By identifying DNA and learning how to manipulate it, science seems to have reduced people to a set of malleable molecules that can be interchanged with those of species that people regard as inferior. Yet unlike the earlier revolutionary discoveries, those in molecular biology are not merely descriptions; they give scientists vast powers for action.

Arrogant Interference with Nature

By what standards are people to guide the exercise of this awesome new freedom if they want to act responsibly? In this context, the charge that human beings are playing God can mean that in "creating new life forms" scientists are abusing their learning by interfering with nature.

But in one sense *all* human activity that produces changes that otherwise would not have occurred interferes with nature. Medical activities as routine as the prescription of eyeglasses for myopia or as dramatic as the repair or replacement of a damaged heart are in this sense "unnatural." In another sense, human activity cannot interfere with nature—in the sense of contravening it—since all human activities, including some gene splicing, proceed according to the scientific laws that describe natural processes. Ironically, to believe that "playing God" in this sense is even possible would itself be hubris according to some religious thought, which maintains that only God can interfere with the descriptive laws of nature (that is, perform miracles).

If, instead, what is meant is that gene splicing technology interferes with nature in the sense that it violates God's prescriptive natural law or goes against God's purposes as they are manifested in the natural order, then some reason must be given for this judgment. None of the scholars appointed to report their views by the three religious bodies that urged the Commission to undertake this study suggested that either natural reason or revelation imply that gene splicing technology as such is "unnatural" in this prescriptive sense. Although each scholar expressed concern over particular applications of gene splicing technology, they all also emphasized that human beings have not merely the right but the duty to employ their God-given powers to harness nature for human benefit. To turn away from gene splicing, which may provide a means of curing hereditary diseases, would itself raise serious ethical problems.

Creating New Life Forms

If "creating new life forms" is simply producing organisms with novel characteristics, then human beings create new life forms frequently and have done so since they first learned to cultivate new characteristics in plants and breed new traits in animals. Presumably the idea is that gene splicing creates new life forms, rather than merely modifying old ones, because it "breaches species barriers" by combining DNA from different species—groups of organisms that cannot mate to produce fertile offspring.

Genetic engineering is not the first exercise of humanity's ability to create new life forms through nonsexual reproduction. The creation of hybrid plants seems no more or no less natural than the development of a new strain of *E. coli* bacteria through gene splicing. Further, genetic engineering cannot accurately be called unique in that it involves the creation of new life forms through processes that do not occur in nature without human intervention. . . . [S]cientists have found that the transfer of DNA between organisms of different species occurs in nature without human intervention. Yet, as one eminent scientist in the field has pointed out, it would be unwarranted to assume that a dramatic increase in the frequency of such transfers through human intervention is not problematic simply because DNA transfer sometimes occurs naturally.

In the absence of specific religious prohibitions, either revealed or derived by rational argument from religous premises, it is difficult to see why "breaching species barriers" as such is irreligious or otherwise objectionable. In fact, the very notion that there are barriers that must be breached prejudges the issue. The question is simply whether there is something intrinsically wrong with intentionally crossing species lines. Once the question is posed in this way the answer must be negative—unless one is willing to condemn the production of tangelos by hybridizing tangerines and grapefruits or the production of mules by the mating of asses with horses.

There may nonetheless be two distinct sources of concern about crossing species lines that deserve serious consideration. First, gene splicing affords the possibility of creating hybrids that can reproduce themselves (unlike mules, which are sterile). So the possibility of self-perpetuating "mistakes" adds a new dimension of concern, although here again, the point is not that crossing species lines is inherently wrong, but that it may have undesirable consequences and that these consequences may multiply beyond human control. As noted, the Commission's focus on the human applications of gene splicing has meant that it does not here address this important set of concerns, which lay behind the original self-imposed moratorium on certain categories of gene splicing research and which have been, and continue to be, addressed through various scientific and public mechanisms, such as RAC [Recombinant Advisory Committee].

Second, there is the issue of whether particular crossings of species—especially the mixing of human and nonhuman genes—might not be illicit. The moral revulsion at the creation of human-animal hybrids may be traced in part to the prohibition against sexual relations between human beings and lower animals. Sexual relations with lower animals are thought to degrade human beings and insult their God-given dignity as the highest of God's creatures. But unease at the prospect of human-animal hybrids goes beyond sexual prohibitions.

The possibility of creating such hybrids calls into question basic assumptions about the relationship of human beings to other living things. For example, those who believe that the current treatment of animals— in experimentation, food production, and sport—is morally suspect would not be alone in being troubled by the prospect of exploitive or insensitive treatment of creatures that possess even more human-like qualities than chimpanzees or porpoises do. Could genetic engineering be used to develop a group of virtual slaves—partly human, partly lower animal—to do people's bidding? Paradoxically, the very characteristics that would make such creatures more valuable than any existing animals (that is, their heightened cognitive powers and sensibilities) would also make the moral propriety of their subservient role more problematic. Dispassionate appraisal of the long history of gratuitous destruction and suffering that humanity has visited upon the other inhabitants of the earth indicates that such concerns should not be dismissed as fanciful.

Accordingly, the objection to the creation of new life forms by crossing species lines (whether through gene splicing or otherwise) reflects the concern that human beings lack the God-like knowledge and wisdom required for the exercise of these God-like powers. Specifically, people worry that interspecific hybrids that are partially human in their genetic makeup will be like Dr. Frankenstein's monster. A striking lesson of the Frankenstein story is the uncontrollability and uncertainty of the consequences of human interferences with the natural order. Like the tale of the Sorcerer's apprentice or the myth of the golem created from lifeless dust by the 16th century rabbi, Loew of Prague, the story of Dr. Frankenstein's monster serves as a reminder of the difficulty of restoring order if a creation intended to be helpful proves harmful instead. Indeed, each of these tales conveys a painful irony: in seeking to extend their control over the world, people may lessen it. The artifices they create to do their bidding may rebound destructively against them—the slave may become the master.

Suggesting that someone lacks sufficient knowledge or wisdom to engage in an activity the person knows how to perform thus means that the individual has insufficient knowledge of the consequences of that activity or insufficient wisdom to cope with those consequences. But if this is the rational kernel of the admonition against playing God, then the use of gene splicing technology is not claimed to be wrong as such but wrong because of its potential consequences. Understood in this way, the slogan that crossing species barriers is playing God does not end the debate, but it does make a point of fundamental importance. It emphasizes that any realistic assessment of the potential consequences of the new technology must be founded upon a sober recognition of human fallibility and ignorance. At bottom, the warning not to play God is closely related to the Socratic injunction "know thyself"; in this case, acknowledge the limits of understanding and prediction, rather than assuming that people can fore-see all the consequences of their actions or plan adequately for every eventuality.

Any further examination of the notion that the hybridization of species, at least when one of the species is human, is intrinsically wrong (and not merely wrong as a consequence of what is done with the hybrids) involves elaboration of two points. First, what characteristics are uniquely human, setting humanity apart from all other species? And second, does the wrong lie in bestowing some but not all of these characteristics on the new creation or does it stem from depriving the being that might otherwise have arisen from the human genetic material of the opportunity to have a totally human makeup? The Commission believes that these are important issues deserving of serious study.

It should be kept in mind, however, that the information available to the Commission suggests that the ability to create interspecific hybrids of the sort that would present intrinsic moral and religious concerns will not be available in the foreseeable future. The research currently being done on experimentation with recombinant DNA techniques through the use of single human genes (for example, the insertion of a particular human hemoglobin gene into mouse cells at the embryonic stage) or the study of cellular development through the combining of human genetic material with that of other species in a way that does not result in a mature organism (for example, in vitro fusion of human and mouse cells) does not, in the Commission's view, raise

problems of an improper "breaching of the barriers." . . .

Evolutionary Impact on Human Beings

Some critics warn against the dangers of attempting to control or interfere with the "wisdom of evolution" in order to satisfy scientific curiosity. Those who hold this view object in particular to crossing species lines by gene splicing because they believe that the pervasive inability of different species to produce fertile offspring by sexual reproduction must be an adaptive feature, that is, it must confer some significant survival advantage. Thus they view species lines as natural protective barriers that human beings may circumvent only at their peril, although the harm such barriers are supposed to shield people from remains unspecified.

Most proponents of genetic engineering argue that the benefits it will bring are more tangible and important and will affect more people than those objecting suggest. Further, the notion of the "wisdom of evolution" that apparently underlies this consequentialist version of the objection to crossing species lines is not well founded. As the scientific theory of evolution does not postulate a plan that the process of evolution is to achieve, evolutionary changes cannot be said to promote such a plan, wisely or unwisely. Moreover, evolutionary theory recognizes (and natural history confirms) that a "wise" adaptation at one time or place can become a lethal flaw when circumstances change. So even if it could be shown that species barriers have thus far played an important adaptive role, it would not follow that this will continue. An evolutionary explanation of any inherited characteristic can at most show that having that characteristic gave an organism's ancestors some advantage in enabling them to live long enough to

343

reproduce and that the characteristic has not yet prove maladaptive for the offspring.

Furthermore, as a philosopher concerned with assessing the risks of genetic engineering has recently noted, the ability to manipulate genes, both within and across species lines, may become a crucial asset for survival.

> There may . . . come a time when, because of natural or man-induced climatic change, the capacity to alter quickly the genetic composition of agricultural plants will be required to forestall catastrophic famine.

The consequentialist version of the warning against crossing species lines seems, then, to be no more a conclusive argument against genetic engineering than the admonition that to cross species lines is wrong because it is playing God. But it does serve the vital purpose of urging that, so far as this is possible, the evolutionary effects of any interventions are taken into account. . . .

Changing the Meaning of Being Human

Some geneticists have seen in their field the possibility of benefit through improving human traits. Human beings have the chance to "rise above (their) nature" for "the first time in all time," as one leader in the field has observed:

> It has long been apparent that you and I do not enter this world as unformed clay compliant to any mold. Rather, we have in our beginnings some bent of mind, some shade of character. The origin of this structure—of the fiber in this clay—was for centuries mysterious. . . . Today . . . we know to look within. We seek not in the stars but in our genes for the herald of our fate.

Will gene splicing actually make possible such changes in "human nature" for the first time? In some ways this question is unanswerable since there is great disagreement about which particular characteristics make up "human nature." For some people, the concept encompasses those characteristics that are uniquely human. Yet most human genes are actually found in other mammals as well; moreover, recent work by ethologists and other biologists on animal behavior and capacities is demonstrating that many characteristics once regarded as unique to human beings are actually shared by other animals, particularly by the higher primates, although an ability to record and study the past and to plan beyond the immediate future appears to be a singularly human trait.

Other people regard the critical qualities as those natural characteristics that are common to all human beings, or at least all who fall within a certain "normal range." "Natural" here means characteristics that people are born with as opposed to those that result from social convention, education, or acculturation.

To consider whether gene splicing would allow the changing of human nature thus breaks down into two questions. Which characteristics found in all human beings are inborn or have a large inborn basis? And will gene splicing techniques be able to alter or replace some of the genetic bases of those characteristics? As to the first, the history of religious, philosophical, and scientific thought abounds with fundamental disputes over human nature. Without a consensus on that issue the second question could only be answered affirmatively if it were clear that gene splicing will eventually allow the alteration of all natural characteristics of human beings.

As it is by no means certain that it will ever be possible to change the genetic basis of all natural characteristics, it seems premature to assume that gene splicing will enable changes in human nature. At most, it can perhaps be said that this technology may eventually allow some aspects of what it means to be human to be changed. Yet even that possibility rightly evokes profound concern and burdens everyone with an awesome and inescapable responsibility—either to develop and employ this capability for the good of humanity or to reject it in order to avoid potential undesirable consequences.

The possibility of changing human nature must, however, be kept in perspective. First, within the limits imposed by human beings' genetic endowment, there is already considerable scope by means other than gene splicing for changing some acquired characteristics that are distinctively human. For example, people's desires, values, and the way they live can be changed significantly through alterations in social and economic institutions and through mass education, indoctrination, and various forms of behavior control. Thus, even if gene splicing had the power that some people are concerned about, it would not be unique in its ability to produce major changes in what it means to be human—although it would be unusual in acting on the inheritable foundation of thoughts and actions. If the technology can ever be used in this way, the heritability of the changes ought probably to be regarded as significantly different from any changes now possible.

Second, according to the theory of evolution, the genetic basis of what is distinctively human continually changes through the interplay of random mutation and natural selection. The concern, then, is that gene splicing will for the first time allow deliberate, selective, and rapid alterations to be made in the human genetic constitution.

Finally, concern about changing human nature may at bottom be still more narrowly focused upon those characteristics of human beings—whether unique to the species or not—that are especially valued or cherished. Here, too, there may be disagreement as to which characteristics are most valuable and the value of a given characteristic may depend upon the social or natural environment in which it is manifested.

In sum, the question of whether gene splicing will enable changes in human nature—and the ethical, social, and philosophical significance of such changes—cannot be determined until much more is known about human genetics, specifically the exact contribution of heredity to many human physical and, more important, behavioral traits. Indeed, one of the most important contributions genetic engineering could make to the science of behavioral genetics may be that it will help resolve the age-old controversy of nature versus nurture. If designed changes were possible, society would have to confront whether such changes should be made, and, if they should, which ones. The problems created by uncertainty are particularly notable here since any decision about what characteristics are "desirable" would depend on the world that people will be living in, which is itself unknowable in advance. . . .

CONTINUING CONCERNS

A distinction has been drawn in this Report between two views: (1) that gene splicing technology is intrinsically wrong or contrary to important values and (2) that, while the technology is not inherently wrong, certain of its applications or consequences are undesirable. Regarding the latter, it has also been noted that genetic engineering involves an array of uncertainties beyond those usually found in technological developments. Not only is the occurrence of specific desirable or undesirable consequences impossible to predict but the application of gene splicing could have far-reaching consequences that could alter basic individual and social values.

The Commission could find no ground for concluding that any current or planned forms of genetic engineering, whether using human or nonhuman material, are intrinsically wrong or irreligious per se. The Commission does not see in the rapid development of gene splicing the "fundamental danger" to world safety or to human values that concerned the leaders of the three religious organizations. Rather, the issue that deserves careful thought is: by what standards, and toward what objectives, should the great new powers of genetic engineering be guided? . . .

POSTSCRIPT

IS GENETIC ENGINEERING A THREAT TO FUTURE GENERATIONS?

When the President's Commission ended its work in the spring of 1983, it urged that an appropriate overseeing body be established to continue to monitor developments in genetic engineering. Such a body, the Commission recommended, should be broadly based and not dominated by geneticists and other scientists. Congress has created a Biomedical Ethics Board which will consider, among other things, genetic engineering.

Meanwhile, the technology is proceeding rapidly. Genetic defects have been corrected in fruit flies, and artificially-inserted genes have functioned in succeeding generations of mammals. Investigators have also succeeded in isolating and studying the gene underlying the Lesch-Nyhan syndrome in humans, a severe disorder resulting in retardation and compulsive self-mutilation. The way has been opened to correct the deficiency in the cells.

Human gene therapy has moved closer to reality, both scientifically and legally. The Working Group on Human Gene Therapy of the Recombinant DNA Advisory Committee of the National Institutes of Health has issued a series of "points to consider" for investigators planning to submit research protocols for review. Only somatic-cell therapy protocols will be considered, that is, therapy that will affect only the genes of the individual and will not be passed on to succeeding generations. The points include anticipated risks and benefits, research design, various laboratory and clinical procedures, the process of selection of subjects and informed consent, and plans to protect confidentiality as well as to deal with media interest.

A comprehensive history of reecombinant DNA techniques and the political and social debates about safety is Sheldon Krimsky, *Genetic Alchemy* (MIT Press, 1982). Jeremy Rifkin's book *Algeny* (Viking, 1983) argues against all forms of genetic engineering. An earlier and influential book with the same point of view is Ted Howard and Jeremy Rifkin, *Who Should Play God?* (Dell, 1977). A positive view of the prospects of genetic engineering is Zsolt Harsanyi, with Richard Hutton, *Genetic Prophecy: Beyond the Double Helix* (Rawson, Wade, 1981).

Daniel J. Kevles *In the Name of Eugenics* (Knopf, 1985) traces the ways in which the control of human genetics has been used to meet social and political ends. The Office of Technology Assessment of the US Congress has issued a comprehensive report called *Human Gene Therapy* (Washington, D.C., 1984). Also see Robert Esbjornson, editor, *The Manipulation of Life* (Harper & Row, 1984). Richard A. McCormick, "Genetic Technology and Our Common Future," *America* (April 27, 1985) presents a cautionary view.

CONTRIBUTORS
TO THIS VOLUME

EDITOR

CAROL LEVINE is the editor of the *Hastings Center Report* and the managing editor of *IRB: A Review of Human Subjects Research*, periodicals published by the Hastings Center in Hastings-on-Hudson, New York. Ms. Levine received her BA in history from Cornell and an MA in public law and government from Columbia University. She is the co-author of *Comparative Government and Politics, Second Edition* (Harper and Row, 1981) and is a frequent contributor of articles on genetic engineering. She is the co-director of the Hastings Center project on "AIDS and the Ethics of Public Health," and she writes and lectures widely on AIDS and other issues in bioethics.

AUTHORS

GEORGE J. ANNAS is Utley Professor of Health Law at Boston University of Medicine. He is also chief of the health law section at Boston University School of Public Health.

MARY ROSE BARRINGTON is a solicitor of the Supreme Court of Judicature of England and an administrator of alms houses for the aged.

THOMAS L. BEAUCHAMP teaches in the philosophy department and in the Kennedy Institute of Ethics at Georgetown University.

SISSELA BOK is a philosopher and author of several books, including *Secrets: On the Ethics of Concealment and Revelation* (Pantheon, 1982).

RICHARD J. BONNIE is a professor of law and director of the Institute of Law, Psychiatry and Public Policy at the University of Virginia.

PERCY BRAZIL is the senior attending physician, president of the medical staff, and chairman of the medical board at Phelps Memorial Hospital Center in North Tarrytown, New York.

ARTHUR CAPLAN is associate director of the Hastings Center.

JAMES F. CHILDRESS is a professor of religious studies and medical education at the University of Virginia.

PAUL CHODOFF is an MD and clinical professor of psychiatry at George Washington University School of Medicine.

WILLIAM P. CLARK was an associate justice of the California Supreme Court. He served as the assistant to President Reagan for national security affairs and in other governmental posts before returning to private practice in California.

STEPHEN COHEN teaches at the Georgetown University Law Center.

ALLEN R. DYER is a professor in the departments of psychiatry and community and family medicine at Duke University Medical Center.

JOHN C. FLETCHER is assistant for bioethics at the Warren G. Magnuson Clinical Center of the National Institutes of Health.

CLIFFORD GROBSTEIN is professor of biological science and public policy at the University of California, San Diego.

BEVERLY WILDUNG HARRISON is a professor of Christian ethics at Union Theological Seminary in New York.

HERBERT HENDIN is a psychiatrist and author.

HANS JONAS is Alvin Johnson Professor Emeritus of philosophy at the New School for Social Research.

C. EVERETT KOOP is the surgeon general of the United States. Formerly, he was professor of pediatrics and pediatric surgery, University of Pennsylvania School of Medicine.

HERBERT F. KRIMMEL is professor of law, Southwestern University School of Law, Los Angeles, California.

JOANNE LYNN is on the staff of the division of geriatric medicine, George Washington University. She was assistant director of the President's Commission for the Study of Ethical Problems in Medicine and Biomedical and Behavioral Research.

GILBERT MEILAENDER is professor of religion at Oberlin College.

BERNARD C. MEYER is in the private practice of psychiatry in New York. He is clinical professor of psychiatry at Mount Sinai Hospital School of Medicine.

The late STANLEY MILGRAM was professor of psychology at the Graduate School and University Center of the City University of New York. He is the author of *Obedience to Authority: An Experimental View* (Harper and Row, 1975).

THOMAS H. MURRAY is an associate in behavioral studies at the Hastings Center.

JOHN T. NOONAN, Jr., is professor of law at the University of California, Berkeley Law School and author of several books, including three works on contraception and abortion.

THOMAS A. PRESTON is chief of cardiology, Pacific Medical Center in Seattle, Washington.

JACK W. PROVONSHA is an MD and a minister who recently retired from practice at the Loma Linda University Medical Center.

JAMES RACHELS is a philosopher who is also the dean of the School of Humanities at the University of Alabama, Birmingham.

JOHN A. ROBERTSON is Mars McLean Professor of Law at the University of Texas, Austin.

ALFRED M. SADLER practices internal medicine in Monterey, California. He served as a chief consultant to the Commissioners on Uniform State Laws in drafting the Uniform Anatomical Gift Act.

BLAIR L. SADLER is president of the Children's Hospital of San Diego. She served as a chief consultant to the Commissioners on Uniform State Laws in drafting the Uniform Anatomical Gift Act.

MARK SCHERZER practices law in New York City. He is also a cooperating attorney with the Lambda Legal Defense Fund.

JOSEPH D. SCHULMAN is director of the Genetics and IVF Institute of the Fairfax Hospital Association in Fairfax, Virginia. He is also professor of human genetics and pediatrics at the Medical College of Virginia.

EARL E. SHELP is assistant professor of medical ethics at Baylor College of Medicine in Houston and resident fellow in theology and ethics at the Institute of Religion.

SEYMOUR SIEGEL is professor of theology and professor of ethics and rabbinic thought at the Jewish Theological Seminary.

PETER SINGER teaches in the department of philosophy at Monash University in Australia. He is also the director of the Monash Centre for Human Bioethics.

THOMAS S. SZASZ is a psychiatrist, writer and educator affiliated with the Upstate Medical Center, State University of New York, Syracuse. He is the author of many controversial books and articles on psychiatry.

HANS O. TIEFEL teaches in the department of religion at the University of Virginia.

MATHEW O. TOBRINER is an associate justice of the Supreme Court of California.

INDEX

245; *in utero,* 234-235; and recognition of humanity of, 16-20; research using aborted, 236, 243; rights of, 20, 21, 23, 231-248

fireplug rule, 169

Fletcher, John C., in defense of fetal research, 230-231; 238-248

Flew, Anthony, 100

for-profit hospitals, 305, 309

France, presumed consent for cadaver organs in, 282-284

frozen embryo(s), and *in vitro* fertilization, 34, 35, 39, 40

full disclosure, and need for confidentiality between physician and patient, 161

gastrostomy, 111

gay men, and AIDS, 314, 317, 325

generic drugs, 308

gene splicing: and improving human traits, 344-346; and breaches of species barriers, 341-343

gene therapy, 41, 49

genetic engineering: and biogenic errors, 337, 338, 343, 344; and cloning, 335, 336; and debate over creation of new life forms, 328-346; and human-animal hybrids, 342; and improving human traits, 344-346; problems of, 336-337; religious viewpoints of, 339-343

genetic remodelling, of bacteria, 332

genetic repair, 336

gene transfer, 41

germ-line therapy, 329

Goodman, Paul, 210

government, *see* federal government; state government

Grobstein, Clifford, on ethics of *in vitro* fertilization, 28, 29, 36-42

guilty but mentally ill verdict, 172, 173, 179

half-sibling marriages, and surrogate mothering, 58

handicapped newborns, and morality of withholding treatment for, 120-130

Hardy, James D., 224

Harrison, Beverly Wildung, on ethics of abortion, 21-27

health care: and AIDS, 318, 325, 326; effects of costs of artificial heart on, 294-302; cost of, and effect on medical decision making, 310; economics and ethics in, 304-312; at home, and

Health Maintenance Organization, 307, 308; market approach to, 311; quality of, and doctors role in reducing cost of, 304-312

health insurance companies, and debate over screening for AIDS virus, 314-326

Health Maintenance Organizations: 305, 306, 311; and home care, 307, 308

hemophiliacs, and AIDS, 317

Hendin, Herbert, and debate over suicide as rational, 132, 133, 142-148

Hinckley, John W.: 164; and trial for insanity, 166-168, 177

Hippocratic Oath, 65, 86, 125, 153

histo-comparability, of tissues in humans and baboons, 222, 225

Hoche, Alfred, 147

home care, and Health Maintenance Organizations, 307

homosexual men, and AIDS, 315, 317

homunculus, 334, 335

Hôpital Général, 184

hospital parole, 172

hospitals: unnecessary admissions to, and ethics of health care, 306, 307; for-profit, and cost of health care, 305, 309; nonprofit vs. private, 289

HTLV-III, and AIDS, 314-316, 318, 319, 323, 325

human-animal hybrids, 342

humanization, question of, concerning fetus and abortion, 18-20, 23, 24

human T cell lymphotropic virus Type III, and AIDS, 315, 316, 318, 319, 323

Hume, David, 133

hybridization of species, and genetic engineering, 343, 344

immune system, and AIDS, 316, 317

imprisonment, compared to commitment, 186-187

incubation period, for AIDS, 317

industry, and genetic engineering, 328

infanticide, withholding treatment from newborns with birth defects as, 120, 125, 126

infants: and euthanasia, 89, 90; and ethical issues of *in vitro* fertilization, 28-42; and surrogate parenting, 44-59; withholding treatment of, with birth defects, 120-130; *see also,* newborns

infertile couples: and *in vitro* fertilization, 28-42; and surrogate parenting, 44-59